THE NEW NATURALIST
A SURVEY OF BRITISH NATURAL HISTORY

MUSHROOMS & TOADSTOOLS

The aim of this series is to interest the general reader in the wild life of Britain by recapturing the inquiring spirit of the old naturalists. The Editors believe that the natural pride of the British public in the native fauna and flora, to which must be added concern for their conservation, is best fostered by maintaining a high standard of accuracy combined with clarity of exposition in presenting the results of modern scientific research.

The text and line illustrations are here reproduced unaltered, but the process of manufacture used to achieve an economic price does not, unfortunately, do full justice to all the photographs; and those originally in colour appear in black and white.

FLY-AGARIC, *Amanita muscaria*; usually growing with birch trees. Poisonous

THE NEW NATURALIST

MUSHROOMS &
TOADSTOOLS

*A Study of
the Activities of Fungi
by*

JOHN RAMSBOTTOM

Bloomsbury Books
London

First Impression   *1953*
Second Impression   *1954*
Third Impression   *1959*
Fourth Impression   *1963*
Fifth Impression   *1969*
Sixth Impression   *1972*
Seventh Impression *1977*

TO FORMER COLLEAGUES

BRITISH MUSEUM (NATURAL HISTORY)

1910-1950

In Friendship

This edition published 1989 by
Bloomsbury Books an imprint of
Godfrey Cave Associates Limited
42 Bloomsbury Street, London WC1B 3QJ
under license from William Collins Son's & Co. Ltd.

ISBN 1 870630 09 2

CONTENTS

* PLATES IN COLOUR

PLATES IN BLACK AND WHITE

X PLATES IN BLACK AND WHITE

It should be noted that throughout this book Plate numbers in arabic figures refer to Colour Plates, while roman numerals are used for Black and White Plates

EDITORS' PREFACE

WITHOUT DOUBT, no one is better qualified to write a book on British Fungi than Dr. John Ramsbottom. The present long-awaited addition to the New Naturalist Series contains the distilled harvest of a life-time's knowledge and experience, much of it, especially in the historical field, never before published in accessible form. We say " distilled " advisably, since Dr. Ramsbottom could undoubtedly have written—in fact, did, in the first place, write—a book of more than double the present length; and, even then, he complained that much had to be omitted!

Dr. Ramsbottom has recently retired after forty years' service in the Department of Botany at the Natural History Museum, South Kensington, having been Keeper of Botany during the last twenty years. As his book shows, however, he is far from being a purely ' museum botanist.' Every aspect of Fungi has fascinated him, and he is equally at home hunting for rare toadstools in the Surrey woods, attending a conference in South America on medical mycology, ransacking old books for reference to the truffle-hunting habits of dogs, and probing the secrets of sex in moulds. He has always been willing to share his knowledge with others, and many will remember him best at his annual autumn exhibit of edible and poisonous toadstools at the Royal Horticultural Society's Shows, surrounded by crowds of eager questioners thrusting forward specimens for identification. The Editors feel fortunate in having persuaded Dr. Ramsbottom to put his unrivalled knowledge on permanent record as a volume in the New Naturalist Series.

The great group of Fungi, comprising perhaps some hundred thousand species, shows an amazing variety of form, from the minute unicellular yeasts to the Giant Puff-balls and bracket Fungi. The group touches human activities at a surprising number of points. In recent years everyone has become familiar with penicillin and other antibiotics produced from moulds, but how many fully appreciate the role of Fungi in wine and beer making, in the diseases of both plants and animals (including man), and as a human food throughout the world? Dr. Ramsbottom has not, of course, been able to deal in detail with all these aspects of Fungi; he has concentrated mainly on the larger kinds, commonly known as toadstools; but he has touched on most groups, and has a final chapter describing fully the story of the development of the penicillin industry from its beginnings in Sir Alexander Fleming's room at St. Mary's Hospital. This is the best short account of penicillin that has been written, in our opinion.

Dr. Ramsbottom, as will be seen, has paid particular attention to the history of Fungi, their names, their uses, and the beliefs and superstitions connected with them, as revealed in old books. The abundant quotations and references he has brought together can be found in no other book and give a special value to his volume. In his chapter on mushroom-growing, too, he has gathered together a mass of obscure information, including particulars of the vast cave industry under the streets of Paris.

Parts of Dr. Ramsbottom's book will be found to be more technical than the majority of New Naturalist volumes. When writing of Fungi this is inevitable. Very few species have English names, and when describing, for example, the sexual behaviour of the ' lower ' Fungi, it is impossible to avoid using technical language. With the help of the glossary-index, however, any reader should be able to understand these sections if he is willing to take the necessary trouble.

This volume is not, of course, intended as a handbook for the identification of British toadstools. Excellent books for this purpose already exist. In several chapters, however, Dr. Ramsbottom has given lists of the species occurring in different types of habitat, together with mention of their main distinguishing characters.

The book is fully illustrated with black and white and with colour plates, and the fine photographs by Mr. de Laszlo do full justice, we feel, to the fascinating colour scheme affected by so many kinds of toadstool.

The Editors, during the production of this book, have come to look upon Dr. Ramsbottom as a sort of Robert Burton of the fungal world, and, with his discursive style, " curious learning," and wide canvas, he has, we feel, given us something approaching a twentieth century " Anatomy of Toadstools."

THE EDITORS

AUTHOR'S PREFACE

THE WRITING OF THIS BOOK has presented several problems, chief of which has been that of giving a sufficiently wide view of the subject in a single volume. It seemed desirable to try to explain the modes of life of this large group, the fungi, and this in its turn meant suggesting its biological relations to other groups of organisms.

The fact had also to be faced that probably only about half a dozen of the larger fungi are recognised by people generally; and consequently there are surprisingly few common names. Names alone, therefore, are likely to mean nothing to the general reader, except irritation, so some indication of what they signify is needed. Unfortunately lack of space has prevented this being done in any detail, but the colour plates will help to determine a number of species, or give an idea of those mentioned in the text.

Doubtless others would have treated the subject differently: but having always been impressed with the influence fungi have on our very existence, I wished to convey some idea of this. Those who specialise in any branch of knowledge naturally tend to magnify its importance—but a mycologist, if he regards fungi as living organisms, can hardly fail to realise the significance of other disciplines. On the other hand scientists generally are beginning to consider that the old-time neglect of fungi—even by botanists—was short-sighted.

The writing of the book has taken far longer than I expected, and when first written greatly exceeded the required length! To preserve some sort of balance meant the cutting out of some portions (which probably will be published elsewhere) and the cutting down of others. The result is, however, somewhat uneven: the chapters on Grasslands (17) and Woodlands (19) are but shadows of their former selves; though what is little more than a list of species should serve as an introduction to their descriptions in systematic works. There is abundant scope for original observations, but it must be stressed that these can have no scientific value without correct identifications. The Penicillin chapter was included at the request of the Editors.

As far as possible scientific terms have been kept to a minimum and all except those which are explained are to be found in standard dictionaries. " *Difficile est de scientiis inscientur loqui*; which is as much

xiii

as to say, that, 'in treating of scientific matters, it is difficult to avoid the use of scientific terms.' But I shall endeavour to be as plain as possible." *

After this apologia there remains the pleasure of thanking those who have been of help. It is not possible to list all those to whom I am under obligation; for it has been my good fortune to be in close touch with amateur and professional mycologists, both here and abroad, for many years—and as Linnaeus remarked, " Sometimes a blind hen meets with a grain of corn," and I must have gleaned.

More particularly I wish to express my indebtedness to Mr. Paul de Laszlo, O.B.E., who, though then serving as Lieut.-Commander in the R.N.V.R. spent much of his leisure time photographing for me; most of his kodachromes were duplicated and together with many others were generously given to me for use in Museum lectures: to my old friend Mr. Somerville Hastings, M.P., who kindly gave me leave to use his large collection of excellent photographs: and to Dr. Erik Björkman, Mr. J. A. Crabbe, The Director, Forest Products Research Station, Sir Alexander Fleming, Glaxo Laboratories, Mr. H. J. Howard, Prof. C. T. Ingold, Mr. H. Meyer, Mr. D. A. Pickford, Prof. A. Stoll, Mr. W. H. T. Tams and The Trustees, British Museum (Natural History), who allowed me the use of their photographs.

I wish to thank many who answered my queries and particularly Mr. Arthur Collins for his notes on truffle-hunting at Winterslow.

I am under many obligations to my former colleagues in the Department of Botany who were willing to help in tracking down some obscure reference, and in every possible way: to Mrs. F. L. Balfour-Browne, my assistant for many years, who helped in numerous ways with the manuscript as it took form, and with the proofs; also to Mr. A. C. Townsend, Museum Librarian, who read much of the manuscript and has applied his wide experience to the proofs; and to Mr. T. C. Denston, Secretary of the British Pharmocopœia Commission who read and advised me upon the pharmaceutical aspects of some of the chapters.

The *Oxford English Dictionary* has been most useful in providing clues to the old literature.

The book has many shortcomings but if it succeeds in adding to the goodly company of those interested in matters mycological it will serve its purpose.

12 *March* 1953   **J. R.**

*Charles Lamb. Letter to an old gentleman whose education has been neglected.

CHAPTER I

GENERAL INTRODUCTION

S INCE THE SECOND WORLD WAR the British public appears to have become fungus conscious. This is not to suggest that it was previously unaware of these organisms or that it was entirely ignorant of mushrooms and toadstools, of moulds and mildews, of yeasts and of dry rot, but rather that events brought the group as a whole more into public notice.

The most outstanding of these was the discovery that *Penicillium notatum*, a green mould of a very common type, is able to produce penicillin, the most valuable antibacterial substance known, which, because it is non-toxic to animal tissues, was of supreme importance in the treatment of war wounds. The so-called food-yeast, which was destined to play an important role in the feeding of starving nations, also impressed the public. A third factor has been a more general realisation that many toadstools may be eaten with perfect safety and can add a spice of variety to diets requiring only this to make them satisfying.

Fungi form a vast assemblage of organisms, probably greater in the number of species and individuals than are flowering plants. They include Moulds, Mildews, Rusts, Smuts, Mushrooms and Toadstools, from extremely small microscopic forms to large bracket fungi the width of a man's height. There is a great variety of structure and texture.

From a physiological standpoint the essential characteristic of all fungi is that they are without chlorophyll, the green-colouring matter of plants. By the aid of this complex chemical substance, the proto-plasm of green plants is able in sunlight to build up, from water and the carbon dioxide of the air, the carbohydrates essential for life and growth. The process is not a simple one and its details are still matters of controversy. However, the important point is that only organisms with chlorophyll* are able to carry out this fundamental process, the building up of organic from inorganic substances. Fungi, not having chlorophyll, must obtain organic material already prepared. In this

*Sulphur bacteria are apparently exceptions to this.

they resemble animals, but they are much more catholic in their tastes. It is in their search for food that they cause disease, decay and destruction, but they also bring about changes beneficial to man and other organisms.

As a nation we have certain characteristics apart from those wished upon us by continental writers. One of them, which does not appear to have called for comment, is our dread of eating any fungus other than the Common Mushroom, either wild or cultivated, though during the friendly invasion by foreigners in the past few years the peculiarity has certainly been remarked.

The general belief that only one, or at most a very few species, are safe to eat, has led to the words mushroom and toadstool being used to denote edible and poisonous fungi respectively. This differentiation takes no account of the large number of species which are so leathery that they are inedible, though not poisonous. Leaving these aside, however, we are faced with the fact that there are hundreds of edible fungi and only a dozen or so which can be described as deleterious. Are we still to call all edible species mushrooms and the few poisonous ones toadstools?

The grete herball (1526) says, " Fungi ben mussherons. . . . There be two maners of them, one maner is deedly and sleeth them that eatheth of them and be called tode stoles, and the other doeth not ": but all are mushrooms. In some parts of the north country we have this same use which leads to awkward phrases like: " Mushrooms as is toadstools." Most of the earliest references to mushroom and toadstool, however, regard them as synonymous. Thus we find in John Maplet's *A green forest* (1567), " The Mushrom or Toadstoole . . . hath two sundrie kinds, . . . for the one may be eaten: the other is not to be eaten," and in Henry Lyte's *A Nieue Herball* (1578), " sicke with eating of venimous Tadstooles or Mousheroms ": and about 1440, " Promptorium Parvulorum " speaks of " Muscheron, toodys hatte, *boletus, fungus*," which is incidentally the second reference to mushroom given in a long series of spelling variations in the *Oxford English Dictionary*, the first being " *Mussetum*, musserouns " (14 . .): the earliest reference for toadstool (tadstoles) is 1398.* To revert fully to this original usage would be inconvenient; one or other word should be inclusive. It would be better to use toadstool in its original sense

---

*The same work (Bartholomaeus Anglicus *De proprietatibus rerum*, 1398) has " frogge stoles and venemous meetes "; " Frogstooles " occurs in 1661 and lingers on in Dorset.

Plate 1. DEATH-CAP, *Amanita phalloides*; showing unbroken volva and emerging cap (*below*) and tearing of ring (*top centre*). The cap is usually olive-green, the gills white. Deadly poisonous (*Paul L. de Laszlo*)

Plate 2a. DESTROYING ANGEL, *Amanita virosa*; closely related to the Death-Cap. Wholly white. The curving of the stem is due to the position in which the specimen was growing.

b. FALSE DEATH-CAP, *Amanita mappa*; patches of the volva remain on the cap. Distasteful but not poisonous (*Paul L. de Laszlo*)

and to restrict mushroom to those species which are usually now so-called, that is to species of the genus *Psalliota*—*Psalliota campestris*, the Field-Mushroom, P. *arvensis*, the Horse-Mushroom, and so on. Mushrooms would thus be regarded as special kinds of toadstools, and no confusion could arise about the meaning.

The word mushroom is usually thought to be derived from the French *Mousseron* (*muceron*) from *mousse*, moss, but it is not used in quite the same sense. It has been said that " mousseron is a barbarous name which has caused endless confusion." *Tricholoma gambosum*, the St. George's Mushroom and its varieties, is " mousseron," " mousseron de la Saint-Georges," or " mousseron vrai"; *Clitopilus prunulus* is " mousseron "; *Marasmius oreades*, the Fairy-Ring Champignon, is " mousseron d'automne, de Dieppe, etc." or " faux-mousseron." Further, the name appears to be used commercially for all fungi sold in a dried state. Strange to say, in Germany " Mousseron (Musseron)" or " echter Mousseron " is *Marasmius scorodonius*, whereas one name for *Clitopilus prunulus* is " grosser Mousseron." It may be recalled that according to Rabelais, Dido did sell " mousserons " in hell.

The derivation of toadstool is obvious, especially when considered in conjunction with toodys hatte, paddocstol (1450), and the modern Scottish and north country paddockstool or puddockstool. John Gerard in *The Herball* (1597) says, " in English Mushrums, Toadstooles or Paddockstooles." Clusius states that Genus xiii of his Fungi perniciosi (*Collybia maculata*) is called Froschen stuel. Ray in *Historia* says such fungi are called Toad-stools by country people here.

A typical toadstool obviously might serve as a resting place for a sedentary batrachian, but it is peculiar that the association is mostly with toads and not with frogs; possibly the explanation is in the old belief that toads were venomous. In Brittany and neighbourhood there are local names meaning toad's hat or toad's bonnet; the most widespread is " tour soc " or " scabello tou soc " (escabeau de crapaud). The belief is that they are formed from the harmful substances of the earth and the venom of toads and that fungi always grow in places where toads abound, and give shelter to them when they take the air.

There have been suggestions that the word has reference to excrement. Certainly stool might have that meaning, but the derivation of toad from the Icelandic tad (dung) is philologically unnecessary having regard to early usage. From the point of view of belief there would be nothing surprising if, originally, the word had reference to such unsavoury similes, but it seems certain that the obvious and more poetic derivation is the correct one: " The grieslie Todestoole growne there mought I se And loathed Paddocks lording on the same."

As would be expected, we find modifications also of the Latin word fungus, though these were usually used with mushroom or toadstool as synonyms. Thus we have funge and fungo. In the " forme of cury compiled of the chef maistes cokes of kyng Richard the Secunde kyng of [E]nglond attir the conquest, the which was accounted the best and ryallest vyand of alle csten|k|ynges " (1390), there is a recipe "10 Funges (mushrooms). Take tunges, and pare hem clene and dyce hem; take leke, and shred hym small and do hym to seeth in gode broth; color it with satron, and do thereinne powdor fort." W. Bullein in *The booke of simples* 1562) speaks of " rotten Moushrimpes called Fungas."

Though fungus in Latin meant the larger fungi generally, it also referred to fleshy excrescences on the human body and on tree trunks. It is commonly believed to be cognate with or derived from the Greek word for sponge, *sphonggos* (σφόγγος), which agrees with the ideas the Romans expressed about the nature of fungi. A derivation which was apparently first suggested by J. Bauhin in *Historia Plantarum* (1650), appealed to several of the herbalists because of its supposed aptness— *funus*, funeral, and *ago*, I lead to. John Ray, in *Historia Plantarum* (1681), says whatever the etymology the idea is not unmerited.

The Greeks used the word mykes (μύκης) for mushrooms generally, presumably because of the slimy nature of some of them. It also denoted any knobbed round body shaped like a mushroom, such as the chape or cap at the end of a sword's scabbard, and fleshy excrescences.

It is significant that both the Greeks and the Romans regarded the snuff or lamp-black of candles and lamps as being sufficiently like fungi to warrant using the same name: its occurrence was supposed to forbode rain. Similarly, they considered soft-headed doltish persons as deserving of the same appellation. Both uses are found with us; thus, Ajax in *Troilus and Cressida*—" Toadstool, learn me the pro-clamation."

The usual term for the study of fungi is mycology. *Mykes* in its plural form is the ending adopted for the names of many groups of fungi without any special reference to rank; thus Eumycetes for the whole of the Fungi; Phycomycetes, Ascomycetes and Basidiomycetes, for the three main classes; Hymenomycetes, Gasteromycetes, Dis-comycetes, and Pyrenomycetes, for orders.

The name of the old Greek city Mycenae was derived by the

ancients either from an eponymous heroine Mycene, or from the word mykes. Pausanias in his *Description of Greece*, says that Perseus, when he had received the kingdom of Proteus, founded Mycenae because there the cap of his scabbard had fallen off; he regarded this as a sign to found a city. " I have also heard that being thirsty he chanced to take up a mushroom, and that water flowing from it he drank, and being pleased gave the place the name of Mycenae."

CHAPTER 2

NAMES

———————————————

THERE ARE SEVERAL FUNGI mentioned in Greek and Latin authors but, though some of the names are still in use, they now have a different significance. Thus, the boletus of Latin authors, Βωλίτης of Galen, is *Amanita caesarea*; pezica of Pliny, πέξις of Theophrastus, is *Lycoperdon giganteum*; agaricum of Pliny, ἀγαρικόν of Dioscorides, is *Polyporus (Fomes) officinalis;* ἀμᾶνιται of Nicander is *Psalliota campestris*, and ὕδνον of Theophrastus is a truffle.

Most writers before the time of Linnaeus endeavoured to apply these names correctly. J. J. Dillenius, however, in *Catalogus Plantarum sponte circa Gissam nascentium* (1719), a work which led to his employment by William Sherard and to his nomination in Sherard's will as the first (Sherardian) Professor of Botany at Oxford, used *Boletus* and *Peziza* (also *Amanita*) in a sense entirely different from the original. Linnaeus, who in matters of nomenclature was occasionally autocratic, adopted Dillenius's interpretation of *Boletus* and *Peziza*, and for some reason, or whim, altered the application of the names *Agaricus, Hydnum* and *Elvella (Helvella)*, which last, in Cicero, is not even a fungus, but a vegetable. In *Species Plantarum* (1753), Linnaeus used these names among the ten genera that he described; the remaining five names were " modern "—and unaltered. The influence of this work was so great that the misuse of the old names was generally adopted, though not without some pointed protests, for in it the binary system of nomenclature was established; the specific names of all plants henceforth consisted of two words, a generic name and a specific epithet. This innovation is regarded by some as Linnaeus's most useful service to science.

The necessity for the convention will be best understood by glancing through the pages of a work of one of Linnaeus's immediate predecessors, for example, Ray's *Synopsis Methodica Stirpium Brittanicarum*

(1724, edited, anonymously, by Dillenius*). At first one has the same bewilderment as had Jacob when wrestling with the angel—" what is thy name? " The account of fungi begins with the Field Mushroom; " I. Fungus campestris albus superne, inferne rubens *J.B.T.* 111, *P. 2, p. 824*, esculentus 13, sive pileolo lato and rotundo livido, *C.B.Pin. p.370.* parum rubens inferne, pileo albo plano, quandoque umbilicato, *Sterb.Th.F. p. 28, Tab. I. Fig. A.* esculentus 12 *Park.Th. p. 1317 Champignon.* In pascuis sterilioribus sub finem aestatis."

Apart from the name Champignon† and the last sentence giving the place and season, there is no description beyond what is contained in the names bestowed by four previous authors, J. Bauhin, C. Bauhin, Sterbeeck and Parkinson, and presumably the first of these synonyms was favoured by adoption. There is, however, no regular procedure; for some species we find the phrase name written separately, followed by a description; with many of the newly added species, moreover, there is no attempt at anything beyond a description, though this may contain seventy words or more.

How did such clumsy names arise? Greek authors who wrote about plants were writing for the general public and used the names of everyday speech; indeed, occasionally, more than one name was given to the same plant obviously drawn from different localities, where, incidentally, many of the names are still in use. I had this impressed on me early in 1919 when sitting on the slope of the so-called Clytemnestra's tomb at Mycenae in company with Capt. T. S. Hele (later master of Emmanuel College, Cambridge). An old shepherd came along and with obvious enthusiasm pointed to the different places of interest within sight. I was puzzled by a plant which was forming abundant spirals on the ground, but was not in flower. More as an acknowledgment of his friendliness than with a hope of acquiring knowledge, I drew his attention to the plant, which he at once called " heliotropion." It was *Heliotropium supinum*, and an unkempt, illiterate shepherd knew it by the same name that Theophrastus had used in *Enquiry into Plants* about 300 B.C. In this, the earliest known botanical

---

*Because of " some apprehension (me being a foreigner) of making natives uneasy, if I should publicate it in my name."

† Champignon was formerly used, as in French, for all larger fungi, but later was restricted to the Field-Mushroom: Lyte (1578) has " venemous Champions or Tode Stooles " and there are various other spelling modifications. In the nineteenth century it became generally transferred to the Fairy-Ring Champignon, *Marasmius oreades*, but remains as a local name for the Horse-Mushroom: Champignon (Warwickshire), Champilion (Cheshire), Champion (Lancashire).

work and one which served as a text for several centuries, we find plant names of different kinds. About five hundred plants are mentioned, the majority cultivated, and all from a restricted area. Many of the names are single words (nouns) referring to the only species then known (e.g. *Asparagos*). Sometimes, however, plants recognised as not being closely related had some character in common which led to a name which described this similarity. Often this resemblance was in the roots which were well known, for the root-gatherers* of antiquity provided the materials for medicines. Thus for Theophrastus, Sweet Flag was compared to a reed κάλαμος, and was called the sweet-smelling reed κάλαμος ὁ εὐώδης, just as we have Ivy and Ground Ivy, Nettle and Dead Nettle.

The same system of naming was followed for species; the commonest species was given the generic name, and other species were distinguished by adding an adjective such as " broad-leaved," or, as is frequent in Greek, the adjective was joined on to the noun to make a compound word κυνόρροδον, dog rose. All plant names in Theophrastus, whether of genus, species or variety, are either a noun, or a noun qualified by an adjective. When, later, the Romans began to take an interest in plants, they based their ideas on Greek lore. They used Latin words of common speech for the species known to them; for others they borrowed names from Greek writers, Theophrastus particularly. Consequently almost all their plant names are of the same kind as those of the Greeks, namely a noun, or a noun and an adjective, the latter, in Latin, always written as two words no matter what the Greek form was.

Latin became the acknowledged medium for natural history works at the time of the Revival of Learning, and in the Herbals we find that the classical names used, being mainly unitary or binary, have a much more modern appearance than those of the first half of the eighteenth century. Though generic names were rarely descriptive, the qualifying adjective was invariably so. So long as comparatively few species of a genus were known it was simple to give names sufficiently distinctive to recognise them. As knowledge increased so simple a nomenclature was sure to break down. It did so almost at once with fungi because of the impossibility of finding a distinctive character definable in a word. Pliny distinguished different truffles as *Tuber colore nigro*, *Tuber colore intus candido* and *Tuber colore rufo*, which

---

*Their influence is seen in the old Herbals, which, as they were mainly medical in object, always represent the character of the roots in their figures.

clearly indicate the method that led to his using *Boleti veneni, diluto rubore, rancido aspectu, livido intus colore, rimosa stria, pallido per ambitum labro* for *Amanita muscaria*, and *Boleti sicci, nitri similes, veluti guttas in vertice albas ex tunica sua* for *Amanita pantherina*, whereas, as we have seen, *Amanita caesarea* was simply *boletus*. Similarly, in the period following the Herbalists, when the spread of knowledge and the opening up of new lands had greatly increased the numbers of known plants, the distinguishing phrase replaced the descriptive adjective. Some authors showed considerable ingenuity in keeping these phrases within reasonable bounds, for all were free to use whatever name they chose. Linnaeus originally set himself a limit of twelve words for the formation of a specific name; others left nothing out and the name was in fact a detailed description of the plant. The result was that the study of natural history—for animal names were similar in kind—was hampered and confused; it was becoming as difficult to find a way through the tangle as it would be to travel hopefully if all places had such descriptive names as Llanfairpwllgwyngyllgogerychwyrndrobwllllandysiliogogogoch.*

Linnaeus eventually realised that a name and a description need have nothing in common. A generic name and a specific epithet are sufficient to denote an organism; the description gives its distinctive characters. The epithet may be erroneous or even ridiculous, but this signifies nothing so long as we have a convenient name to use and know precisely to what it refers.

Like the Greeks, we have few popular fungus names. A popular name is a sure sign that a species is recognised by country people, and, indeed, it is usual to find more than one such name for the few fungi so endowed. Occasionally in these pages English names are given, but most of them are not folk-names, having been coined in an effort to popularise the study of fungi. Many writers of books which aim at a wide appeal, think it wise to criticise the use of Latin names for organisms, as if this were pedantic, even if not cryptic. Doubtless, as a knowledge of the larger fungi becomes more popular, names will be invented by or for those who prefer homely appellations, but myriads of microscopic species are unlikely to have bestowed upon them anything additional to their baptismal names. It is really only at the outset that Latin names appear forbidding: amateur gardeners soon talk of *Antirrhinum* and *Delphinium* instead of Snapdragon and Larkspur;

*The Church of St. Mary in a wood of white hazel near a rapid whirlpool and near St. Tysilio's cave close to a red cave. The Ordnance Survey map of Anglesey slightly abbreviates the name; the Post Office uses Llanfairpwll or Llanfair P.G.

Chrysanthemum, Rhododendron, and suchlike, occasion no comment. Genuine English names should be treasured; made-up book-names, which are often merely translations of the Latin names, should be regarded as makeshift stepping stones and discarded so soon as they have served their purpose.

When writing the name of a plant it is customary to add the name of the author who first described it, either in full or in an abbreviated form. This " authority " is really a shortened reference, but it also indicates which species is meant when the same name has been used in different senses by two or more authors. The name of the Chanterelle is written *Cantharellus cibarius* Fr. meaning that F. M. Fries, the illustrious Swedish mycologist, gave this name to the fungus, which he also described in a manner which permits of certain identification. To be more precise the name should be written *Cantharellus cibarius* Fr. Syst. Myc. I 318 (1821), for Fries wrote much from 1815 till 1874, and, moreover, gave several descriptions of this fungus. He was not the first to describe it; he was the first to call it *Cantharellus cibarius.* Frequently two authorities are given, the first within brackets, for example, *Amanitopsis strangulata* (Fr.) Roze. This indicates that the specific epithet was bestowed on the fungus by Fries but that he had placed it in another genus—here it was *Agaricus*— and that E. Roze transferred it to *Amanitopsis,* which, incidentally, was a new genus proposed by him. Thus in *Cantharellus cibarius,* Fries is the authority for the specific name, in *Amanitopsis strangulata,* only for the specific epithet. No matter for what reason a transference is made, the fact that it has occurred is shown by such a " double citation." For example *Agaricus echinatus* Roth, because of its puzzling characters* has been placed in different genera; it is *Agaricus (Psalliota) echinatus* (Roth) Fr., *Agaricus (Chamaeota) echinatus* (Roth) Cooke, *Agaricus (Inocybe) echinatus* (Roth) Cooke, *Agaricus (Pholiota) echinatus* (Roth) Pat., *Pratella echinata* (Roth) Gill., *Lepiota echinata* (Roth) Quél., *Cystoderma echinatum* (Roth) Sing., *Naucoria echinata* (Roth) Schroet. and *Melanophyllum echinatum* (Roth) Sing.; the check to the identity is the specific epithet and the authority for it.

Some mycologists favour genera with narrow circumscription, others are more catholic. This brief account is merely to explain the significance of what often puzzles the uninitiated. The subject of

---

*Agaricus haematospermus Bull. (1792) is synonymous with *A. echinatus* Roth (1800) and is adopted by some authors. We have a further list of names though not, as yet, so long!

nomenclature is full of difficulties, not excluding psychological ones. International Rules of Botanical Nomenclature have been drawn up with the object of straightening out some of the tangles, but as they are retroactive it is not always easy to apply them both logically and reasonably; it is possible to legislate for ourselves, and perhaps for our successors, but our predecessors cannot be influenced. The names in this book are without " authorities," for, except where comment is made, they are used in the sense accepted in British mycological writings.

CHAPTER 3

HISTORY

I N ADDITION to the outstanding fact that fungi, though very occasionally green, do not possess chlorophyll, is the equally significant one that like mosses, ferns, liverworts and other cryptogams, they reproduce by spores and not by seeds. The spores of fungi are very small and those of only three or four species are sufficiently large to be within the range of unaided vision. Those of toadstools average about 10 μ in length, a μ (micron or mu) being $\frac{1}{1000}$ of a millimetre, i.e. $\frac{1}{25400}$ of an inch. Though the smallest seeds, those of orchids, are much larger than any fungus spore, the essential difference between a seed and a spore is not in size but in structure. That of a seed is highly organised with, typically, an embryo and surrounding tissues: that of a spore is extremely simple, for there is no tissue and no embryo, merely, as a rule, an outer cell-wall enclosing protoplasm with a little oil or other reserve food-material, though sometimes the spore is divided by cross-walls and, less frequently, also by vertical ones.

A seed, when it germinates, first puts forth the young root of the embryo or germ, and later the stem apex with or without the seed leaves (cotyledons). The fungal spore, as it does not contain an embryonic fungus, does not germinate in a similar way; indeed, strictly speaking, as it has no " germ " it does not germinate, though it is customary and convenient so to speak of the first stage of development. This, in all the larger fungi, consists in the protrusion of a part of the spore wall as a tube, the germ-tube, which gradually lengthens until it becomes thread-like, and then with continuous growth, branching, and anastomosis, spreads in all directions. The thread-like portion is called a *hypha*, the more advanced stage a *mycelium*. There is no hard and fast distinction between the two, and usually hyphae and mycelium are spoken of as though synonymous. The flesh of mushrooms, toadstools and other fungi with similarly definite shapes, is formed by the massing together of these hyphae. It is " tissue " in a descriptive rather than a strictly anatomical sense.

Though spores are produced in enormous numbers, and deposits containing millions of them can often be seen on leaves and stumps as well as on parts of a fungus itself, it was long before their significance was realised. To the Greeks and Romans the origin of fungi was a mystery. They had no conception of spores and therefore marvelled at the absence of seeds, and though mycelial threads must have been noticed, their import was not grasped. But there were occasional surmises about the mystery. A common belief was that fungi, truffles especially, were produced by thunder, a belief still held in the Philippines. Theophrastus, however, speaks of this as a peculiar belief, as also the fact that some thought that truffles were produced from seed, because those that grew on the shore of the Mityleneans appeared only after floods which brought down the seed from Tiarae, where truffles abound.

Pliny, over three centuries later, says about truffles:

" Among the most wonderful of all things is the fact that anything can spring up and live without a root. . . . Now whether this imperfection of the earth—for it cannot be said to be anything else—grows, or whether it has at once assumed its full globular size, whether it lives or not, are matters which I think cannot be easily understood. In their being liable to become rotten, these things resemble wood."

" The origin of boletus [*Amanita caesarea*] is from mud and the acrid juices of moist earth, or frequently from those of acorn-bearing trees; at first it appears as a kind of tenacious foam, then as a membranous body: afterwards the young boletus appears."

Nicander, about 185 B.C., refers to a fungus as " the evil ferment of the earth "; and, generally, " the central heat of the globe forms them by rarefying the mud of the earth."

It seemed so unlikely that fungi could be produced in any normal manner that Petronius commenting on the extravagancies of the gourmand Trimalchio, joked about his having sent to India for seeds of boletus.

The writers of Herbals stuck rather closely to classical authority in most things, and not least in the explanations given about the origin of these " earthie excrescences " or " bastard plants."

It is fascinating to follow the threads of ideas about the nature of fungi from their earliest mention until they were woven as the warp and weft of definite pattern. This took longer to attain than with most other organisms, for as fungi did not appear to fit into the notions conceived at different periods about the " Order of Nature," their characters were sometimes regarded philosophically rather than interpreted factually. The problem was whether fungi were manifestations of some phenomenon, or were entities, and how they were produced, and reproduced.

The earlier herbalists were occupied for the main part in elucidating *De Materia Medica* of Dioscorides. Their interpretations were not simply literary exercises but commentaries with reference to the floras of their own countries, which became more and more valuable as it was gradually realised that many of the plants were different, and illustrations were made from living specimens. William Turner in *A new Herball* (1551-1568), the first important English botanical work, realised the difficulties, and in his forthright manner—a manner which at that period proved perilous for a prelate—wrote that he had:

> " taught the truthe of certeyne plantes. . . . And because I would not be lyke unto a cryer yt cryeth a loste horse in the marketh, & telleth all the markes and tokens that he hath, & yet never sawe the horse, nether coulde knowe the horse if he sawe him: I wente into Italye and into diverse partes of Germany, to knowe and se the herbes my selfe."

Mixed with ideas about the nature of fungi which are derived directly from writers of antiquity, we find modifications due to personal observations and independent judgment. Thus Caesalpinus in *De Plantis* (1583), wrote that:

> " Some plants have no seed; these are the most imperfect, and spring from decaying substances; and they therefore have to feed themselves and grow, and are unable to produce their like; they are a sort of intermediate existence between plants and inanimate nature. In this respect fungi resemble zoophytes, which are intermediate between plants and animals."

Here we have a fairly clear statement that fungi arise spontaneously and a suggestion that they are not plants. They played a notable part in the controversies about spontaneous generation, which held on, with shifting ground of argument, until almost the end of last century. Whether fungi are plants or not depends upon definition. The question repeatedly arose, and several, like Linnaeus, thought fungi might form a new natural kingdom between those of plants and animals.

Mycologists, in this country at least, are tending again towards this view though they would express it differently.

Porta, in *Phytognomonica* (1588), asserted that:

" contrary to the opinion of the ancients, all plants are provided with seed. . . . From fungi I have succeeded in collecting seed, very small and black, lying hidden in oblong chambers or furrows extending from the stalk to the circumference."

As he describes black " seeds " he had probably examined species of *Coprinus, Panaeolus*, or some other dark-spored forms. If so, it is possible that he saw the spores on the gills, but with whatever lens he had they would appear as minute dots, so it is a little surprising that he should have been so dogmatic about their function. Obviously discussions on whether fungi had seeds could not then get very far, and advance waited on the ability to make closer observations than were possible by the aid of a simple lens. With the invention of the microscope the means was to hand but progress was slow; there was much to observe and observers were few.

The first " observations " of the new kind occur in Robert Hooke's *Micrographia, or some Physiological Descriptions of Minute Bodies made by Magnifying Glasses, with Observations and Inquiries thereupon*, which was published in 1665. A great variety of objects were examined; two sections relate to fungi, one (observ. 19) " Of a *Plant* growing in the blighted or yellow specks of *Damask-rose-leaves, Bramble leaves* and some other kind of leaves," the other (observ. 20) " Of *blue Mould*, and of the first Principles of Vegetation arising from *Putrefaction*." The rose blight is the rust-fungus *Phragmidium*, and the description is accompanied by the first known illustration of a microscopic fungus. Hooke's views on plant disease are worth noting.

" Though the original cause, or seminal principle from which this minute Plant on Rose leaves did spring, were, before the corruption caus'd by the Mill-dew, a component part of the leaf on which it grew, and did serve as a *coagent* in the production and constitution of it, yet might it be so consummate, as to produce a seed which might have a power of propagating the same species. . . . So that the little cases which appear to grow on the top of the slender stalks, may, for ought I know, though I should suppose them to spring from the perverting of the usual course of the parent Vegetable, contain a seed, which, being scatter'd on other leaves of the same Plant, may produce a Plant of much the same kind."

Several moulds are mentioned in the other section:

" The Blue and White and several kinds of hairy mouldy spots, which are observable upon divers kinds of *putrify'd* bodies, whether Animal substances, or Vegetable, such as the skin, raw or dress'd, flesh, bloud, humours, milk, green Cheese, *&c.* or rotten sappy Wood, or Herbs, Leaves, Barks, Roots, etc. of Plants, are all of them nothing else but several kinds of small and variously figur'd Mushroms, which, from convenient materials in those *putrifying* bodies, are, by the concurrent heat of the Air, excited to a certain kind of vegetation, which will not be unworthy our more serious speculation and examination."

He figures a small white speck of hairy mould which he found growing on the red sheepskin cover of a book. This was probably a *Mucor,* but here as elsewhere " what these heads contain'd I could not perceive; whether they were knobs and flowers, or seed cases, I am not able to say." Hooke's views on fungi are thus expressed:

" First, that Mould and Mushroms require no seminal property, but the former may be produc'd at any time from any kind of *putrifying* Animal or Vegetable Substance, as Flesh, *&c.* kept moist and warm. . . . Next, that as Mushroms may be generated without seed, so does it not appear that they have any such thing as seed in any part of them; for having considered several kinds of them, I could never find any thing in them that I could with any probability ghess to be the seed of it, so that it does not as yet appear (that I know of) that Mushroms may be generated from a seed, but they rather seem to depend merely upon a convenient constitution of the matter out of which they are made, and a concurrence of either natural or artificial heat."

We find similar ideas about the nature of fungi and fungal disease extending over the next century and a half, in spite of the gradual accumulation of new facts.

We owe to Hooke our first knowledge of the internal structure of the larger fungi—hidden away in his section on Sponges (observ. 22). Examining " several kinds of Mushroms " he found " their texture to be somewhat of this kind, that is, to consist of an infinite company of small filaments, every way contex'd and woven together, so as to make a kind of cloth."

It is somewhat surprising that Hooke did not see the spores of the moulds he examined. These, however, were figured by M. Malpighi in *Anatome Plantarum* (1679), who gives sketches of common moulds found growing on second-rate cheese, on the putrescent skin of melons, on lemons and oranges, on wood and on bread, but the spores are regarded as florets borne in an inflorescence (the sporangiophore). He also figures the mycelium of an Agaric.

In 1707, J. P. de Tournefort gave the first scientific account of mushroom-growing, and therein described the mycelium (spawn) which he regarded as nothing other than the developed seeds or germs of the mushroom, which cannot be perceived until they have grown into little hairs. Despite Tournefort's eminence as a botanist his reasoned opinions received far less attention than the speculations of his contemporaries. L. F. Marsigli, so keen a mycologist that he collected fungi on the battlefield, published a dissertation in 1714 which greatly influenced contemporary thought. His views, however, were very similar to those of Pliny in kind, but were stated in the idiom of the period: fungi occur where there is a fatty substance, consisting of some sort of oiliness mixed with nitrous salt, which penetrates through the roots and between the fibres of the wood by means of a fermentation caused by mild warmth and dampness. The ligneous matter becomes transformed into a compact substance, which insinuates itself either between the wood and the bark, or through the pores of the bark, and engenders woody fungi. The same product of fermentation coagulates in the ground and becomes the *situs*, which, swelling and emerging above the surface, acquires the nature and form of toadstools.

In reading the old accounts one finds a strange mixture of fact and fantasy. Some are so fantastic that if they had not been accepted by other authors they would not find a place in even a most detailed historical summary. Then there comes an observation of such merit that all seems set for real progress. But these facts, even when accepted, are often misinterpreted, almost as if in a superfluity of naughtiness, and again there is confusion.

Nova Plantarum Genera published by P. A. Micheli in 1729 is outstanding. Micheli, a Florentine, was the first to pay special attention to fungi as a whole, though his researches also comprised flowering plants, mosses, liverworts and lichens. Among his new genera were *Aspergillus, Botrytis, Clathrus, Geaster, Mucor* and *Polyporus*, all of which are still recognised. His researches on fungi were doubtless guided by the desire to discover flowers and seeds in them so that they could be brought in line with flowering plants. He found his " seeds " in al kinds of fungi—Polypores, Agarics, Gasteromycetes, Discomycetes, Truffles and Moulds; they were obviously the spores. Not satisfied with a belief that his seeds were what he thought them to be, he carried out a series of experiments to find out whether they grew and gave rise to the same fungus which bore them. For these experiments he used *Fungus* [*Agaricus*] and the three common moulds *Botrytis*, *Aspergillus* and *Mucor*. He planted the spores of the agaric on dead leaves and those of the moulds on freshly cut pieces of melon, quince, and pear. The experiments with moulds were immediately successful, and the spores were again sown and the same fungi again obtained; the experiments were repeated and varied, with convincing results. The agaric needed a much longer time for development; some months after sowing the spores a mycelium was seen on some of the leaves and later gave rise to fruit-bodies of the fungus. Obviously these experiments were not conducted with the precautions afterwards found to be necessary, and, indeed, now a routine in all laboratory work.

Micheli did not adopt the old divisions of Dioscorides which found expression in most of the earlier accounts as Fungi esculenti and Fungi perniciosi. He classified his genera on morphology which, however, in moulds such as his *Aspergillus*, *Botrytis* and *Mucor*, meant the spores and the manner in which they are borne.

Though in the larger fungi external morphology is a guide to their classification, it is not wholly to be relied upon, for occasionally similar forms occur in more than one group. Micheli, though inadvertently, gave the clue to a more scientific system; this is based on the manner in which spores arise.

Fungi are classified in three major groups: Phycomycetes, Ascomycetes, and Basidiomycetes (a subsidiary group, Fungi Imperfecti, includes those genera in which the complete life-cycle is unknown or may not exist). Phycomycetes (literally algal fungi) are mostly filamentous forms which resemble colourless green algae, hence their name.

The fungi with which we are specially concerned fall into the two groups: Ascomycetes, which include cup-fungi, morels, ergot, candle-snuff fungus, and yeasts, having their spores—characteristically eight, contained *within* an enclosing membrane or sack, known as an *ascus*— (Pl. V*a*, p. 134): Basidiomycetes, which include mushrooms, toadstools and bracket-fungi, having characteristically four spores borne on the *outside* of a structure called a *basidium* (Pl. V*e*, p. 134). Most frequently both asci and basidia are club-shaped.

If a thin section taken down the cap of a Field-Mushroom be examined under a microscope the narrowly triangular gills will be seen to have an interior portion of interwoven hyphae (*trama*) enclosed on the almost parallel sides by a layer of closely packed hyphae which

Paul L. de Laszlo

Plate 3. BLUSHER, *Amanita rubescens;* the patches of volva on the cap vary in size, shape and consistency according to the weather during growth. Edible

Plate 4. Tawny Grisette, *Amanitopsis fulva.* Edible

end in very compact cells vertically arranged. These latter form the spore-bearing portion, the *hymenium*. The principal components of this are club-shaped structures (*basidia*) with four teeth-like projections (*sterigmata*) to each of which a spore is originally attached: though many spores will have been detached in making the section the mature basidia are easily recognisable from their sterigmata. Such a section gives a clue to the enormous number of spores produced on the hymenium which completely covers the gills.

In some genera, as for example *Coprinus*, the hymenium shows prominent projecting cells. These *cystidia* vary in size and shape and are sometimes the most conspicuous component.

Micheli was the first to note that the spores of some agarics are arranged in fours (Pl. V*d*, p. 134). There is no indication of the species in which he saw this quaternate arrangement, for the figure is on a plate devoted to illustrating his general description of agarics. As it is most easily seen in dark-spored forms like *Panaeolus* it is probable that the figure is from one of them. He makes no mention of how the spores were attached. He was obviously looking down on the surface of the gill and thus on the ends of the basidia, but the definition of his microscope was not sufficient for him to see that the spores were borne on these above the general surface. In other species he described the spores as being scattered irregularly. Possibly this was in species of *Coprinus* where the basidia are of different lengths; he figures this irregularity in *Coprinus narcoticus*. The irregular arrangement is also shown in *Volvaria gloiocephala*, a pink-spored species, and in an oyster-shaped lignicolous form which is possibly a species of *Crepidotus*; here the spores are too light in colour to show clearly against the general background with the instrument used.

Micheli also observed asci for the first time. These are figured and described in the truffle, with two, three or four warted spores in the ascus (Pl. XVIII*c*, p. 243). He also noted how the spores of cup-fungi were ejected by " puffing."

In his search for flowers Micheli discovered the hairs on the edges of the gills of some agarics. These marginal hairs (*cystidia*) he interpreted as apetalous flowers, a view which seems peculiar to modern minds for they are situated far from where the " seeds " are formed. He also described cystidia on the gill surface of many species, particularly those growing on animal dung (*Coprinus* spp.) and he correctly interpreted their prop-like function in keeping the gills apart: the conical or pyramidal transparent bodies " are made by a wise device of nature so that one lamella does not touch another lest by chance the seeds produced between them shall be hindered in their development and they should not fall only where they ought to fall."

It might have been expected that Micheli's fascinating studies would have aroused some enthusiasm for fungi, for he showed beyond all doubt that they are entities and not degeneration products. Most botanists, however, were, and remained, of the opinion expressed by Sébastien Vaillant in 1728 in the paper from which Linnaeus got his first ideas about the sexuality of plants:

" Je sape entierement . . . ces captieuses Fleurs sans fleur, race maudite, qui semble n'avoir été créee ou inventée que pour en imposer aux plus habiles, & désoler absolument les jeunes Botanistes, lesquels en étant debarassez, se trouvent d'abord en état d'entrer tête levée dans le vaste empire de Flore."

We are accustomed to find a clarity of ideas both on botany and zoology in the writings of Linnaeus, due in part to his amazing ability in picking out essential characters which he made use of in his general classifications. His influence, particularly on botany, was remarkable both for the world-wide acceptance of his opinions and for the length of time that even his *obiter dicta* were regarded as beyond criticism: " Deus creavit, Linnaeus disposuit "; " Un sentiment que M. Linnaeus appuie, est pour moi presque une vérité "; " The very dreams of so great a genius merit our attention." Linnaeus, however, did not advance the study of mycology. Indeed, it may be reasonably held that he definitely retarded it. He began well by describing the species he found on his Lapland tour, and later he gave a competent treatment of fungi in *Flora Suecica*. In *Philosophia Botanica* (1751) he gets a little restive; " The order of Fungi is still Chaos, a scandal of art, no botanist knowing what is a Species and what is a Variety." Such a statement about any subject is both inspiring and hopeful; it is the settled, orthodox belief which stultifies and depresses the " back room boys." But in the same year Otto von Münchhausen wrote to Linnaeus that he had placed the spores of *Ustilago frumenti* (*U. Hordei*), the Smut of corn, in water and in more than two hundred experiments found that their development proved them to be the eggs of insects. This was a period when many possessing microscopes were examining infusions of pepper, hemp and other vegetable seeds. Münchhausen, but not until 1766, published a short account of what he found when fungus spores, especially those of the puff-ball, *Lycoperdon*, were kept in water. They changed into oval, mobile, animal-like balls, and the next day formed clumps of hard weft and from these arose moulds or fungi. Two years later he stated that the spores of toadstools are the eggs of small animals and that the fungus fruit-body should not be regarded as a plant but as the dwelling and edifice of innumerable small animals, and that Linnaeus had confirmed his results. Linnaeus meanwhile had the problem made the subject of a thesis, *Mundus invisibilis*, by his pupil, J. C. Roos. In it we are told that the realm of nature is an immense museum; the large theatres are open to everyone, but the numberless small rooms are locked, and can be entered only by those possessing the key. The immortal Münchhausen had dared to enter a door before which many had stood with hair erect and spirit stunned, desiring to explore the treasures of the room.

With the "facts" before him, Linnaeus, as was his nature so to do, tackled the fundamental problem. Are fungi to be referred to the vegetable or to the animal kingdom, or should they form a new natural kingdom which should be called neuter or chaotic? Should Polyps, Infusoria, and fermentatives be referred there? And in the twelfth edition of *Systema Naturae* we have a genus *Chaos* grouped under Vermes which includes *Chaos Fungorum* and *Chaos Ustilago* for the motile organisms arising from the spores of fungi. The result may have been foreseen. "These thieving and voracious beggars which seize upon the odds and ends which plants leave behind them when Flora is leading them into their winter quarters," as Linnaeus described them, proving unamenable to the Linnaean discipline, attracted many investigators, and not a few impostors. There were also several who tried to wrest the pride of priority for Münchhausen's immortal discovery. What may be called the Münchhausen doctrine with various modifications vying with each other in absurdity, had a tremendous vogue for a time. Even J. Lyly's "I am of this minde with Homer, that . . . the Snayle that crept out of his shell was turned eftsoones into a Toad, and thereby was forced to make a stoole to sit on, disdaining her own house" could doubtless have found supporters. Then it gradually faded out of sight, though it continued into the nineteenth century. Probably without Linnaeus's adherence it would have been still-born.

While this was going on there were variations put forward of the Nicander-Pliny-Marsigli theme, one such notion which regarded fungi as arising by vegetable crystallisation being very popular. For over half a century "the opinions of naturalists on the nature of Fungi, their origin and reproduction were so discordant that whoever wrote about them thought it his duty, either necessarily or legitimately, to form a new theory in order to win the favour of his readers."

One author of the period, commenting on the imbroglio, summarised the position thus: " Es ist so süss etwas zu träumen was noch keiner geträumt hat." ˙

Meanwhile, in 1787, J. Hedwig made the first proper microscopical analysis of the structure of fungi. He described and illustrated twenty species of Discomycetes in his monumental *Descriptio et Adumbratio Muscorum Frondosorum*, in so clear a manner that he established once for all the fact that their spores are enclosed in club-shaped structures (thecae : asci) in a definite number, eight. Previously all cup-shaped fungi were classed together in the genus *Peziza*, which thus included the Bird's nest fungi. Hedwig used the name *Octospora* for the species with eight-spored asci. Moreover, by showing that the fruit-bodies of some Lichens had similar asci he proved the close relation of fungi and lichens.

The presence of asci was readily confirmed in the fleshy Discomycetes and it was at once assumed that all the larger fungi had their spores so arranged that the essential part of the spore-bearing layer (*hymenium*), which appears as a skin to the naked eye, was the ascus. Many authors figured asci on plates illustrating toadstools. Thus, R. K. Greville, in *Scottish Cryptogamic Flora* (1823-28), shows asci containing spores in nineteen Basidiomycetes, e.g. *Cantharellus cibarius* (*Pl.* 258), *Phlebia merismoides* (*Pl.* 280) and *Clavaria rugosa* (*Pl.* 328). However, there were occasional records of a spore arrangement in fours as exceptional occurrences worthy of note, and there was the classical observation of Micheli which awaited explanation. The hypothesis propounded by H. F. Link in 1809, was that the spores of toadstools are contained in asci, in a single series except in *Coprinus* where there are four series; the quaternate arrangement seen in surface view was accounted for by assuming that it was due to the disposition of the spores of contiguous asci. For a quarter of a century every author continued in this opinion. So early as 1780, O. F. Müller, in a plate of *Coprinus comatus*, had given figures of magnified portions of gills, and in one had shown the spores arranged in fours around circular structures, and basidia were figured by C. Vittadini in 1831, though the spores were shown as originally enclosed and passing thence to the exterior. Then B. Ascherson, in a short note in 1836, announced that he had made numerous microscopical observations on the "higher fungi" and had come to the unexpected conclusion that instead of being contained in asci their spores stand on small stalks on cylindrical structures usually to the number of four. The following year (1837) J. H. Léveillé published the results of twelve years' study of the hymenium with a full analysis of the various constituents, basidia, cystidia and paraphyses. M. J. Berkeley published a paper, in 1838, on the "fructification" of the pileate and clavate Hymenomycetes; in *English Flora* (1836) he had noted the quaternate arrangement in several species and had described basidia in *Clitopilus prunulus*, "very minute conical papillae, ending in four spiculae, Sporules . . . often seated upon the spiculae." In 1839 he extended his observations to Gasteromycetes. F. Klotzsch, in 1838, figured basidia in plates of twenty-one Basidiomycetes. P. Phoebus figured them in eight species the same year, but a full account of a paper he had communicated in 1837 was not published till 1842. Further it may be noted that A. C. J. Corda in 1839, claimed that he had described the true structure of the hymenium of Basidiomycetes before the Royal Prussian Academy of Science in 1833 with forty-one drawings, ten of which he later published, but the greatest German microscopists would have none of it, the quaternary arrangement was false, the cystidia, and partly also the basidia, were insect eggs.

The facts just related illustrate in a remarkable way how knowledge advances. It is perhaps most frequent that one more discerning or more brilliant than his fellows makes some discovery. If his contemporaries are in a receptive state the controversies which arise consolidate the position and knowledge advances; if not, the matter remains either as a curiosity or is for the time forgotten. In the present instance the discovery required nothing but exact observation; the facts are such that they can be verified by anyone with an elementary knowledge of the use of a microscope, though their recognition was not so simple merely with a double lens. But practically simultaneously— for apparently none knew of any other investigations until his own were complete—Ascherson, Berkeley, Corda, Klotzsch, Léveillé and Phoebus startled their own coteries by what was an epoch-making discovery, as revolutionary in its effects on the understanding of the structure and classification of fungi as it was simple to confirm. It is of little consequence to assign priority. The veteran mycologist, C. H. Persoon, when Léveillé demonstrated basidia to him, could not conceive how organs so constant and so easy to see could have escaped notice. Berkeley probably hit the nail on the head when he wrote, " the eyes of modern mycologists were for years blinded by Link's celebrated paper, or the real structure would long since have been recognised." Authority has served mycology many scurvy tricks.

Fungi from their very nature played their part in several controversies, and, moreover, were themselves the subject of much discussion later.

CHAPTER 4

HABITATS

JUST AS FLOWERING PLANTS—trees, shrubs and herbs—grow in more or less well defined communities in fields, hedgerows, marshes, sand-dunes, woodlands, so do mushrooms and toadstools. If we consider microfungi this is self evident, for many of them are specialised parasites strictly confined to definite host plants, and their distribution has its limits set by that of the possible victims; entomogenous fungi are dependent upon the presence of the host insect for their occurrence; and saprophytic species, as they are frequently particular in their diet, may be assumed to be restricted in their range in relation to the substrata capable of providing them with nutriment.

Since about the beginning of the present century, the study of plant and animal communities has become a specialised, almost a separate, branch of biological discipline, called Ecology. It is usually overlooked that the germ of many of our ideas about plant groupings is to be found in writings of antiquity (Theophrastus), in those of the herbalists (Porta), in those of Linnaeus and of many others, until the period when natural history in its older sense became so extensive that research had to be more intensive, and teaching more circumscribed. With the advent of the so-called " New Botany " in the 1860's, the work of the laboratory with its microscopes and physiological apparatus proved so fascinating and so convenient for teaching and examinations, that all other branches of the study were for the time neglected. The appeal which Ecology has made is due to its having cut across some of the old barriers and co-ordinated several of the artificially separated aspects of biology. Ecology is by derivation simply the study of organisms in their environment (*o'kos*, abode).

There is no attempt here to treat fungi on a purely ecological basis, although, indeed, it is not possible to consider them as living organisms without regard to their mode of life. Their existence is obligate on that of the other living constituents of the environment.

25

Fungi can be described as a collection of individuals with such and such morphological, anatomical, histological, cytological and other characteristics, but as living organisms they do not exist in splendid isolation. A fungus grows as a member of a community which often may be regarded as a closed system, but it is necessary to consider a community as a very complex and varying structure. One must beware of seeing nothing but trees in a wood, or even of restricting one's view to flowering plants. The south country beech-wood on chalk is, for example, a characteristic community marked by the dominance of the tree, which, owing to the dense shade it casts, determines to a great extent the nature of the ground flora. In some beech-woods herbaceous plants are almost or entirely absent. But other organisms have their rôle, numerous insects and animals of various kinds, including man. Moreover, toadstools abound, several species being confined to such woods or being most frequent there. In addition, microfungi are abundant in the soil and play their part with other organisms in the processes which ensure the continued fertility of the soil. Further, the roots of many forest trees, including beech, are intimately associated with fungus mycelia (see Mycorrhiza, Chap 18). Disease also is a factor which has to be considered, and here again fungi play an important part.

The view stressed here is that though the green mantle of the earth is that which can be most readily apportioned into its constituent units, and though vegetation is " the head stone of the corner " of life as a whole, it is not self-contained nor independent of other organisms. In particular, though fungi, on account of their comparatively small size, may appear insignificant in an assembly of organisms so obviously dominated by a tree that the biologist, in common with the local man, calls it, say, a beech-wood, they are essential components of the community as it exists. As, in the main, toadstools are dependent for their food on the vegetable detritus in and on the soil, they tend to be associated with special plant societies, though the ordinary factors of growth (moisture, temperature, and to some extent, light) also have their effects. As a consequence there are fungi characteristic of different kinds of pasture, of marshes and fen-land, of moors, of heaths, of sand-dunes, and of the various types of woodland.

Little investigation has been carried out on the factors which determine specific distribution. As with all other organisms, fungi must be considered as part of their own environment, affecting it and being affected by it, but with them the complexity of the environment is almost too obvious to permit of trite hypotheses. The least complicated relation is that of parasite to host, and as this is bound up with economic problems—though despite Theophrastus and many moderns, disease is not the result of civilisation or of cultivation—it has received a good deal of attention, as has the search for Haemony " of sov'ran use 'gainst all inchantments, mildew, blast, or damp, Or ghastly furies apparition." It is from the researches of plant pathologists that we may hope to obtain clues to the solution of the more recondite problems which face us when we wish to understand the occurrence of species in certain situations, and their relative frequency.

If one wants to generalise one may say that all organisms, living or dead, and all organic material are liable to be used by fungi as a source of food. Several results follow from this. One which is of primary importance is the effect of fungal growth on organic material. Moulds growing on substances such as fruit, jam, bread and meat, trouble civilised man who wishes to store such foods for future use and, as we know, civilisation had not proceeded far, before he began to baulk famines by laying up reserves in plenteous years; in his primitive state he was probably not less prudent than the squirrel. The use of brine against mould attacks and those of the analogous bacteria, was followed by the various methods so well known—sterilisation, freezing, the use of oil, dehydration—the advantages of which have been abundantly evident during the recent war years when food ousted weather from general conversation.

Obviously from this standpoint fungi are a dreadful scourge, but their ravages are not confined to food. The housewife finds that boots put away damp become covered by a green mould, either *Penicillium* or *Aspergillus*, or her wallpaper, where damp, becomes spotted with black *Macrosporium*, or if wet through a burst pipe or cistern, there may be in addition a pink covering of the small confluent fruit-bodies of the Discomycete *Pyronema*. *Macrosporium* may also cause black diamond-shaped spots on her casement curtains, later to turn into holes. Similar " diamond spots " destroy tentage and sails, and cutching is to prevent this. Great losses are brought about in food products stored in warehouses, and by the mildewing of cotton and cotton fabrics. No householder who has experienced an attack of dry rot will need further evidence of the powers of fungi for evil.

The fungi concerned in all these trials and tribulations are able to act only when there is sufficient moisture and heat for them to grow; they are impotent if moisture is lacking or if the temperature is too high or too low. Consequently their attack can be circumvented by sterilisation if the substratum is such that it can be kept sterile, but all other methods of preservation depend upon desiccation, upon temperature, or upon treating with some fungicide which prevents growth.

The wastage of material of all kinds by fungal attack proved to be one of the major horrors of tropical warfare. The climatic conditions in some of the areas of the Far East, where war recently raged, are ideal for mould growth, for nothing suits them better than a hot, moist atmosphere, and the more luxuriant the growth the more devastating its result: the relative humidity in the jungles of Burma and the Pacific Islands may be between 90 and 100 per cent for considerable periods. Apparently no army foresaw what must happen and when matters took a normal course and materials of all kinds—food, clothing, precision instruments, arms, ammunition, electric and electronic mechanisms—were rendered useless, it seemed to be assumed at first that there had been malevolence and malfeasance by some power of evil. Many optical instruments operated only from four to eight weeks in New Guinea—vision through binoculars and telescopes was obscured by mould growth and films of moisture, with eventual etching of the glass. Instruments shipped from Australia were often useless before they could be issued. The official designation was " tropical deterioration " and the code-word " tropicalisation " for emergency protective treatment. Since the war, evidence has accumulated that" moisture and micro-organisms, particularly fungi, can and do cause just as serious damage (if not quite so rapidly) in areas far from the equator." Moulds cannot grow on clean glass or metal; " dust " or the bodies of minute insects must be present. They are, however, able to spread from affected parts of equipment which provide them with nutriment, and may cause damage by substances produced in their growth.

To deal adequately with these various matters would require a volume. They are mentioned here not merely to indicate how saprophytic fungi can be a menace to man's design for life, but also to suggest that it is this very menace which in the long run is his salvation.

Man, taught that the kindly fruits of the earth are for his enjoyment, finds such an anthropocentric conception of world organisation consoling to his dignity. What happens, however, if he for whatever reason fails to make use of these fruits? What of the fruits of the wild and of tropical forests? We know that, apart from those eaten by birds or other frugivorous animals, they fall to the earth in their due season. We also know for a certainty that they do not accumulate on the ground over the centuries. They rot, mainly through the action of fungi, and eventually the material of which they are composed helps to keep the soil fertile. Similarly, leaves, twigs and branches, tree trunks and all vegetation when it has run its span, rot and decay and are gradually removed by serving as a pabulum for fungi and bacteria. Other organisms, such as insects, are concerned in the general process, but they are secondary: the main scavenger work is done by saprophytic fungi and bacteria.

The picture would be incomplete without some effort to envisage what the state of things would be if such organisms were eliminated. Obviously every tree and sparrow that fell, every animal and insect, every leaf, everything dead would remain throughout the ages where it rested. There would be a gradual accumulation of undecayed and undecayable dead matter which would encumber the earth until life would cease because it would be impossible. If there were no device for decay there would soon be no need for it.

Though green plants are the basis of life, because of their unique ability to form organic from inorganic substances and thus serve as food for all other living creatures, one must not simply be satisfied by the eternal verity that " all flesh is grass " or with the statement that " Life, as we know it, is impossible without chlorophyll." This is abundantly true, but few seem to grasp that it is also beyond question that the cycle of life could not revolve unless there were also organisms without chlorophyll, which, in their search for food, clear away the impedimental remains.

The natural fate of all dead organic material is change, which has as a result the eventual return to the soil of substances necessary for plant life, for as Lucretius said, " No body can be born unless others contribute to it by their death." If man wishes to reserve any of this material for his use he must protect it from fungal attack. He must season wood and keep it dry, or paint it, or treat it with a preservative; otherwise decay is inevitable. The various methods of preserving food have been devised to restrain fungi from fulfilling their natural proclivities.

CHAPTER 5

POISONOUS AND EDIBLE
FUNGI: I

THE DIFFICULTY in writing popularly about fungi is that no general
exact knowledge about them can be assumed. Thus, though
everyone would probably claim to be able to recognise a mushroom,
many have no clear picture in their minds of the essential points to
be looked for in the only species they would think of eating. Some
have an eye for these things and know a mushroom in the same way
as they do a cow, but if asked why, would have difficulty in answering.
The majority, however, are not so sure, but regard " peeling " as an
infallible test, perhaps bolstering this up with some other ancient or
local fancy.

During the years of war there was a good deal of interest here in
the possibility of using fungi as food. When hostilities began official
circles were much concerned lest we should have to face serious
shortages in essential foods, but good fortune attended the schemes
for circumventing the danger and consequently the chief concern of
most people was to arrange variety in an otherwise satisfactory diet,
lest flavour became a war-time casualty. Obviously it was not sound
official policy to strive for this at the expense of staple foods, though
the omission of onions as an essential commodity was one which was
soon remedied in response to widespread complaints. For the most
part the problem was left to individual ingenuity, though advice was
given both officially and unofficially by means of published recipes
and public demonstrations on how to make appetising dishes from the
calorifically correct available foods.

More than two centuries ago, Richard Bradley, Professor of Botany
at Cambridge and a voluminous writer on horticulture and agriculture,
wrote " Whoever has been accustomed to eat *Mushrooms* will certainly
allow them to be one of the greatest Dainties the Earth affords," an

opinion which many hold to-day. Unfortunately for them, mushroom-growing could not be regarded during the war as nationally economic food-production and, moreover, the price was not controlled. Consequently there was a steady increase from 2s. 6d. a pound until 1943, when London prices reached a steady 15s. to 16s. a pound; moreover, even mushroom stalks have been sold at 5s. a pound. The prices of wild mushrooms, which in certain years, for instance 1934, were from 1d. to 3d. a pound in markets, showed similar rapid commercial inflation, and even in 1942, when almost every aerodrome in the country appeared to suffer from overabundance, London prices were 6s. to 8s. 6d. a pound. Obviously there was a ready market at such exorbitant prices, for mushrooms are so perishable that sale must be fairly rapid.

The common belief in this country is that only the Field-Mushroom and possibly the Horse-Mushroom are edible. However, the Morel (*Morchella*) is eaten, particularly in northern counties, and Blewit (*Tricholoma personatum*) in many parts of the country. The rest are generally regarded as dangerously poisonous.

About eighty years ago, half a dozen species were commonly sold in Covent Garden market and this at a time when only the cultivated mushroom was on sale in Paris: there seems to have been no particular reason why it became no longer profitable to offer them for sale. True, the cultivated mushroom was to be had in plenty and it may be held to have ousted others, but that hardly seems a sufficient reason, for the Field-Mushroom continued to find purchasers. Somehow or other the ancient dread of toadstools again arose and this " feare of hid mischance " was fanned by newspapers and magazine articles and by teaching in country schools. Among British people, those who had travelled on the Continent and had learned to know some edible species, and those who had espoused foreigners, were almost alone in indulging in what were regarded as dangerous practices; the outlook has altered greatly, however, in the last ten years, though some people have remained most " indecently and impolitely positive in incredulity " as Boswell remarked of Hume.

The wide knowledge of natural history acquired by country people is generally recognised. They observe the habits of bird, beast or flower with an accuracy which often surprises the trained biologist, but the information to be gained from them about toadstools is amazingly meagre. They know mushroom-meadows, but otherwise there is endless repetition of the old herbalist lore. Pliny, commenting on the difficulty in recognising the different kinds of fungi, said, " Who in fact is able to distinguish them, except those who dwell in the country, or the persons who are in the habit of gathering them? " The only people in Britain who have been in the habit of gathering them are mycologists—which does not take us very far.

Fungus-eating was common in Greek and Roman times. As with fruits there were occasionally serious mishaps through partaking of poisonous species. Indeed, the first two references we have to fungi both refer to accidents. When Euripides (480-406 B.C.) was on a visit to Icarus, a woman and her family gathered fungi and were " strangl'd " by eating of them." " O Sun, that cleavest the undying vault of heaven, hast thou ever seen with thine eye such a calamity as this— a mother and maiden daughter and two sons destroyed by pitiless fate in one day? "

The second case had a happier ending. Hippocrates relates how the daughter of Pausanius, having eaten a raw fungus, was seized with nausea, suffocation and stomach pains. An emetic and a hot bath put matters aright.

For the most part references to fungus-poisoning appear to be of the " news " type; there was danger lurking in common food. Some authors, however, misreading the evidence, advocated banning them from the table. As C. D. Badham says in *Esculent Funguses of England* (1847), " No article of diet was ever half so roughly handled as the fungus. What diatribes against it might be cited from the works of Athenaeus, Dioscorides, Galen, Pliny, the Arabian physicians, and all their commentators! " Tertullian, in one epigram, went so far as to say that for every different colour they display there is a corresponding pain, and just so many kinds of death as there are species. But the denunciations were disregarded: " it is safer to send a messenger with gold and dress than with boleti." Wealthy Romans had special collectors, and it was probably to these that Pliny referred as being able to distinguish the different kinds of fungi. Claudius Cæsar was amongst those who employed them, a custom which excited the wrath of Seneca—" Good God! how many men labour for a single belly! " As is well known, Claudius is reputed to have fallen a victim to a dish of fungi. In all probability the fungus was *Amanita caesarea*, a species which has not been found in this country. It has a scarlet cap and yellow gills, stem and volva, in structure much like *Amanita phalloides*, the Death-Cap (Pl. 1, p. 2), in appearance not unlike *Amanita muscaria*, the Fly-Agaric (Frontispiece). No harm would have come to Claudius if his wife Agrippina, doubtless with the assistance of her son Nero, that " angler in the lake of darkness," had not manipulated the dish. Suetonius, Pliny, Tacitus, Juvenal, and Dio Cassius agree that Claudius was removed, though the precise method adopted to administer the poison is in doubt. Suetonius's account says:

> " and verily it is agreed upon generally by all, that killed he was by poison, but where it should be, and who gave it, there is some difference. Some write that as he sat at a feast in the Capitol castle with the priests, it was presented unto him by Halotus, the eunuch, his taster; others report that it was at a meal in his house by Agrippina herself, who had offered unto him a mushroom empoisoned, knowing that he was most greedy of such meats."

However the assistance was given, Claudius descended into heaven (in coelum descendit) and so made way for another poison (venenum alterum) his stepson Nero, who in reference to Claudius having been deified irregularly at Colchester and officially at death described fungi as food of the gods ($\beta\rho\tilde{\omega}\mu\alpha$ $\Theta\epsilon\tilde{\omega}\nu$).

About twenty species have been identified in Greek and Latin authors with more or less certainty: the most prized by the Romans were boletus (*Amanita caesarea*), fungi suilli (*Boletus edulis*) (Pl. 23, p. 158), and tuber (truffles). There was obvious difficulty in describing fungi in such a way that they could be identified. Added to this there is uncertainty of occurrence both in habitat and in season, together with the evanescent character of the fleshy species which alone can serve as food. It is all very different from what obtains in trees, shrubs, and herbs, and many of the accounts were obviously written from memory or from hearsay. Pliny says that Cratevas, Dionysius and Metrodorus adopted the very attractive plan of delineating the various plants in colours; but there is no suggestion that any but flowering plants were painted. However, the earliest illustration known of a fungus occurs on a fresco from Herculaneum (buried in A.D. 79): it probably represents *Lactarius deliciosus*.

When it was realised that there might be death in a pot of fungi it was obvious that care should be taken in selecting them, or that all should be avoided. If it was not possible so to describe them that they could be recognised, then rules for testing whether a species was safe or dangerous should be drawn up. In view of the frequent references to poisoning, it is remarkable that so little information is given about the fungi believed to be responsible. Indeed in Pliny's opinion one of the reasons for avoiding fungi is that they are very convenient for administering poison (venenis accommodatissimi), and to illustrate this he records the death of the prefect of Nero's guard, together with a number of tribunes and centurions at a banquet where they partook of suilli. At that period of Roman history it must have been difficult to decide whether or not a fungus was responsible for ensuing trouble. Possibly the practice that " fungi are the only food which dainty voluptuaries prepare with their own hands and thus, as it were, feed upon them by anticipation, using amber knives and silver service " was not quite so foolish as Pliny suggests: they could at least know where trouble, if any, originated.

With so little fact to go upon it is not surprising that the rules promulgated for deciding which species were safe should be nonsensical. But they were accepted without question by the Herbalists and some enjoy widespread belief even to-day. Everyone has heard of two at least of them: an edible fungus " peels " and does not tarnish a silver spoon when cooking; the latter is current even amongst the native cooks in Indo-China. A Field-Mushroom certainly peels, but peeling is not a distinguishing character, for *Amanita phalloides*, the most deadly of fungi, also peels. Neither blackens silver; indeed no fungus of itself does.

No useful purpose would be served by detailing the different rules and tests that are, or have been, current. They refer to colour and shape; smell and taste; exudation of " milk " when broken, or change in colour of the flesh; coagulation of milk or changing the colour of onion or parsley in cooking; time and place of appearance. All are equally valueless. Perhaps more logical is the idea that fungi nibbled by rabbits or squirrels, or eaten by slugs are edible: obviously they are so for these animals, but are not necessarily wholesome for man. Slugs seem to be particularly fond of *Amanita phalloides*, and the stomach contents of rabbits are able to neutralise the poison of this most dangerous species. Furthermore, it is unwise to place reliance even in trials on domestic animals.

The fact that none of these ancient and widely believed criteria is of any worth is less surprising than that any credence should ever have been placed in them, for such rule-of-thumb methods play no part in deciding for or against other foods.

The only certain test is eating. This may sound irrelevant to anyone intent on procuring information, but it is the time-honoured

Plate Ia (*above*). **Corner of fungus-market at Munich, 1936.**

(*Photograph by G. Beal*)

b (*left*).   Fresco from disused church at Plaincourault (Indre, France) dating from 1291, showing *Amanita muscaria* as the tree of good and evil.

method by which we have acquired enlightenment on what we shall eat. We know that one fruit or plant is edible, another poisonous, from knowledge obtained in the remote past by accident or by design, presumably so soon as man could comprehend cause and effect and was able to pass on the information. If asked how to distinguish between a Blackberry and the Deadly Nightshade, the answer would be an attempt to describe them, not a series of tests to be applied to all fruits. We know that the Deadly Nightshade is poisonous because it has proved to be so whenever it has been eaten.

To know whether a fungus is safe to eat we must be able to recognise it and know its proved reputation.

There is abundant evidence about which fungi are poisonous as well as those which are most palatable. For most people the wisest plan is to learn some of the second group and eschew the rest. Those who have the urge to try everything once would be well advised to learn first to distinguish, so as to avoid, the poisonous species and especially the deadly Amanitas.

Our national attitude to fungi appears to have its origin in the writings of the sixteenth and seventeenth centuries, though none of the authors apparently wrote from experience, but based his accounts on what was contained in ancient writings, which had gradually become known as printing spread. The Herbalists had as their chief consideration the elucidation of *De Materia Medica* of Dioscorides, which was " as it were, the foundation and groundeworke of all that has been since delivered in this nature." Thomas Johnson's *An Advertisement to the Readers*, appended to the (1636) " second Edition of revised Gerrard," gives a contemporary view of the purpose of Herbals:

" I judge it requisite that we should labour to know those Plants which are, and ever are like to be Inhabitants of this Isle; for I verily beleeve that the divine Providence had a care in bestowing Plants in each part of the Earth, fitting and convenient to the foreknowne necessities of the future Inhabitants."

Dioscorides, an Asiatic Greek military surgeon in Nero's Army, describes about 500 plants, though he deals principally with their healing virtues. The earliest manuscripts of Dioscorides are lost and are thought not to have been illustrated; the famous Vienna Codex, a Byzantine version dating from about *c.* 512, has large-scale wash drawings believed to be derived wholly or in part from originals by

---

Plate II.   Parasol-Mushroom, *Lepiota procera,* often forming large rings amongst grass. (*H. J. Howard*)

Cratevas.* No fungi are figured. Indeed, there is only one described, the *Agarikon*, still in use under the name *Agaric* or *White Agaric* (*Polyporus officinalis*), as a purgative or to check sweating,† but reported by Dioscorides to have an amazing range of medicinal virtues, being efficacious for fractured limbs, dysentery, asthma, epilepsy, and so on, an antidote to poisons and a relief against serpent bites. Less space is given to general remarks about fungi: " Of Fungi there is a double difference, for either they are edible, or they are poisonous, and come to be so on many occasions." The occasions are when they " growe where olde rustie iron lieth, or rotten clouts, or neere to serpents dens, or rootes of trees that bring foorth venemous fruits."‡

The influence of Dioscorides was so strong that his statements were repeated by most if not all who mentioned fungi, particularly the Herbalists. The first British herbal—Banckes's *Herball*, 1525, does not refer to them, but *The grete herball** (1526) says:

" There be two maners of them. . . . They that be not deedly have a grosse gleymy moysture, that is dysobedyent to nature and dygestyon and be peryllous and dredfull to eate therefore it is good to eschew them."

John Gerard in *The Herball* (1597), a translation for the most part of Dodoens's *Pemptades*, but rearranged according to de l'Obel, says:

" Many wantons that dwell neere the sea, and have fish at will, are very desirous for change of diet to feede upon the birds of the mountains; and such as dwell upon the hils or champion grounds, do long after sea fish; many that have plenty of both, doe hunger after the earthie excrescences, called Mushrums: whereof some are very venemous and full of poison; others not so noisome; and neither of them very wholesome meate. . . . To conclude, few of them are good to be eaten; and most of them do suffocate and strangle the eater. Therefore I give my simple advice unto those that love strange and newe fangled meates, to beware of licking honie among thornes, least the sweetenes of the one do not countervaile the sharpnes and pricking of the other."

*Cratevas was a physician to Mithridates. Linnaeus dedicated the genus *Cataeva* (Capparidaceae) to him. There was another herbalist of the same name mentioned by Hippocrates.

†It enters into the composition of the " Elixir de longue vie " (*Tinct. Aloes compos.*).

‡Presumably because they absorb deleterious substances. In southern Italy a piece of metal is placed in the water in which fungi are cooked, in the belief that it will attract and withdraw any poison which may be present.

**The grete herball whiche geveth parfyt knowledge and understandyng of all maner of herbes and there gracyous vertues . . . was " translated out of ye Frensshe " mostly from *Le grand Herbier*.

John Parkinson in *Theatrum Botanicum: The Theater of Plants; or an Herball of a large extent* (1640), more closely follows Dioscorides. He has a chapter headed " Fungi esculenti. Holsome Mushromes that may be eaten," followed by one on "Fungi pernitiosi. Dangerous Mushromes." These last "whereof there are many sorts . . . dangerous if not poysonous," but there is no need to caution against them, " seeing our Nation is not so inclined to the good." This remark about native aversion is not supported by J. E. [John Evelyn] in *Acetaria. A Discourse of Sallets* (1699). He would have banished fungi from the work " were I to order the Composition," but not for reason other than that they were not to be eaten crude.

" However so highly contended for by many, as the very principal and top of all the rest ; whilst I think them tolerable only (at least in this *Climate*) if being fresh and skillfully chosen, they are accommodated with the nicest Care and Circumspection; generally reported to have something malignant and noxious in them: Not without cause; from the many sad Examples, frequent Mischiefs, and funest Accidents they have produc'd, not only to particular Persons, but whole Families."

The accounts of these last, however, all have reference to the ancients.

Meanwhile, in *Sylva Sylvarum* (1627), Francis Bacon had shown that he had other views.

" The Mushromes have two strange properties; the one that they yield so delicious a Meat; the other, that they come up so hastily, as in a night, and yet they are unsown. And therefore such as are Upstarts in State, they call in reproach, *Mushromes*. It must needs be therefore, that they be made of much moisture; and that moisture fat, gross, and yet somewhat concocted. And (indeed) we finde, that *Mushromes* cause the accident, which we call *Incubus*, or the *Mare* in the stomach. And therefore the Surfeit of them may suffocate and empoyson. And this sheweth, that they are windy; and that windiness is gross, and swelling, not sharp or griping. And upon the same reason *Mushromes* are a venereous Meat."

Thus it is not very clear what was the attitude of people generally towards fungus-eating. Parkinson says definitely that as a nation we did not favour them, but I can find no confirmations of this. Evelyn relates that " at no small charge we send for them into *France*; as we also do for *Trufles* . . . rank and provocative Excrescences," which suggests that they were considered to be delicacies by some at least of the wealthier classes. There is also the statement by W. Harrison in Holinshed's *Chronicles* (1577) that "the English eat dangerous fruits, like mushrooms."

The impression I have gained is that there was no general aversion from fungi as food. Doubtless even if the ancient Britons refrained from eating them, which is unlikely, the Romans would introduce the practice, and from medieval monastic diet rolls, we know that monks, often much travelled men in constant contact with Rome, made use of them; they have always been valued for replacing meats during fasting, particularly where fish is not readily obtainable. It is said that Pope Clement VII was so fond of them that he forbade their use in his States for fear there should be a shortage: the tradition that his death in 1534 was due to them is not true. St. François de Sales, however, in his *Introduction à la vie dévote* (1609), compares medical opinion on fungi with his own on dances, considering even the best worthless, and advising that if fungi are eaten they should be well cooked and taken in moderation.

Two medieval references seem to bear on the matter. The one is the recipe already quoted from *the forme of cury*: "Take funges, and pare hem." An earlier one dating from the ninth or tenth century, translated in O. Cockayne's *Leechdoms, Wortcunning and Starcraft of Early England*, is in a recipe for making a woman pregnant: "and for meat she shall use mushrooms."

Of minor significance is that they figured in quit or peppercorn rents. Thus John de Warrenna, Earl of Sussex and Surrey, who died in 1347, held a manor of Gymygham (Gimingham), County Norfolk, by the rendering to the king a campernolle (mushroom) yearly.

That they should appear in coats-of-arms is not surprising. A drawing of the arms of Dryland in the Harleian Manuscripts shows Wert, a chevron purpure; between three mushrooms slipped argent. In the same Harleian manuscript are the arms of three French families showing mushrooms. It would be reasonable to assume that the Normans would have brought with them their taste for fungi and that their consumption would have been considered a badge of aristocracy if it had not been already customary to eat them in this country.

It is possible that the introduction of printing was the cause of the Englishman's later attitude towards fungi. The constant stress laid on the accidents that had occurred well over a thousand years previously had its effect when a classical education was the only possible one. Later the diminution of woodlands—an ever present concern to those connected with the navy—and the comparative abundance of other foods doubtless damped desire for them, and eventually a stage was reached where it was taught and believed that the Dioscoridean " Fungi good to eat " was an exaggeration and that there is only one edible fungus, the common mushroom, preferably cultivated: this, moreover, at a time when every other European nation regarded fungi as a valuable constituent of their diets. Everywhere they are on sale, and in some towns, as formerly at Munich, there are special fungus-markets (Pl. Ia, p. 34). In devastated Europe they have been eagerly sought. If the belief common in this country were true, there would scarcely be a living person in most of Continental Europe.

There are very few poisonous fungi even if we use poisonous in its widest sense; less than there are of noxious flowering plants. But amongst them are species that kill, and kill mercilessly. Deaths attributed to fungus-eating are almost invariably due to *Amanita phalloides*, the Death-Cap (Pl. 1, p. 2) or its close allies, *Amanita verna*, the Fool's Mushroom, and *Amanita virosa*, the Destroying Angel (Pl. 2a, p. 3). Two other species of Amanita, *Amanita muscaria*, the Fly-Agaric (Frontispiece), and *Amanita pantherina*, the Panther, are definitely poisonous.

In the genus *Amanita* a membrane surrounds the young fungus. In addition to this wrapper or volva there is another membrane, stretching from the margin of the cap and joined to the stem, as in the mushroom. Thus it is as if the " button stage " were surrounded by an outer skin. As the fungus develops this is torn apart. If its texture is sufficiently tenacious to hold together, it is left as a cup at the base of the stem (*A. phalloides*); if it is friable the part covering the cap remains there and becomes broken up into wart-like particles (*A. muscaria*, *A. pantherina*). An intermediate type is seen in *A. mappa* (Pl. 2b, p. 3). With growth the membrane covering the gills tears and is left as a ring on the stem. The spores are white and the gills in most species are also white: they do not quite reach the stem.

Amanita phalloides has a hemispherical, then flattened, greenish olive silky cap with blackish fibrils radiating from the centre; occasionally it is more yellowish or brownish or even whitish. The gills, stem and ring are white, but may have a slight greenish tinge. It has no particular smell or taste. Before the volva breaks the fungus looks somewhat like a pigeon's egg half-buried, or like a small *Phallus* " egg " (Pl. 38a, p. 247). It is common in glades in woods and adjoining pastures after the first summer rains, and continues through early autumn.

Amanita verna and *A. virosa* are rare. Both grow in woods in summer and autumn, the former especially under beeches. *A. verna* closely resembles *A. phalloides*, but is usually entirely white, though the centre of the cap may be slightly brownish. The stem is more slender and the volva usually more sheathing. *Amanita virosa* has a slightly viscid cap which is at first conical, often asymmetrical, giving it rather a tipsy look, and always retaining a central swelling when fully expanded. The stem is slender and covered with floccose scales, and the ring is silky and usually lower on one side and often remaining attached to the rim of the cap. It is entirely white.

How is it that *Amanita phalloides* is mistaken for the Field-Mushroom? *A. verna* and *A. virosa* have a closer resemblance because of their white caps, but they are too rare to account for any of the thirty-nine fatal cases of fungus poisoning in England and Wales recorded by the Registrar General between 1920 and 1950. It is difficult to find any explanation other than that reliance has been placed on the presence of a ring on the stem and " peeling ": indeed victims have stated that they " knew they were mushrooms because they peeled." Deaths on the Continent are not due to this confusion, but rather to the practice of eating every species that looks appetising, though in most countries posters are displayed contrasting its characters with those of the mushroom. It is worth noting that deaths among English people have not been caused by eating toadstools intentionally but what were thought to be mushrooms.

The symptoms of *Amanita phalloides* poisoning are characteristic and terrible. Several distinct clinical forms have been described but the precise conditions determining them are not yet known. The general course is, however, the same. After ingestion there is an incubation period of from ten to twelve hours during which no discomfort is felt. This late onset is almost diagnostic. It is followed by sudden and intense abdominal pains with vomiting, cold sweats, diarrhoea and excessive thirst. The symptoms subside after two days, but this period of a few hours' quiescence is most dangerous, for after it they recur in a more intense form. Usually the nervous system is gradually paralysed, the liver degenerates, there is delirium following coma, then collapse and death.* There are often accompanying symptoms of an equally

---

*The celebrated mummies of the Tour St. Michel at Bordeaux, moved from an ancient cemetery in 1810 and ranged along the wall of the crypt, date from the beginning of the fifteenth century. Of the seventy there is a family of seven which show strong evidence of having died from poisoning by *A. phalloides*: the traces of pain still show on the faces.

distressing nature. Death occurs three to ten days after ingestion, depending upon the resistance of the victim and the amount of fungus absorbed. All parts of the fungus, including the spores, are poisonous, and a surprisingly small amount will cause illness and even death. The percentage of recoveries is difficult to estimate because formerly *Amanita mappa* was assumed to be equally poisonous and, indeed, is often misidentified as *A. phalloides*. It has been put as high as 50% and as low as 10%. What is certain, however, is that at least 90% of the recorded deaths through fungus-poisoning have been caused by the *Amanita phalloides* group.

The search to determine the source of the toxicity has been long and difficult. Early investigators were obviously not competent to tackle the problem efficiently and there was, moreover, the confusion between *A. phalloides* and *A. mappa*. Modern research began when R. Kobert in 1891 isolated a haemolytic substance which he called phalline. At first he considered this to be the active principle and this opinion was widely adopted even when his later experiments in 1899 showed that there were two poisons, the water soluble haemolytic phalline rapidly destroyed by much less heat ($140°$-$150°$ F.) than is usually employed in cooking, and a non-haemolytic substance which is heat-resistant and responsible for most of the symptoms. W. W. Ford, from 1906 onwards, made a more exact study which formed the basis for future research. He called the two substances Amanita-haemolysin and Amanita-toxin, and showed the first to be a glucoside with the formula $C_{50}H_6O_{32}N_{10}S$, destroyed by digestive juices, present sometimes in only small amounts, and occurring also in some well-known edible species, e.g. *Amanita rubescens*. Very rarely are there symptoms of haemolysis in *A. phalloides* poisoning. Amanita-toxin is heat resistant, is not acted on by digestive juices, and injected into animals produces the characteristic symptoms.

Since 1940 a group of German chemists (H., T. and U. Wieland and their collaborators) has made a detailed study of this Amanita-toxin. They have shown that it consists of a complex of three substances which they have obtained in a crystalline state—α amanitine, β amanitine and phalloidine.

Amanitine is a polypeptide containing an indol group and having the formula $C_{33}H_{45}(47)O_{12}N_7S$ and forming about 60% of Amanita-toxin. It is slow in action, causing hypoglycaemia and caryolysis, being responsible for the principal symptoms. The least trace inflamed the eyes of the investigators and caused running eczematous slowly-healing sores on the skin. Phalloidine is a hexapeptide having the formula $C_{30}H_{39}O_9N_7S$. It is rapid in action causing degeneration of the liver, kidney and cardiac muscle and possibly some haemorrhage of the digestive tubes.

Experiments on mice gave the relative toxicities per 25 grams weight: α amanitine, 2.5γ kills within five days; β amanitine, 8-10γ within three days and phalloidine, 40-50γ within two to three days.

With such a long incubation period it is useless to try to ameliorate the poisoning by removing the remains of the fungus from the stomach when the symptoms are recognised. The Institut Pasteur has produced an antiphalloidian serum by immunising horses. This has given consistently good results when injected hypodermically or intravenously shortly after the first sign of poisoning. The sporadic occurrence of the poisoning and its comparative rarity, make it impossible for pharmacists to stock fresh serum.* Consequently a country pactitioner will need to look to other methods.

It has been found that there is a considerable lowering of the percentage of glucose in the blood in *A. phalloides* poisoning. This hypoglycaemia is one of the causes of the lesions of the liver and the kidneys. Intravenous injections of 20 c.c. of 4% glucose in normal saline solution four or five times a day gradually restores the amount of sugar, and modifies the effects of the poison, with frequent recovery. It is not advisable to administer the sugar by the mouth because of the constant vomiting. In fault of glucose, saccharose or ordinary sugar may be used. It is worth recording that J. Roques, in 1821, recommended a large quantity of honeyed or sugared water as an antidote.

A similar treatment originated when Le Calvé in 1936 was called to attend to eight nuns who had eaten *Amanita phalloides*; a ninth nun had died. Seeing their excessive nausea he recalled to mind that salt had been recommended as a cure for rebellious vomiting and administered a coffee-spoon full in a glass of water to relieve their distress, at first every half-hour and then hourly. The vomiting diminished. Normal saline solution was then injected hypodermically and there was recovery. The suggestion is that the frequence and abundance of the evacuation leads to dehydration, which brings about cramp, and causes hypochloraemia: this accelerates the rhythm of the evacuations

*Emergency applications for the serum (sérum antiphalloïdien) may be made to the Public Health Laboratory, Hendon. Supplies can be dispatched by air at short notice from the Institut Pasteur, 28 Rue du Dr. Roux, Paris XV. Telephone Ségur 01-10.

and produces a serious disintegration of the albumins of the tissues. Thus both these treatments add to the blood. Both seek to reconstitute the proper percentage of an important constituent, the one sugar, the other salt. They are not antidotes but remedies for two of the serious effects.

A third method which has had a good deal of publicity both in the medical and in the lay press, is difficult to regard with due seriousness. It is based on the belief that a rabbit can eat *Amanita phalloides* without ill-effect. The assumption is that the poison contained in the fungus consists of a portion which brings about degeneration of liver and kidneys and irritation of the intestine (hepato-toxin) and another which acts on the central nervous system, bringing about progressive paralysis (neuro-toxin). The rabbit's stomach contents must therefore contain some substance capable of neutralising the hepato-toxin, its brain some antidote to the neuro-toxin. The stomachs of three rabbits and the brains of seven are chopped up finely and made into pellets and administered with sugar or jam. It is a strange mixture to give raw to the patient suffering from distressing vomiting; it calls to mind the ancient Mithridate. That rabbits are easily obtainable and that they afterwards may be served at table, are regarded as favourable accessories of the treatment. Cures have been reported, but possibly the sugar may have had some effect. It should be noted that though rabbits, in common with some other animals, do not suffer from eating the fungus in small amounts, the immunity is only relative and is due to a neutralisation *in vivo* of the toxin by gastric juices; they succumb with larger quantities.

One of the best known of all fungi is *Amanita muscaria*, the Fly-Agaric. With its bright scarlet cap covered with white or yellowish warts, white gills and a white stem with a white or yellowish ring, it attracts attention and admiration as it glistens in the autumn sun amongst birches or under pines. But it is usually known from earliest childhood as it forms the motif of numerous toys and decorations.* As it is so unlike a Field-Mushroom there is little likelihood of its being eaten unawares. Possibly because it is so far removed in appearance from the one species known to be edible, it is frequently said to " look poisonous." There is no danger in this of itself, but there is in

*The film *Fantasia* showed a ring of this fungus to translate into colour, form and visible movement, the music of one of the dances in Tchaikovsky's Nutcracker Suite. Before Pearl Harbour a " still " of this was sent inscribed " From *Fantasia*. To Chiang Kai-shek—In admiration. Walt Disney."

believing that those fungi without this theoretical distinction are safe. Many will recall that soldiers in New Guinea ate Finger-Cherries (*Rhodomyrtus macrocarpa*) because of their attractiveness. One or two of these fruits did no apparent harm, but nine to ten caused total and apparently permanent blindness. The Fly-Agaric is poisonous, but, in spite of its popular reputation, is not deadly: indeed it is probable that it does not cause death in healthy people.

The incubation period is much shorter than with the Death-Cap, usually one to three hours. Typically there is then a period of excitement and hallucinations simulating alcoholic intoxication, followed fairly rapidly by a deep coma and an awakening to complete forgetfulness. Sometimes the illness may consist merely of colic, vomiting and diarrhoea, though there may be accompanying delirium, loss of memory, convulsions and prostration with a tendency to sleep. Recovery is rapid. The poison appears to reside principally in the skin on the cap, which, incidentally, " peels."

In contrast with the Death-Cap the Fly-Agaric seems to vary considerably in its effects. It is eaten in some districts in France and this suggests either that special local methods of cooking eliminate the poison, or that its presence is somehow dependent upon environmental conditions. Personal idiosyncrasy may account for the immunity of certain individuals. Another possibility is that strains occur which are little, if at all harmful, though this would not explain the facts given by various writers.

Amanita muscaria has been used since medieval times, broken up in milk, to stupefy flies. Albertus Magnus in *De vegetabilibus* (before 1256) mentions this—" Vocatur fungus muscarum, eo quod in lacte pulverizatus interficit muscas "—and the old popular name was adopted by Linnaeus, who called the fungus *Agaricus muscarius*. The method is still in use in country districts on the Continent; in Poland and Czechoslovakia a sugar solution replaces the milk, or sugar is sprinkled on the cap. The fungus is placed on window-sills in Roumania to discourage flies from entering. It was formerly used both in this country and in Sweden for getting rid of bugs: hence the name Bug-Agaric which is to be found in old books.

It is perhaps not surprising that a fungus having the power to produce intense excitement should have been deliberately used for that purpose. There is a tradition that the Vikings sought its aid to go berserk—apparently started by S. Ödman in 1784—and stories were told in the days of prohibition in U.S.A., that it was found less expensive and just as effective as boot-leg liquor. What would doubtless be regarded as a fable but for its repeated confirmation over two centuries, is the use made of the fungus by the Koryak and neighbouring tribes of Kamchatka:ᛋ P. J. Strahlenberg (1736)*, S. Krasheninnikov (1737-41), [J. Grieve (1764), La Harpe (1780)], G. H. Langsdorff (1804-5), K. v. Ditmar (1851-5), G. Kennan (1865-7), H. Lansdell (1882), N. V. Slunin (1900), W. B. Vanderlip (1903), and S. Bergman (1927) all refer to it. W. I. Jochelsen, in 1900-01, carried out a study of the Koryak tribes. The Fly-Agaric is among the objects believed by the Koryak to be endowed with particular power.

" Once, so the Koryak relate, Big-Raven had caught a whale, and could not send it to its home in the sea. He was unable to lift the grass bag containing travelling-provisions for the whale. Big-Raven applied to Existence (Vahīyñin) to help him. The deity said to him, ' Go to a level place near the sea: there thou wilt find white soft stalks with spotted hats. These are the spirits wāṕaq. Eat some of them, and they will help thee.' Big-Raven went. Then the Supreme Being spat upon the earth, and out of his saliva the agaric appeared.† Big-Raven found the fungus, ate of it, and began to feel gay. He started to dance. The Fly-Agaric said to him, ' How is it that thou, being such a strong man, canst not lift the bag? '—' That is right ' said Big-Raven. ' I am a strong man. I shall go and lift the travelling-bag.' He went, lifted the bag at once, and sent the whale home. Then the Agaric showed him how the whale was going out to sea, and how he would return to his comrades. Then Big-Raven said ' Let the Agaric remain on earth, and let my children see what it will show them.' "

The Koryak's idea is that a person drugged with the fungus does what the spirits residing in it tell him to do.

" The Koryak are most passionate consumers of the poisonous crimson fly-agaric, even more so than the related Kamchadal and Chukchee,

*It is apparently from Strahlenberg that Oliver Goldsmith derives the account given in *Letters from a Citizen of the World to his friends in the East* (1762).

†This recalls the tradition current in Poland and adjoining regions. When Christ and Peter were passing through a forest after a long journey without food, Peter, who had a loaf in his sack but did not take it out for fear of offending his Master, slipped a piece in his mouth. Christ, who was in front, spoke to him at that moment and Peter spat out so that he could answer. This occurred several times until the loaf was finished. Wherever Peter spat out, edible fungi appeared. The devil who was walking behind saw this and decided to go one better by producing brighter and more highly coloured mushrooms. He spat mouthfuls of bread all over the country-side. The wonderfully coloured mushrooms as well as those which looked very much like St. Peter's mushrooms, were, however, all poisonous.

probably because the fungus is most common in their territory," and a very profitable trade results from gathering and drying it. " The Koryak do not eat the fly-agaric fresh. The poison is then more effective, and kills more speedily. The Koryak say that three fresh fungi suffice to kill a person. Accordingly, fly-agaric is dried in the sun or over the hearth after it has been gathered. It is eaten by men only; at least, I never saw a woman drugged by it. The method of using it varies*. As far as I could see . . . the men, before eating it, first let the women chew it, and then swallow it . . . the alkaloid of fly-agaric produces intoxication, hallucinations, and delirium. Light forms of intoxication are accompanied by a certain degree of animation and some spontaneity of movements. Many shamans, previous to their seances, eat fly-agaric in order to get into ecstatic states. . . . Under strong intoxication, the senses become deranged; surrounding objects appear either very large or very small, hallucinations set in, spontaneous movements, and convulsions. So far as I could observe, attacks of great animation alternate with moments of deep depression. The person intoxicated by fly-agaric sits quietly rocking from side to side, even taking part in the conversation with his family. Suddenly his eyes dilate, he begins to gesticulate convulsively, converses with persons whom he imagines he sees, sings, and dances. Then an interval of rest sets in again. However, to keep up the intoxication, additional doses of fungi are necessary. Finally a deep slumber results, which is followed by headache, sensations of nausea, and an impulse to repeat the intoxication. . . . There is reason to think that the effect of fly-agaric would be stronger were not its alkaloid quickly taken out of the organism with the urine. The Koryak know this by experience, and the urine of persons intoxicated with fly-agaric is not wasted. The drunkard himself drinks it to prolong his hallucinations, or he offers it to others as a treat. According to the Koryak, the urine of one intoxicated by fly-agaric has an intoxicating effect like the fungus, though not to so great a degree. . . . From three to ten dried fungi can be eaten without deadly effect."

The Fly-Agaric is one of the easiest fungi to recognise and to describe. Consequently its poisonous properties were early known, though doubtless it had attributed to it powers beyond its possession. In a fresco in a ruined chapel at Plaincourault (Indre, France), dating from 1291, a branched specimen is painted to represent the tree of good and evil (Pl. I*b*, p. 34). Presumably it was the artist's conception

*M. Enderli who accompanied the expedition, describes how a woman sat between her husband and his friend and chewed the fungus, then rolled it between her hands into small " sausages " which the men then thrust to the back of the throat. The Fly-Agaric has a burning and sickly taste, and readily causes vomiting, which would interfere with the men's enjoyment.

of the essence of evil made more terrible by enlargement and prolifera-
tion. The serpent is shown winding round the stem, offering the
traditional apple to Eve, who, apparently having eaten of the " tree,"
is shown in an attitude which suggests that she is " suffering from colic
rather than from shame."

The poisons of the Fly-Agaric have been studied for well over a
century. In 1869 Schmeideberg and Koppe isolated muscarine, which
they thought was the essential constituent. It is present in variable
but always very small amounts. There has been much research on
its constitution. Recently (1956) the molecule has been shown to contain three N-methyl groups, its formula corresponding to $C_9H_{20}O_2N_+$.
Its physiological effects are well known—abundant sweating and
salivation, augmented intestinal peristalsis, colic, diarrhoea, pupils contracted, myosis, slowing down and finally stopping of the heart—but
they are not those of *Amanita muscaria* poisoning. As the experiments
were carried out with synthetic muscarine (isomuscarine) it is usual to
distinguish that in the fungus as mycetomuscarine. Schmeideberg himself found that the muscarine he isolated would not kill flies, and moreover, realised that it could not be the cause of the observed symptoms.
He suspected the presence of another alkaloid (muscaridine). If muscarine is eliminated the fungus still retains its poisonous properties
practically unaltered. These are so similar to those caused by deadly
nightshade (*Belladonna*, atropine) that it is assumed to be of the same
nature and called mycetoatropine although its chemical structure is not
yet ascertained. It is only very occasionally that any symptoms
suggesting muscarine poisoning have been recorded with *Amanita
muscaria*, though certain other fungi give such symptoms. Occasionally,
there are also accompanying gastro-intestinal discomforts. These are
attributed to choline, which is fairly abundant and is an oxidation
product of muscarine, and possibly other resinoid substances which
are present are also concerned.

The old treatment of administering atropine as an antidote to muscarine, aggravates the symptoms. Emetics and purgatives should be
given and chloral hydrate or potassium bromide to appease the delirium.

Amanita muscaria is used in homoeopathic practice under the names
Agaric, Agar., or Aga; the dried cap is powdered or a tincture made
of the fresh fungus. " Sunstroke is within the curative range of Agaric."
It is said to be efficacious against chilblain and chorea and many
homoeopathic practictioners have recorded it as specific for bunions.
It has also been alleged to clear up certain types of cataract.

Amanita pantherina is very similar in its effects and in its chemistry.* It somewhat resembles the Fly-Agaric, but has a brownish grey or brown cap, darker in the centre, with white spots and a striated margin. It grows principally in woods, in summer and autumn. In some German books this fungus is given as edible owing to confusion with *Amanita spissa*, which differs in the cap being smoky brown and having smaller, less well-defined warts, sometimes even a powdery covering, and in the stem being slightly striate above the ring and the bulbous base being obconic and rooting.

The real danger, however, is that *Amanita pantherina* should be mistaken for the much commoner well-known edible species *Amanita rubescens*, the Blusher (Pl. 3, p. 18), which appears from late summer throughout the autumn. In this species the cap is more reddish brown and the warts are usually less distinct. It is a most variable fungus and both size and appearance seem to be definitely related to the conditions of growth: when growing in dry places it is small, firm and compact, and the warts are well defined; in moist places it is large, lax and soft, and the covering of the cap shows as grey patches, or may even be absent owing to rain washing it off or the cap slipping through the volva. The specific epithet refers to the flesh turning pink when broken. This may take a considerable time in more compact specimens, but in lax ones it can usually be noted as pink spots on the gills, or these may become wholly coloured with age. Further, if the base of the stem is maggot-ridden it will be found to be already pink; many species are liable to be infected with fly maggots, but *A. rubescens* seems particularly prone to attack.

Addendum. Mr. R. Gordon Wasson, of New York, an authority on the folk-lore of fungi, writes to me as follows (cf. p. 46): Rightly or wrongly, we are going to reject the Plaincourault fresco as representing a mushroom. This fresco gives us a stylized motif in Byzantine and Romanesque art of which hundreds of examples are well known to art historians, and on which the German art historians bestow, for convenience in discussion, the name *Pilzbaum*. It is an iconograph representing the Palestinian tree that was supposed to bear the fruit that tempted Eve, whose hands are held in the posture of modesty traditional for the occasion. For almost a half century mycologists have been under a misapprehension on this matter. We studied the fresco *in situ* in 1952.

*It is used in Japan for killing flies and has a popular name, "Hayétoritaké," denoting this.

CHAPTER 6

POISONOUS AND EDIBLE
FUNGI: II

EVER SINCE the time of the conquest of Mexico by the Spaniards in 1522 there have been references to a sacred fungus employed as a narcotic by the Indians. The Aztecs and Chichimecas were the earliest recorders of this *teonanacatl*, but its identity has remained obscure, and, indeed it has been confused with *peyote*, a cactus, *Lophophora Williamsii*, which also has narcotic properties. R. E. Schultes, in his ethnobotanical studies among the Mazatec Indians of north-eastern Oaxaca in 1938, learned that a fungus was being used as a narcotic. " When identifiable specimens of the fungus had been secured and when ample information regarding its use was obtained, it became evident that *Panaeolus campanulatus* var. *sphinctrinus* was the teonanacatl of the ancient Aztecs." In further investigation it was learned that the Chinantecs and Tapotecs, other tribes of southern Indians, also still use the fungus. *Teonanacatl* means " dangerous mushroom," *nanacatl* being the generic name for mushroom: in Mexican provision markets mushrooms in general are still called *nacatl*. In most writings, however, the word is interpreted as " bread of the gods " or " flesh of the gods."

Panaeolus campanulatus var. *sphinctrinus* is usually given specific rank as *P. sphinctrinus*. From the evidence that three kinds of mushroom are used by Mazatec witch-doctors " it is probable that these are all species of *Panaeolus*," possibly *P. campanulatus* and *P. papilionaceus* in addition to *P. sphinctrinus*. All three species are common in this country on dung and in rich pastures. They are small, with slender stems. The cap is slightly fleshy, conical or bell-shaped, viscid when moist and shining when dry, not expanding, with the margin exceeding the gills and often bearing the remains of the fugacious veil. The gills are mottled grey-black and often have a white edge. Though, when

49

typical, the species are readily differentiated, intermediate forms occur. *P. sphinctrinus* has an oval then bell-shaped cap, reaching about 1 in. in diameter, often with a central prominence, and a firm, hollow stem about 3 in. in height. The cap is dark smoky grey when moist and paler when dry, the margin at first fringed with the white fragments of the veil. The stem is hollow, smoky grey, and often reddish and a little swollen at the base. *P. campanulatus* is slightly larger, the cap a smoky brown or greyish red, the remains of the veil not so prominent, and the white powdery stem, with a striate apex, becomes pinkish red. (Pl. 26*a*, p. 167 shows a form of this species). *P. papilionaceus* has a pale grey cap, with a reddish disc which is always obtuse, rimosely cracked when dry, and a greyish stem which has a powdery apex and is greyish red at the base.

Fray Bernardino de Sahagun, one of the famous band of priests who went to Mexico in 1529, was the first European to record the use of teonanacatl as a narcotic in *Historia general de las cosas de Nueva Espana* (1585).

" The first thing which they ate at the gathering was small, black mushrooms which they called *nanacatl*. These are intoxicating and cause visions to be seen and even provoke sensuousness. They ate these [mushrooms] before dawn, and they also drank chocolate before daylight. They ate these little mushrooms with honey, and when they began to be excited by them, they began to dance, some singing, others weeping, for they were already intoxicated by the mushrooms. Some did not want to sing but sat down in their quarters and remained there as if in a meditative mood. Some saw themselves dying in a vision and wept; others saw themselves being eaten by a wild beast; others imagined that they were capturing prisoners in battle, that they were rich, that they possessed many slaves, that they had committed adultery and were to have their heads crushed for the offence, that they were guilty of a theft for which they were to be killed, and many other visions which they saw. When the intoxication from the little mushrooms had passed, they talked over among themselves the visions which they had seen."

According to Schultes the fungus is sought for eagerly and dried for future use. Because it is regarded as semi-sacred it is difficult to purchase. Professional diviners earn a livelihood by endeavouring through mushroom intoxication to locate stolen property, discover secrets and give advice. The fungus is used to induce a semi-conscious state accompanied by a mild delirium; the incoherent utterances of intoxication are regarded as prophecies and warnings. These divinators

Plate IV. P.sathyrella disseminata.
Very fragile and short-lived, it
spreads by means of brownish
red mycelical threads (*Ozonium*).

(S. C. Porter)

Plate IIIa (above). *Mitrophora hybrida*, a morel-like fungus, mostly near poplars. *(John Armitage)*

b (right). Jew's Ear, *Hirneola auricula-Judae*, on old elder. *(S. G. Porter)*

are said to age rapidly and show evident senility at the age of thirty-five. The use of the fungus is by no means confined to them, and that the consumption is large was shown by the fact that it was only with difficulty Schultes was able to secure two dozen specimens.

" The doses which the Indians employ vary with the size and age of the individual. Usually fifteen mushrooms are sufficient to induce the desired effect, but larger doses are reported. Overdoses of fifty or sixty mushrooms result in poisoning, while continued use of excessive quantities is said to produce permanent insanity. Whether or not this is true could not be ascertained.

" According to Indian descriptions, the intoxication lasts about three hours. Shortly after ingestion of the mushrooms, a general feeling of exhilaration and well-being is experienced. This state of exhilaration is followed within an hour by hilarity, incoherent talking, and later, is accompanied by fantastic visions in brilliant colours."

The first missionaries to the Mexican Indians were strongly opposed to the use of teonanacatl because it was accompanied by idolatrous ceremonies. These Catholic fathers declared that eating it was as grave a sin as cannibalism. Fray Bartholome Garcia in a small religious manual (1760) prescribes as questions to be put in the confessional, " Have you eaten human flesh? " " Have you eaten the fungus of the devil? "

There is a reference to two cases of poisoning by *Agaricus (Panaeolus) campanulatus* in a note by W. Salisbury to the *Gentleman's Magazine* in 1815. The fungus had been mistaken for *Agaricus campestris* or White Champignion—written " Shampillions " by another contributor. No details are given except that the poisonous influence had been counteracted " by which means two whole families have been rescued from the grave." " In consequence of the necessity arising therefrom I have undertaken to teach Botany by making excursions into the fields near London, as was the usual practice of my late Partner, Mr. William Curtis."

A full account of " A Case proving the Deleterious Effects of the *Agaricus campanulatus* . . ." is given by G. Glen in 1816. A poor man of Knightsbridge collected some fungi which he cooked and ate for breakfast. Eight or ten minutes after beginning the meal he was suddenly seized with giddiness, trembling, loss of power and of memory. This soon wore off but returned on his way to the doctor. There was no pain or nausea, but he was greatly inclined to sleep; his pulse was slow and feeble. He rapidly recovered after an emetic

M.T.   E but on the following day had pains in his calves, weakness and languor.

Sowerby in 1809 gives two plates of what he calls *Agaricus virosus*, which for the most part is *Stropharia semiglobata* (Pl. 18*b*, p. 131), though four figures of *Panaeolus* are included. He believed that all the figures referred to the same species which "may be equally noxious, under every form in which it may appear . . . and which were the same sort that had fatal effects at Mitcham upon those who eat of them." The name was coined to serve as a caution—"else I do not like new names."

No investigations have been carried out on the toxins of *Panaeolus*. The parallelism with the cerebral symptoms in poisoning by *Amanita muscaria* and *A. pantherina*, suggests a similarity of causes.

The only other species known to have caused a death in this country is *Inocybe Patouillardii*. It occurs in summer in deciduous woods, especially beech; it is not uncommon. In its young stage there is a slight resemblance to a Field-Mushroom, but the cap is conical with an inrolled margin and there is no ring on the stem. It is distinguished at once by the fact that it immediately stains red where touched or handled, and that with age it becomes more or less completely vermilion or brownish red. The mature fungus has a central boss to the cap, the gills are almost free, whitish pink, then rusty brown or olivaceous, with a white floccose edge, becoming blotchy with red. There are several species of *Inocybe* which redden on touching; they are difficult to distinguish without microscopical examination. The symptoms are those of muscarine poisoning—vertigo, blindness, cold sweats, low temperature, very dilated pupils—and several species of *Inocybe* produce these in experimental animals.

Some white species of *Clitocybe*, *C. dealbata* (which sometimes invades mushroom-beds) and *C. rivulosa*, particularly, have been recorded abroad as causing this type of poisoning and have been shown experimentally to contain muscarine. They are small, and distinguished by having white decurrent gills. There are a number of similar species, and more mycological knowledge is required for their discrimination than is usually possessed by the practitioners who have recorded the cases. Certainly not all small white species of *Clitocybe* are poisonous, but they should be avoided. Care needs to be taken not to confuse them with the well-known edible *Clitopilus prunulus*. This has a white or yellowish cap, at first convex then flattened and finally depressed in the middle, with an irregular undulating margin and decurrent gills which are white when young but become pink as the spores ripen. It has a pleasant smell of meal, and is common in woods, especially under oaks, and in pastures.

Another definitely poisonous fungus is *Entoloma lividum*. It is responsible for a large number of accidents in France and is known about Dijon as " le grand empoisonneur de la Côte d'Or "; death, however, very rarely results and probably never in healthy persons. To a casual observer it might be mistaken for a Field-Mushroom, but it has no ring on the stem and the gills are sinuate. The cap is tawny or greyish, often becoming white here and there, with a central fleshy disc and an inrolled edge when young, which later becomes irregularly raised. The gills are yellowish at first, but become pink as the spores ripen, though the edge often remains yellow. It grows in grassy places, especially in deciduous woods. It smells and tastes agreeably of new meal, but usually causes violent sickness and diarrhoea. The treatment is that for acute indigestion.

It is probable that other species also contain similar emetocathartic substances sufficient at times to promote post-prandial regrets. Often, however, the poisons are destroyed in cooking, as in many species of *Russula* and *Lactarius*, the acrid species of which are usually avoided, although in Russia and Poland all species of these genera are eaten with avidity.

Lactarius torminosus and *Boletus Satanas* (Pl. 25, p. 166) deserve special mention, for it is usual to regard them, wrongly, as very poisonous.

Lactarius as a genus is characterised by all parts of the fungus exuding a " milk " when broken. This in *L. torminosus* is white and very acrid, which distinguishes the species at once from the much prized *L. deliciosus*, which has a saffron-coloured mild milk. The cap is usually rosy pink with darker concentric zones and a paler margin; it is depressed in the centre and the margin, which is much inrolled in the young stage, is covered with woolly fibrils. When eaten raw it may cause the internal pains signified by the epithet *torminosus*—griping —but the irritant substance is destroyed by cooking. It is a favourite species in Finland, eaten at once, or salted down. In Norway it is strongly roasted and added to coffee.

When *Boletus Satanas* was described over a century ago, it had caused sickness and diarrhoea in several who had eaten it, or merely tasted it, and H. O. Lenz epitomised its attributes by the epithet *Satanas*, for it proved so devilishly poisonous that even its emanations caused him to be ill when he was describing it. Its evil reputation has diminished with the years, and it is commonly eaten in Czechoslovakia and parts of Italy, though there is general agreement that it should always be cooked. Possibly there may be differences in toxicity due to varying amounts of some irritant substance, and it is probably very indigestible. It is a very handsome fungus, occurring in late summer in woods and pastures on chalky soil. The cap is dirty white or greenish grey, soft and smooth to the touch. The pores are yellow then bright crimson. The short swollen stem is usually yellow above and below and bright red in the middle, the whole covered with a network of bright red veins. The flesh, when broken, changes slightly from yellow to pink and blue.

Two species which are often mistaken for *Boletus Satanas* are the much more common *Boletus luridus* and *B. erythropus*. The caps of these are some shade of brown, and never whitish, and do not reach so great a size, the pores are red-brown or orange-red and not vermilion, the flesh is yellow and not white, and they are not calcicolous. The stem of *B. luridus* has a blood-red network; that of *B. erythropus* is covered with reddish dots. Though both species are given in most books as poisonous, they are not only harmless but are of good quality.

Gyromitra esculenta, Helvella crispa (Pl. 41*a*, p. 262) and several other Discomycetes contain helvellic acid, which has a strong dissolving action on the red corpuscles of the blood. *Gyromitra* is allied to the Morels. It has a chestnut-coloured cap which is irregularly folded or grooved and turned in on the white stem so that it has a brain-like shape. It grows in coniferous woods in spring, often appearing under snow in burnt or open places; it is not uncommon in flat, wet " slacks " of sand-dunes. Large quantities of the raw fungus are exported from Poland, particularly to Germany: the factory workers suffer from eye trouble either from the spores or from irritation by the poison on the fingers. All accidents due to this fungus have been reported from Germany, none from France. Some were fatal and were apparently not simple haemolysis, and, as a second meal caused trouble after the first was without apparent effect, it has been held that the explanation must be sought in anaphylaxis. When cooked or dried, *Gyromitra* and its allies are perfectly safe, for helvellic acid is removed by washing and destroyed by cooking and drying.

All fungi, including cultivated Mushrooms, are very indigestible, and indulgence in even the most choice may lead to dolour. It must always be remembered that they should be eaten fresh; they are organic and therefore liable to the changes consequent upon their serving as pabulum for other organisms.* Without doubt some of the ill-consequences occasionally recorded as caused by well-known edible species are due to the eating of old and altered specimens.

There are, however, a few species which are so indigestible that they frequently cause illness. The Yellow-Staining Mushroom, *Psalliota xanthoderma* (Pl. 15, p. 126), which is very like the Horse-Mushroom, *P. arvensis* causes sickness, headache and diarrhoea in a small proportion (not more than 10%) of those who eat it; others find it palatable. In the button stage the cap is usually flattened in the middle and not rounded as in the Horse-Mushroom, and the fungus has a disagreeable smell: the gills remain whitish for a long time. The most obvious character is that wherever it is touched or rubbed the skin almost instantly becomes bright yellow, the colour of poppy juice, changing after some time to chocolate colour; the same yellow is seen in the flesh at the base of the stem. There are growth forms which have been described as varieties but var. *obscuratus* which has a cap beset with blackish or brownish scales, and likened to a guinea-fowl and partridge, and grows in woods often associated with oaks seems better regarded as a species, *P. meleagris*. Another mushroom, the delicate-tasting *Psalliota sylvicola*, is sometimes mistaken for *P. xanthoderma*. It is a woodland species, with a slender habit and the base of the stem usually curved. It is white when young and changes to yellow when rubbed, but much less readily and less intensely than does the Yellow-Staining Mushroom. With age it becomes ochraceous reddish both outside and inside.

Coprinus atramentarius (Pl. 22b, p. 151) also shows selection in its manifestations, for with some people there is a strange effect if wine or other alcoholic drink is taken at a meal which includes it. A short time afterwards the face, and sometimes the neck, arms and other parts of the body become purplish red, and this may recur in a lesser degree at the next meal if alcohol be again drunk. This cardiovascular erythrism appears to be due to the solubility in alcohol of a toxin present in the fungus.

A similar effect is produced by antabuse (tetraethylthiuram disulphide: disulfiram) used in treatment of alcoholism—no alcohol, no symptoms.

Although most of the large branched Clavarias have a high reputation as edible species while they are young, *Clavaria formosa* is to be

* " Beware of musherons . . . and al other thinges, whiche wyll sone putrifie " (Sir Thomas Elyot: *The castel of helth*, 1533).

avoided as it acts as a purgative. This beautiful fungus is rare in this country, occurring in beech-woods where it forms rings of what look like miniature bushes, with a short, stout, pinkish buff trunk and numerous elongated, erect, salmon-pink branches with divided blunt yellow or pinkish yellow tips. It is pleasant smelling and slightly acrid.

In contradistinction to definite poisoning by some specific substance, or by alterations caused by other organisms, and by simple indigestion, there is the strange phenomenon of personal idiosyncrasy. This is common with all organic food—strawberries, eggs, butter, cream, fish, and so on, and to most drugs of the Pharmacopoeia, including sulphonamides and penicillin. Indeed, if toadstools were not regarded from so particular a viewpoint no special allusion would need to be made to it. Such food idiosyncrasy has been known from earliest times: Hippocrates (c. 400 B.C.) mentions that " cheese does not prove equally injurious to all men, for there are some who can take it to satiety without being hurt by it in the least . . . but there are some do not bear it well." Lucretius says, " What is food for one may be fierce poison for others," which suggests the old saw, " What's one man's meat is another man's poison." Food idiosyncrasy is now regarded as an aspect of allergy, a general phenomenon denoting an altered capacity to react. It comprises hay fever, anaphylaxis and contact allergy (e.g. with cosmetics). We have little information about toadstools in general, for any upset has almost invariably been considered as due to poisoning. It is known that some people are allergic to mushrooms, even to a drop of mushroom ketchup.

The idea that changes in colour in the flesh denote poison may be particularly referred to, not because it is of any more value than others as indicating the possibility of internal insurrections, but for its intrinsic interest. The change is most noticeable and best known in species of *Boletus*, a genus which has a cap and stem of the typical mushroom type but instead of gills has narrow tubes, with the openings below showing as pores—often referred to as " spongy underneath "—where vivid blues appearing almost as the flesh is broken are excusedly taken for colour warnings. But a change in colour occurs in many species, even in the Field-Mushroom, *Psalliota campestris*. Indeed in the genus *Psalliota*, which is recognised by having a ring on the stem, gills just free from the stem and gradually changing from whitish to pink then purplish or blackish brown, and by having purple spores, there are two series; the one beginning with *P. campestris* with flesh turning slightly pink, through *P. sylvatica*, a woodland species with a scaly cap and a slender hollow stem, where the flesh becomes clearly reddish, to *P. haemorrhoidaria*, often growing under conifers, with a more scaly cap and a robust stem, and flesh that turns instantly blood-red; the other beginning with the Horse-Mushroom, *P. arvensis* with flesh becoming slightly yellow, through *P. sylvicola*, clearly yellow, to *P. xanthoderma*, bright yellow.

The flesh of *Lepiota rachodes* turns pink then brown, that of *Amanita rubescens* (Pl. 3, p. 18) becomes pink, that of *Russula nigricans* and *R. densifolia* red then black, that of *R. albonigra* blackens directly. In *Lactarius* the presence of milk which may itself change colour, adds complexity. Sometimes flesh and milk act somewhat differently as in *L. fuliginosus*, where the flesh reddens much more markedly than does the milk. In *L. scrobiculatus*, *L. chrysorrheus* and *L. theiogalus*, the milk changes from white to yellow; in *L. acris* and *L. lignyotus*, to reddish; in *L. vietus* to grey or greenish; in *L. uvidus* and *L. flavidus* (*aspideus*) to violet. In some species the milk changes colour only when in contact with the flesh and gills; thus in *L. uvidus* a drop placed immediately after exudation on to a glass slide remains unchanged. On the other hand that of *L. theiogalus* changes extremely slowly on the gills, but soon turns yellow on a slide or on the fingers.

Boletus cyanescens, with a whitish or pale yellow cap and stem, and white then yellowish tubes, has white flesh which becomes dark indigo colour instantly on exposure to air. The flesh of *B. Satanas* becomes pale blue and pink, that of *B. luridus* and *B. erythropus* blue then green, that of *B. versipellis* (Pl. 24, p. 159) finally blackens, with green at the base of the stem: *B. badius* has a brown cap and stem, and bright yellow pores which rapidly become blue when touched, while the flesh hardly changes. The allied *Strobilomyces strobilaceus*, distinguished by its very scaly cap and stem, has white flesh which becomes reddish then blackish bistre.

The changes seen in these and other fungi, though so visibly different, are of the same character as those commonly occurring in fruits when cut. The flesh of some varieties of apple quickly changes to brown; apple juice when expressed is pale honey colour but rapidly darkens. It has been shown that ferment- or enzyme-like substances of the oxidase type are present, that is substances which have the power at ordinary temperatures of bringing about the oxidation of certain compounds in the presence of free oxygen. G. Bertrand has been the principal worker in this field. In a *Boletus* with flesh turning blue there is a chromogen which he called boletol, and laccase (phenolase).

They are separated in the tissues, but when these are bruised or broken, oxygen gains admittance and the laccase acts on the boletol (an anthraquinone) producing a deep blue coloration (boletoquinone). Where there is scarcity of laccase the coloration is slight, where there is none, as in the common coniferous species, *Boletus variegatus*, the cut flesh remains yellow: the addition of apple or potato juice to the cut surface produces an immediate blue coloration. For this action there must be boletol, laccase, oxygen, water and metallic ions; it is now known that the laccase of fungi is a copper protein compound. A shrivelled specimen usually reacts very slowly and only slightly, because of the lack of water.

The change of colour in other forms, as for example, *Russula nigricans*, is due to another oxidase, tyrosinase, which acts on tyrosine, an amino-acid containing a phenol group. The colour on exposure to air becomes pink then red, violet, blue-black and finally black, owing to the production of the pigment melanin. Many fungi apparently have this sort of reaction, but there are probably several different chromogens. Bertrand has lately found that *Strobilomyces strobilaceus* has one such, namely strobilomycol.

Methods of neutralising the poisons in fungi by special methods of cooking are described by Celsus and Pliny: the former advocates boiling them in oil or with the young twig of a pear tree, the latter says they are rendered safe if cooked with meat or with pear stalks, and in a much quoted sentence adds, " Vinegar being of a nature contrary to them neutralises their dangerous qualities."

It is well known that in many parts on the Continent—Russia, Poland and Hungary in particular—peasants are accustomed to eat large numbers of species with no precaution other than giving them a preliminary boiling in salt water. Fabre, in *Souvenirs entomologiques*,* says that in the thirty-odd years he had lived at Sérignan he had never heard of even a mild case of fungus poisoning in the village, though plenty are eaten—a little of everything.

" How, with such careless picking, are accidents avoided? In my village and for a long way around, the rule is to blanch the mushrooms, that is to say, to bring them to the boil in water with a little salt in it. A few rinsings in cold water conclude the treatment. They are then prepared in whatever manner one pleases. In this way, what might at

*Mushrooms were Fabre's " botanical joys from my earliest youth. I have never ceased to keep up my acquaintance with them." He left a collection of nearly 700 coloured drawings which are preserved at l'Harmas.

first be dangerous becomes harmless, because the preliminary boiling and rinsing have removed the noxious elements . . . When it leaves the purgatory of the stew-pan, the doubtful mushroom can be eaten without fear."

Fabre mentions several species he saw in peasants' baskets, but, though many were described as poisonous in older works, none except *Amanita pantherina* is so. As a result of Fabre's popularity and his statement that the treatment does not reduce the mushrooms to mash nor take away their flavour and succulence, there arose a vogue for this safety first method of cooking, with results that caused an outcry from French mycologists. Although Fabre knew the deadly Amanitas he never tried them, and as he did not mention them, apparently did not intend to be understood as including them.

Frederick Gérard, a naturalist attached to the Jardin des Plantes, had already, in 1851, experimented with the method. He included *Amanita venenosa, A. muscaria* and other fungi then thought to be poisonous. He cut 500 grammes of fungus into large pieces, and put them in a litre of water adding two or three tablespoonfuls of vinegar (or salt); if neither vinegar nor salt was added the water was changed two or three times. The fungi were left to macerate for two hours, washed well in water, then placed in cold water and brought to the boil. After half an hour they were again washed and then wiped. He first experimented on himself, in a month eating 75 kilograms of poisonous fungi, and 250 to 300 grammes daily for a week. He was in no way inconvenienced, and so he tried the method on all the members of his family one by one, and in spite of the differences in age, sex and temperament, none of the twelve suffered any ill-effects. He wrote an illustrated memoir and submitted it to the Council of Hygiene and Health of Paris. They appointed a Commission who watched Gérard experiment on himself and his son, and then themselves took part. After repeated tests they reported favourably. The Council adopted the report and then pigeon-holed it. There was a suggestion that they did not wish to publicise it for fear of interfering with the sale of cultivated mushrooms, then the only fungi allowed on the Paris market. Gérard persisted in his efforts for several years. It is said that he eventually contrived to poison himself effectively. Opponents of the method say that it renders the toadstools leathery, tasteless and odourless, and reduces their nutritive value. All expert opinion is against the method, for it is considered too laborious always to be carried out properly. Moreover it is not at all certain that it renders

Amanita phalloides innocuous. It is possible that Gérard may not have been dealing with any of the deadly species. *Amanita venenosa* as described by Persoon in his *Traité sur les Champignons* (1818), refers almost entirely to *Amanita mappa*; three varieties are distinguished, the white and yellow forms of *A. mappa* and *A. phalloides*. Three of the four drawings on the accompanying plate are typical *A. mappa*, the other badly represents *A. phalloides*. *Amanita mappa* (Pl. 2b, p. 3) until about twenty years ago, was regarded as being as poisonous as *A. phalloides*; it is, however, perfectly safe but nasty. It is often confused with *A. phalloides* in the field. It is a very common species and appears in two well-marked forms, the one with a lemon-yellow cap, the other white. There is no sign of the fine radiating fibrils seen in *A. phalloides*, and the cap has patches of skin-like volva of various shapes, so that the whole has been likened to a geographical map. The specific epithet *mappa* refers to this. As so much of the volva is left on the cap there is not the cup-like portion at the base of the stem as in *A. phalloides*; it is torn away from the edge of the truncated bulbous base of the stem.

As Pliny remarked, fungi are very convenient for poisoning and attempts to use them have not been restricted to writers of detective stories. In this country there appear to have been few suspicions and no convictions.*

The most remarkable case on record was l'affaire Girard of 1918. Girard had first studied pharmacy and then, after being invalided from the army, dabbled in insurance. He used his slight knowledge of pharmacy and of life insurance to furnish the necessary funds for maintaining a luxurious flat at Neuilly for his wife and mistress. His plan was to make the acquaintance of someone of means, much of his own age or that of the women, and to impersonate the intended victim at the necessary medical examination for taking out a policy: the premiums were to be collected at Girard's residence and, naturally, he was named as sole beneficiary. The acquaintance was then stimulated by lavish entertainment and eventually the poisoned dish was served. At first, use was made of pathogenic bacteria such as typhoid and anthrax, but later poisonous fungi were employed. These

---

*At the Central Criminal Court, 24th September, 1873, a gardener was indicted for the murder of a barmaid by giving her mushrooms from the eating of which she died. The Grand Jury threw out the bill.

At Clerkenwell Police Court in March, 1937, the defence argued that a man accused of being drunk in charge of a motor car was suffering from the effects of a rather liberal meal of mushrooms.

were collected by a picturesque vagrant who eked out an existence by gathering edible species for sale. He was provided with an illustrated book and told to gather only specimens with white gills, a ring and a volva. There were, however, some miscarriages—and a return was made to bacteria or some non-fungal poison. The failures were apparently due to the old belief that *Amanita mappa* is deadly poisonous —a copy of the first volume of Dumée's *Petit Atlas* wherein this is upheld, had been in Girard's possession. The crimes were discovered when Girard took out insurances with four different companies on the life of a woman whom he murdered three weeks later. Three companies paid, but the doctor of the fourth, unable to believe that so well-nourished a woman (Mme. Girard) should have died so unaccountably, went to see the corpse, and found a semi-rickety body.

In comparison with poisonous fungi there is little to be said about those which are edible. It is unlikely that in this country there are any species beyond those already mentioned which are really dangerous, though it must be remembered that many have never been sampled, either because they are very rare, or very small, or too leathery—for it is only the aboriginal who delights in excessive mastication. But fungi of beauty and tenderness are not necessarily of sufficient culinary merit to warrant the expenditure of trouble and rations. It is best, therefore, for savour as well as safety, to confine one's gastronomic attention to species which are above suspicion. Most of them do not resemble the ordinary mushroom in flavour; indeed as they are different species it would be remarkable if they did. There are very many ways of cooking them and tastes differ in this as in other matters.

The number of fungi admitted to continental markets ranges from very few to over three hundred as at Stockholm, and some species admitted to one market are forbidden others.

The species of good repute of which there are coloured illustrations in this book, are: *Amanita rubescens* (Pl. 3, p. 18), *Amanitopsis fulva* (Pl. 4, p. 19), *Boletus edulis* (Pl. 23, p. 158), *B. versipellis* (Pl. 24, p. 159), *Cantharellus cibarius* (Pl. 20, p. 147), *Clavaria vermicularis* (Pl. 29, p. 182), *Coprinus comatus* (Pl. 22a, p. 151), *Helvella crispa* (Pl. 41a, p. 262), *Lepiota gracilenta* (Pl. 5, p. 66), *Lycoperdon giganteum* (Pl. 32a, p. 191), *L. perlatum* (Pl. 31a, p. 190), *Marasmius oreades* (Pl. 10, p. 103), *Peziza aurantia* (Pl. 42c, p. 263), *Pleurotus ostreatus* (Pl. 19a, p. 146), *Psalliota arvensis* (Pl. 16, p. 127), *Sparassis crispa* (Pl. 27b, p. 174), *Tricholoma nudum* (Pl. 7, p. 82), *T. personatum* (Pl. 6, p. 67).

Others which are not usually so highly esteemed, are: *Armillaria mellea* (Pl. 11*a*, p. 110), *Choiromyces meandriformis* (Pl. 39*c*, p. 254), *Clavaria pistillaris* (Pl. 30, p. 183), *Clavaria rugosa* (Pl. 28*b*, p. 175), *C. stricta* (Pl. 28*d*, p. 175), *Collybia radicata* (Pl. 9*a*, p. 102), *Coprinus atramentarius* (Pl. 22*b*, p. 151).

Though in this country there has fortunately been no real need to look to fungi for nutrition, this does not hold elsewhere. Darwin relates how *Cyttaria Darwinii*, which grows in vast numbers on the "beech-trees" (*Nothofagus*) at Tierra del Fuego, "in its tough and mature state is collected in large numbers by the women and children, and is eaten uncooked. It has a mucilaginous, slightly sweet taste, with a faint smell like that of a mushroom. With the exception of a few berries, chiefly of a dwarf arbutus, the natives eat no vegetable food besides this fungus."

In countries with severe winters where it is impossible for the peasants to obtain vegetables, great use is made of fungi collected in the autumn and dried or pickled in brine. Fungi prepared in this way are also used when the eating of meat is forbidden; pickled fungi, chiefly species of *Lactarius*, are eaten throughout Russia during the three great feasts of the Orthodox Church.*

C. F. Schwaegrichen, Professor of Natural History at Leipzig, a century ago records how finding that the people in the neighbourhood of Nuremberg subsisted on raw fungi and black bread, he experimented on himself and for several weeks ate nothing but these, and drank only water. He suffered no ill effects, but, on the contrary, felt stronger. He concluded that fungi, if used moderately, are very nutritious, but that they lose their goodness and their natural flavour in cooking. According to M. Glenne there is an interesting tribe, numbering only about two hundred, who, in the dry season, live in caves near the summits of the mountains of the mandated territories of New Guinea. "Their food consists of fungus and palm sprouts and what rats and snakes they can catch with their hands." During the Kaiser's war much use was made of fungi in many parts of Europe to eke out the frugal fares of both man and beast; they were also found most valuable in the French Cameroons. In the East African Campaign the German forces were constantly on the run. Von Lettow-Vorbeck in his account of the campaign says that his troops, dodging through the forests to

*According to Stabitchwski's *History of Russian Censorship from* 1700-1863, when Krassarski was censor he forbade a small book which was published to aid in distinguishing edible and poisonous fungi "considering that fungi constitute the food of orthodox people in times of fasting, and that to write of their ill consequences is to undermine faith and spread unbelief."

escape the Allied forces, were often compelled to exist almost entirely on the fungi they met with, which were to them as, formerly, manna was to the children of Israel. " Though fungi, as sole diet, were somewhat indigestible and not very strengthening, yet they were to us of very real help."

Most wild animals, even carnivores like wolves and bears as well as domesticated cattle eat fungi, chiefly *Boletus* and *Lactarius*, though turkeys are partial to *Lepiota procera*. They form an important part of the food of reindeer; in winter they dig up frozen fungi from under the snow and also eat young *Polyporus betulinus* and similar species. It has long been the custom in rural parts of Finland to feed either fresh or salted toadstools to cattle or to use them for luring cattle from pastures. They are valuable fodder for pigs and poultry, replacing fish meat.

Many chemical analyses of different species have been made and, as would be expected, there is some variation in the ratios of the constituents, and more in the conclusions drawn from the figures, for some have held that these show that fungi are as rich in proteins as is meat. Fungi, like vegetables, contain a large amount of water (84-92%), and consequently a wrong picture is drawn if comparison is made between fresh meat and dried fungi if no account is taken of it.

A series of analyses of ten different toadstools show the following composition:

Water   —84-92% (av. 89.2%).
Nitrogenous materials—1.31-5.39% (av. 3.0%).
Carbohydrates—Cellulose and Chitin 0.91-9.14% (av. 4.22).
    Sugars—trehalose   } 0.79-2.18% (av. 1.09).
            mannite, etc.
Fat—0.2-0.76% (av. 0.44).
Minerals—0.45-1.12 (av. 0.82), chiefly potassium and phosphoric acid
    (as lecithin), with small and varying amounts of sodium,
    calcium, magnesium, iron, manganese, aluminium, silica,
    sulphur, and chlorine, principally in the skin of the cap.

45.4%-84% (average 66.8%) of the nitrogenous material is assimilated, and about 95% of the carbohydrates.

These figures compared with those of the same number of vegetables show that the average is practically the same, though on the whole slightly in favour of fungi. Dried, *Boletus edulis* and the cultivated mushroom are richer in protein than any dried vegetable except nuts. So long as food values are taken merely in terms of calories, fungi may be regarded as more or less of the same value as vegetables: moreover they usually give out moisture on cooking.

Sufficient attention has not yet been paid to the vitamin content of toadstools for any satisfactory conclusions to be drawn, though it may be pointed out that the yeast fungi contain almost all the known vitamins, and have played a leading part in their discovery and investigation.

Vitamin A occurs in appreciable quantity in *Cantharellus cibarius* (which is rich in carotene), though there is little or none in *Boletus edulis*, *B. badius* and *Psalliota campestris*.

Vitamin B complex occurs in all the higher fungi, though usually in insignificant amounts.

Vitamin C (ascorbic acid) has been mentioned as occurring occasionally in very small amounts.

Vitamin D (antirachitic) which is absent from green vegetables is present in appreciable quantities:

Boletus edulis 0.83, international units per gramme (i.u./g.) *Cantharellus cibarius* 0.83, *Morchella esculenta* 1.12, Cultivated mushroom (grown in darkness) 0.12, Cultivated mushroom (grown in light) 0.62.

Ergosterol which, when irradiated gives Vitamin D, is widely dispersed among fungi though the vitamin is curiously infrequent.

E. E. Anderson and C. R. Fellows (1942) found that the cultivated mushroom contained in mg/100 g.:

Vitamin A	None
Thiamine	0.12
Riboflavin	0.52
Ascorbic acid	8.60
Vitamin D	None
Vitamin K	+ +
Nicotinic acid	5.85
Pantothenic acid	2.38

Potassium and phosphorus salts are the chief constituents of the ash, with no significant amount of calcium but with appreciable copper and iron.

Rats receiving mushrooms as the sole source of protein in their diet survived a six-week test period and made a gain in weight equivalent to 30% of that shown by rats on a casein diet.

CHAPTER 7

MUSHROOM GROWING

Psalliota campestris, the common white mushroom of the fields, was known to the Greeks and Romans. It is probably the white fungus the gathering of which Ovid lists as one of the tasks of the frugal peasant housewife, and is possibly intended by Horace when he says that fungi which grow in meadows are the best. Galen recommends it next after *Amanita caesarea*. But there is no special mention of its being commonly eaten or greatly prized. Its present popularity appears to date from the introduction of the cultivated mushroom.

The evidence points to mushroom-cultivation having started in France some time early in the seventeenth century, probably in the neighbourhood of Paris. It doubtless originated from the observation that mushrooms arose spontaneously on melon-beds or other spots in gardens where there was abundant half-decomposed stable-manure. It has been frequently stated that it had its origin in the demonstration by Nicolas Marchant before the French Academy in 1678, of how the mushroom first formed in moulded horse-droppings as white filaments (spawn) which swell at their ends, but he was merely attempting an explanation of their spontaneous appearance on prepared hot-beds, which presumably was already a well-known phenomenon

The earliest account of mushroom growing appears to be that in *Le jardinier francois* by R. D. C. D. W. B. N. [N. de Bonnefons*] first published in 1650, and, after six French and one Dutch editions, " transplanted into *English* " in 1658 by Philocepos [John Evelyn]† as *The French Gardiner*, with three editions.

" Of all these *species* there is only the *Bed-mushroms* which you can produce in your *Garden*, and to effect this, you must prepare a *bed* of

*Initials in reverse of N. de Bonnefons, Valet de Chambre du Roi.
†6th Dec. 1658, " Now was published my *French Gardiner*, the first and best of the kind that introduced the use of the Olitorie [pot-herb or kitchen] garden to any purpose."

65

Mules, or *Asses soyl*, covering it over four fingers thick with short, and rich *dung*, and when the great heat of the *bed* is qualified, you must cast upon it all the *parings*, and *offalls* of such *Mushroms* as have been dressed in your *Kitchen*, together with the *water* wherein they were *washed*, as also such as are *old* and *Worm-eaten*, and a *bed* thus prepared, will produce you very good, and in a short space. The same *bed* may serve you two, or three years, and will much assist you in making another.

" If you poure of this *water* upon your *Melon-beds*, they may likewise furnish you with some."

The famous French horticulturist, Jean de La Quintinye, describes the current practice in his posthumous *Instruction pour les jardins* (1690), which was " Made English " by Evelyn as *The Compleat Gard'ner*, in 1693*. The hot beds, to serve for mushrooms in all the seasons of the year, are made by digging a trench about six inches deep and three or four feet wide. Horse- or mule-dung which has been heaped up for some time is then pressed and piled in the trench to a height of two feet and so disposed " that the upper part of it may be raised into a ridge like the Back of an Asse that it may the better shoot off the waters to the right and left." The whole is cased with earth and then covered with litter as protection from frost in winter and excessive heat in summer. The beds are watered twice or thrice a week and mushrooms " may be expected to shoot up about three or four months after." Thus the general procedure is much like that followed in open-air cultivation to-day except that nothing is said about spawning: the mushrooms arose " naturally."

That this was so is seen also from Martin Lister's *A Journey to Paris in the year 1698*:

" But after all, the French delight in nothing so much as *Mushroomes*; of which they have daily, and all the Winter long, store of fresh and new gathered in the Markets. This surprised me; nor could I guess where they had them, till I found they raised them on hot beds in their Gardens.

" Of *Forc't Mushroomes* they have many Crops in a year; but for

*George London and his partner, Henry Wise, published a shortened form as *The Complete Gard'ner* in 1699, which included the " Asses back " mushroom hot beds: it was very popular and went through five editions in eleven years.

London was the principal of the four founders of the " noble " Brompton Park Nursery in 1681, one of the first English commercial nurseries. It occupied most of the ground from Kensington Road in the north to Old Brompton Road in the south, part of which later became the Gore House Estate, purchased in 1856 by the Commissioners of the 1851 Exhibition. The neighbourhood remained famous for its fruit trees, its market gardens and especially for its mushroom beds until it was built over.

Plate 5. *Lepiota gracilenta;* one of the group of edible Parasol-Mushrooms. Uncommon

Paul L. de Laszlo

Plate 6. BLEWIT, *Tricholoma personatum*; lasting until early winter. Commonly eaten, particularly in the Midlands

the Months of *August, September, October,* when they naturally grow in the Fields, they prepare no Artificial Beds.

" They make in the Fields and Gardens out of the Bar of *Vaugerard* (which I saw) long narrow Trenches, and fill those Trenches with Horse Dung 2 or 3 foot thick, on which they throw up the common Earth of the place, and cover the Dung with it, like the ridge of a House, high pitched; and over all they put long Straw or long Horse Litter; Out of this Earth springs the *Champignons* after Rain, and if Rain comes not, they Water the Beds every day, even in Winter.

" They are 6 days after their springing, or first appearance, before they pull them up for the Market.

" On some Beds they have plenty, on others but few, which demonstrate they come of Seed in the Ground; for all the Beds are alike.

" A Gardner told me, he had the other year near an Acre of Ground ordered in this manner, but he lost a 100 Crowns by it; but mostly they turn to as good profit, as any thing they can plant.

" They destroy their old Beds in Summer, and dung their Grounds with them.

" They prepare their new Beds the latter end of *August,* and have plentiful Crops of Mushrooms towards *Christmas,* and all the Spring, till after *March.*"

The most famous account of mushroom-growing is that by Tournefort in 1707. As one would expect from so eminent a botanist, though his description of the structure of the beds is very like that of La Quintinye, he is more concerned with the manner in which the mushrooms arise. It was still the time of controversy about their reproduction and Tournefort's paper did something towards orientating ideas in the right direction. He asserted that the " seeds " of the mushroom were in the manure. As to practice he gave " the secret for obtaining mushrooms promptly and in abundance." This was to allow manure to become mouldy, and when the beds were made, insert pieces of it as large as the fist before casing. Whether this was a trade secret or Tournefort's own is not divulged, but its adoption was a great step forward.

In later years great stress was laid upon the advisability of using " virgin spawn " for impregnating the beds. According to growers, if spawn was taken from old beds, more often than not a poor crop resulted. Virgin spawn was, in theory, that which had not already given rise to fruit-bodies—in other words, that originating directly from spores. In this country there were special spawn-gatherers who went into the highways and by-ways and harvested in the appropriate season. Apparently they were able to distinguish the mycelium of the mushroom from the multitude of other mycelia by its appearance, feel and odour, a remarkable achievement and one of which the mystery was not readily divulged. Mill-track mushroom-spawn had a great reputation even after steam engines had replaced the horses which, moving in monotonous circles, gave motive power to grinding mills and threshing machines. Riding schools, under haystacks and any well-manured spots were also worked. The virgin spawn was used for inoculating " bricks." These were made of soil and manure of a standard size, $9 \times 6 \times 2$ in., and allowed partially to dry before small portions of spawn were inserted. The mycelium in gentle heat soon penetrated the whole brick. These were then stacked in open sheds in such a way that air could circulate round them. In France bricks were not used but flakes of infected manure, obtained much as Tournefort described.

It must have occurred to many that a good deal of trouble would be saved if the mycelium was obtained directly by germinating the spores. This was tried time and again with little success. Germination was irregular and of no practical use. In 1893, however, J. Costantin and L. Matruchot announced that they had found a method of obtaining mushroom-spawn from spores, but kept the details secret, and took out a patent. The process was carried on for some time at the Pasteur Institute and then taken over commercially. It was the first of the pure culture methods and achieved considerable success.

About the beginning of the century many complaints were made about the unsatisfactory state of the mushroom industry in the U.S.A. Growers had to depend on foreign spawn, and about 3,000,000 pounds of canned mushrooms were imported annually. There was a suggestion that the climate was against successful mushroom culture. Examination of the spawn on sale, however, showed that most of this was dead, possibly because of conditions of shipment and lack of care in storage. Attention, therefore, was paid to the possibility of spawn-making. M. Ferguson, in 1902, had determined some of the factors governing spore germination, and found that she got the best results when a portion of mycelium was present, but no practical method resulted. B. M. Duggar subsequently experimented with fragments of tissue and found that mycelium developed, an application of a well-known laboratory procedure. This was the beginning of the tissue-culture method of spawn production which, after extended trial, was fully described in 1905. The essence of the process is that small pieces of

internal tissue are taken from button mushrooms under aseptic conditions and placed on culture media. The enormous development of
mushroom-growing in America dates from the use of spawn obtained
in this way.

There can be no doubt that the difficulty in germinating mushroom spores has been over emphasised. Germination is delayed, but
if fresh spores are used mycelium results after ten to twenty days on
a wide range of media. Spawn is now produced in this country both
from spores and from tissue, but until the outbreak of the late war
some " pure-culture " spawn was imported, chiefly from the States,
but also from France. The advantages of this so-called " Bottle,"
" Carton " or " Sterilised " spawn, is that a strain which has desirable
qualities can be propagated vegetatively much as are many horticultural
plants; results obtained from virgin spawn were haphazard.

The mycelia of the forms of the cultivated mushroom are very
sensitive to temperature; growth begins at 3° C., reaches its optimum
at 24° C., and decreases until it ceases at 33° C. The acidity of the
medium is also important, growth taking place from pH 4.4 to pH 9,
but under most conditions pH 6.9 is the optimum.

There are many excellent accounts of mushroom cultivation and
there is no need therefore to enter into details. With the gradual
eclipse of the horse the chief problem for growers is to find a substitute
for stable manure. Synthetic composts, as they are called, are
gradually coming into use. The basis of most experiments has been to
add organic matter and nutrient salts to wheat straw. Recently, however, C. Treschow has shown that the top layer of litter from Norway
Spruce plantations may be turned into a suitable medium for mushroom growing by adjusting the pH to 7-8 by adding calcium carbonate,
and partially sterilising: it is said to be " fully as good as the composted
horse manure usually employed."

Though there is now a prevalent idea, at least amongst towns-
people, that mushrooms grow better in the dark, it was long before
any attempt was made to grow them indoors. The first mention of
indoor cultivation seems to be by Lundberg from Sweden in 1754.
The method was introduced to this country when Isaac Oldaker, after
managing the Imperial Gardens at Peterhoff, the Versailles of Russia,
returned to England to take charge of Sir Joseph Banks's exotic garden
at Spring Grove. He constructed a famous Mushroom House. His
method of growing mushrooms was doubtless based on a knowledge
gained in Russia. According to J. C. Loudon it was a common practice

with German gardeners to grow mushrooms on shelves, and in pots and boxes, placed behind stages, or other dark parts of their forcing houses otherwise unoccupied, and that this method was carried to Russia. Whether it came originally from Sweden or Germany, the eminence of Banks assured it prominence, and adoption.

Most of the enormous numbers of mushrooms sold in the Paris markets are grown in disused stone quarries. These were formerly almost exclusively confined to the left bank of the Seine outside the fortifications, and extended even under Paris itself as far as the Val de Grâce quarter, where they are well-known as " Catacombs." Fresh excavations were later made further and further from Paris as transport became easier and many of them were put into use for mushroom-growing, sometimes while part of the quarry was still being worked. They are for the most part in coarse limestone, a few in chalk as at Meudon, or in gypsum as at Argenteuil.

The growing of mushrooms in these caves apparently began at the beginning of last century. One tradition is that the idea came to a youth who evaded conscription in the Napoleonic Armies by sheltering there with full appreciation of their amenities, but naturally others, some of much later date, have claimed credit for so profitable a suggestion.

The caves are very numerous, about 3,000 of them being in use in the Department of the Seine alone: it has been computed that there are over 1,200 miles of mushroom beds in the suburbs of Paris. They are nothing like quarries in our sense of the word. The more ancient ones are really mines, the stone being extracted like coal with no interference with the surface. The entrance to the quarry shows as a circular hole, resembling the mouth of an old well, from which a pole with cross bars projects, down which descent is made to labyrinths of long, narrow galleries, 20 to 100 ft. below. The more recent quarries have lofty and wide galleries, with strong supporting pillars hewn from the limestone; the entrance is usually a great arch cut into the rock. Ventilation, a necessity for successful cultivation, offers no difficulties where the opening is at ground level; in the older caves it is provided for by draft chimneys. The caves are under Government supervision and are regularly visited like other working mines.

During the last war the Germans made use of the caves in various ways; flying bombs were stored in some. When the American Army advanced in the Saar they were in time to prevent the massacre of

1,700 German civilians, who with their goods and cows, horses, goats and poultry, were resisting transportation by sheltering in a roomy cave under Sversburg Mountain, in the property of the notorious von Papen, which had been used for growing mushrooms for more than a century.

Underground cultivation has spread to other countries; a small amount is carried on here. The most extensive is in disused Bathstone quarries at Corsham in Wiltshire. It is also carried on in caves at Godstone, Surrey, from which a smooth calcareous sandstone was quarried and used in the building of Westminster Abbey; and in Chislehurst Caves, Kent, long galleries driven underneath the overlying Tertiary hill, from which chalk was excavated for many years, and which were much used by Londoners as shelters during the blitz periods.

The best known, however, was the Scotland Street Tunnel which runs from Waverley Station, Edinburgh, northwards under the city for about three-quarters of a mile: it was formerly part of the Edinburgh, Leith and Granton Railway, and was abandoned when the line was closed in 1868. In 1887 it was used for mushroom-growing and was successful until 1903 when disease became rampant. Another start was made in 1908 and abandoned in 1917. The last effort was in 1927, with the same result—success for a few years, then disease and failure. During the war the tunnel was made into an air raid shelter for 3,000 railway staff, and an emergency control centre there was protected from intruders by invisible rays.

The heat generated in the fermentation of composting—itself a biological process—as it reaches 160° F. provides an effective original sterilisation. In the compost-heap, however, the manure temporarily at the surface is too cold to ferment, and the middle bottom portion may be fermenting under wrong conditions because of having exhausted the available oxygen. Ill-made compost is likely to introduce fungi to the beds which either cause disease in the mushroom or compete with the spawn and prevent its normal development.

The compost heap as it cools is liable to be invaded by such coprophilous fungi as *Coprinus* spp., *Anellaria separata*, *Panaeolus* spp., and *Peziza vesiculosa* (Pl. 41*b*, p. 262); occasionally they appear on the beds before casing.

To obtain more sterile and more uniform compost in the beds many modern growers carry out a final stage of fermentation, peak heating or Pasteurisation, in the mushroom-house. Heat is turned on as filling begins; the house is then closed and the aim is to reach a temperature of from 120 to 145° F. within two days and to hold it there for some hours. In this way any excess moisture is driven from the beds and most fungi and insects are destroyed.

The soil used for casing is another source of infection. It is now customary to steam sterilise this at 212° F.

Mushroom-growing was formerly an art but under the stress of modern conditions it is rapidly becoming a science. The factors of health and disease are studied and experiments are conducted with a view of achieving the one and preventing the other.

Mushroom-spawn thrives in the prepared beds but obviously other organisms are present initially and some gain access later. The various factors, chemical, physical and biological, set up an equilibrium that is favourable to the growth of the mushroom, and spawning, which is usually done at 75° F., gives it a preliminary advantage which, normally, assures its supremacy in the bed.

Mushrooms, like all other organisms, are subject to disease. These are caused by moulds (Hyphomycetes) which kill the fruit-body or, at least, make it unsaleable. There are other fungi which may almost be regarded as diseases of the beds themselves as they make them less serviceable for the purpose for which they have been constructed, sometimes flourishing to such an extent that the crop is a failure. Such fungi may be considered either as " weeds " or " competitors."

The most interesting of them is *Pseudobalsamia microspora*, a truffle which almost completely prevents the development of spawn in beds that are too wet or too tight, particularly with high temperature and poor ventilation. The variously shaped fruit-bodies, almost round to irregularly lobed are $\frac{1}{8}$ to 1 in. across, and creamy white to reddish brown. They occur abundantly in the casing soil and in the surface layer of the compost amongst a dense mass of mycelial threads. It may be called a new disease in that when first reported from America in 1930 it was unknown to science: it was later recorded from Denmark and was noted here in 1936. Several problems arise in connection with it. Mushroom-growing is so liable to failure that the grower is ever watchful for his crop, and it is improbable that invasion would have previously passed unnoticed, or indeed that some popular name, such as the growers' " calves' brains " would not have been given to it. It looks as if invasion of beds occurred independently and more or less simultaneously in America and in Europe. There seems no doubt that in this country the fungus was introduced into the beds from casing soil, but as this is taken from the same sort of places as formerly why the sudden appearance? It is worth noting that the fungus has not yet been detected in its natural habitat.

Two toadstools introduced with casing soil have occasionally caused trouble. The best known is *Clitocybe dealbata*, a common species in pastures. The compost and casing both soon become permeated with the mycelium and the fruit-bodies appear in clusters on the surface often up to three feet across. The cap is shining white and finally becomes revolute and undulated; the gills are white, thin, crowded and slightly decurrent, the stem white and fibrous. It has a smell of new meal.

The other is *Clitopilus cretatus*, an occasional species in woods and pastures usually on bare soil. It has a smooth shining white cap which becomes concave with an incurved edge; the gills gradually become pink as the spores ripen, and are deeply decurrent; the stem is white, velvety and very short and slender. On mushroom-beds it sometimes grows in profusion, the caps commonly superposed in bracket form. It is known to growers as " Cat's Ears."

It is usual to speak of the cultivated mushroom as *Psalliota campestris* as it is assumed that it is the same species as the Field-Mushroom to which the name applies. The common mushroom, which grows in meadows, often forming rings, has four spores on the basidium whereas the cultivated mushroom has only two. This difference was noticed many years ago and it was attributed to the long continued effect of cultivation, a strange view considering the short period elapsing between the obtaining of the virgin spawn and the planting of mushroom-bricks. It gradually became realised that even in the wild mushroom there are at least two well-marked kinds, the one with a pure white silky cap, pure pink gills with a whitish edge, a rather short floccose, fibrillose stem and a narrow ring; the other with a dull-brownish fibrillose cap, dull-pinkish narrow gills, a rather short white stem and a ring which tends to disappear. The first is the Field-Mushroom; the second grows on dung-heaps, on road scrapings and other highly manured ground. There can be no doubt that the second was the fungus which occurred spontaneously on the French prepared hot-beds. Moreover, it can readily be grown on mushroom-beds, whereas the Field-Mushroom will not grow there. Further, its basidia are two-spored. The evidence appears conclusive that there are two distinct species. In other words the cultivated mushroom is not *Psalliota campestris*. It is best called *Psalliota hortensis*. There are several forms of it now in cultivation, but since the introduction of pure culture spawn, it has become difficult to distinguish those which are native. Indeed it is hardly safe to say that all cultivated forms even belong to *P. hortensis*, for there is evidence that some closely allied but distinct American species have found their way here. It should be added that the Horse-Mushroom, *Psalliota arvensis*, can be grown in mushroom-beds and doubtless was occasionally cultivated when " virgin spawn " was used. Indeed Worthington G. Smith held that " the cultivated mushroom of gardeners belongs to this species."

Though the mushroom is the only fungus cultivated on a commercial scale in Europe and America, other species are grown elsewhere. The cultivation of Shii-take in Japan is believed to date back over two thousand years. The fungus has been bandied about in different genera, but is usually called *Cortinellus edodes* or *C. Shiitake*; more recently it has been regarded as a *Lentinus*. Logs of Shii (*Quercus cuspidata*) and other trees, especially hornbeam, are soaked in water for some days and then pounded to soften the bark. Holes are bored at short distances apart and powdered infected wood placed in them. The logs are left in a shady part of the forest and the first crop of the fungus (*take*) appears in about two years: those of different seasons of the year have different names. No successful attempt to put the process on a more strictly scientific basis appears to have been made.

In some parts of China the Jew's Ear is cultivated. Saplings of oak are trimmed, cut into lengths of eight to ten feet and left to lie on the ground. After several months they become infected with the mycelium of the fungus, and are then stacked slantingly in scores or so and the fruit-bodies develop.

The fungus is reported as *Hirneola auricula-Judae*, but the identification has not been critically made, and it may possibly be some other species. Although the Jew's Ear grows in Europe on oak and other trees, it is far more common on old elders. It begins as a cup-shaped growth and finally is ear-shaped, flabby, pinkish brown, veined within and velvety without: it is gelatinous when moist, " swelleth and openeth extremely," and in this condition often resembles the human ear except in colour, but is leathery when dry (Pl. III*b*, p. 50). Though, as Rabelais asserts, it appeared among the hundred salads included in the first course of the Gastrolaters' interlarded fish-days, it is only occasionally eaten in Europe, though it is regarded as a great delicacy by the Chinese.

The name Jew's Ear is a corruption of Judas's ear. There was a

medieval belief that Judas hanged himself on an elder.* Thus in
Piers Plowman:

> *Judas he japed*
> *With jewen silver*
> *And sithen on an eller*
> *Hanged hymselve.*

and Shakespeare in *Love's Labour Lost,* says " Judas was hanged on an
Elder." In *Cymbeline* we find " the stinking Elder " as a simile for
grief, and it is probably the smell of the leaves and flowers, which many
find so unpleasant, that originally associated the tree with Jews, for
it was commonly believed that they suffered from a revolting smell and
loathsome diseases as a penalty for their lack of faith, and that they
used Christian blood, particularly of murdered children, to cure
themselves—tragic nonsense which has had terrible consequences to
this day.

" Some people say that if we bark the white or black poplar,
cutting the bark into pieces and covering it with horse-dung an
excellent kind of fungus will spring up and bear throughout the year,"
according to Dioscorides. Similar methods of cultivation are still
followed in mid and south-east France and in Italy; sometimes the
stump is irrigated, a mixture of wine and warm water being favoured
in some districts; sometimes holes are bored in the stumps, their sides
rubbed with the gills of the fungus, then covered with a light layer of
earth, and watered from time to time. The fungus is *Pholiota aegerita*
which is common on tree stumps in this country, especially elm. It
has a whitish or ochraceous, wrinkled, silky cap, darker in the centre,
finally with an undulated scalloped edge and usually becoming areo-
lately cracked, especially at the disk. The gills are crowded and
smoky brown, the stem white with a large membranous ring.

An ancient and widespread cultivation in the tropics, that of
Volvaria esculenta, was completely overlooked until recent years. The
methods adopted for obtaining growth vary from the extremely
primitive trusting to providence, to the more refined of helping
providence by preliminary spawning.

There are about ten species of *Volvaria* in this country, including
V. volvacea, closely allied to *V. esculenta* which formerly was much more
common than now, for it frequented the tan of hot-beds used for rais-

---

*Sir John Mandeville: " And fast by is yet the tree of elder that Judas hanged
himself upon."

ing tender exotic plants; sometimes the mycelium passed up the walls on to the shelves and there fruited, or through the mortar of the brickwork to fruit outside. It is found in gardens and on roadsides. The cap is grey, streaked with blackish fibrils, the gills white then flesh colour, the stem white and downy; the volva is large, thick, loose, whitish but slightly bistre at the apex.

The evil reputation of *Volvaria* was due to *Volvaria gloiocephala*, our commonest species, being formerly considered not only poisonous, but deadly, appearing in most books as a worthy companion of *Amanita phalloides*. About thirty years ago it was reported as commonly on sale in Algerian markets. Experiments then showed French specimens to be edible. Later it became known that it is commonly eaten in northern Portugal. It grows in grassy places where there is manure, straw or other refuse; it may often be seen on old thatch, particularly when this has been removed and left to rot. The cap is grey, gelatinous, and has a central prominence and a striate margin. The stem is white and the volva is white or grey.

The mushroom proving so amenable to the discipline of cultivation, efforts have been made time and again to bring other desirable species under subjection. The usual method has been to scatter parings or fragments of the fungus or to water the ground with a decoction of it, but although success has been claimed it does not seem to have been attained. Attempts to grow various species on ordinary mushroom beds have met with the failure that would be expected having regard to the specialised habitat. Constantin and Dufour succeeded in cultivating *Tricholoma nudum* (Pl. 7, p. 82) on beds constructed of various materials, of which they found beech leaves the best. Fruit-bodies were obtained after six months in caves, but only after ten to twenty in the open. The results are of no economic importance for such slow growth precludes commercial exploitation. Incidentally, this species is frequent on garden compost heaps.

The Morel, *Morchella esculenta*, offers better promise as it has been recorded several times as occurring spontaneously on apple pomace. Experiments made by inoculating a mixture of apple pulp from cider factories and earth, with fragments of Morel have given good results. This is more economical than the method mentioned by J. G. Gleditsch (1753). The old women of Neo Marchia (Mark Brandenburg) noting that Morels favoured places in woods where there had been fires, gathered together branches, twigs and leaves of trees, heather, and other shrubs, and set them alight to provide suitable habitats for the fungus. As forest fires sometimes resulted the practice was forbidden by royal mandate.*

Though it was the result of a different kind of culture it is perhaps significant that during and after the 1914-18 War the sites of destroyed houses and disused trenches in northern France were, in spring, veritable gardens of Morels.

*Morels appeared in my garden at Richmond, Surrey in May 1953 where quantities of paper had been burned !

CHAPTER 8

GROWTH

A CONSIDERATION of the practices attendant upon mushroom growing brings out some principles of general application. First, for
spore-germination certain conditions are necessary. These are not
the same for all fungi, but there must always be a degree of moisture
and a definite temperature—germination not occurring outside limits
which are strictly defined for each species, with an optimum temperature
for growth in given conditions. The acidity of the mushroom bed is
an important factor; this is also of general application—a lower and
an upper limit beyond which growth does not occur, and an intermediate value where it is at its maximum. Other factors influencing
growth are more obscure and necessitate laboratory investigations to
reveal them. The problems are essentially the same as in flowering
plants, and, as with them, their nutrient requirements cannot be
ascertained while they are growing in the soil. So early as 1699 John
Woodward grew plants in water—spring, river, rain, and distilled—to
find out whether it was water or the solid particles of the soil which
provided their nourishment. J. Sachs (1860) and W. Knop (1865),
published formulae of standard culture solutions for plants, and
various others have been proposed since.

The first standard culture solution for fungi arose out of Pasteur's
researches, his pupil, J. Raulin, working for several years to find a
medium capable of giving the maximum growth of the well-known
mould *Aspergillus niger*. This contained eleven substances in the following proportions (in grammes): water (1500), cane sugar (70), tartaric
acid (4), ammonium nitrate (4), ammonium phosphate (0.6), potassium
carbonate (0.6), magnesium carbonate (0.4), ammonium sulphate
(0.25), zinc sulphate (0.07), iron sulphate (0.07), and potassium silicate
(0.07). He studied the part played by each of the constituents, varying
the quantities, taking away one substance and adding another, and

78

so on. He found for example that the fungus was extraordinarily sensitive to zinc, a slight decrease in the percentage greatly depressing the amount of growth. Another point of interest was the deleterious effect of other substances. Thus growth ceased if $\frac{1}{1.600.000}$ grammes of silver nitrate were added to the liquid; indeed if the solution were placed in a silver goblet instead of a china saucer, growth did not begin, though it was almost impossible to detect chemically any dissolved silver. Though fungi are still grown in liquid solutions it is more usual to use solid nutrient media with a basis of agar sufficient (2%) to form a jelly. There are many different media in use, and most of them are known by the name of their originators.

The details of making what are described as pure cultures can be found in most text books. An essential step is the sterilisation of the culture medium so that no living organism is present when it is inoculated with the fungus which it is desired to grow.

Fungi are grown in pure culture for several reasons: it may be that it is more convenient for studying a life-history, or abundant material may be needed of a parasite for inoculation or other purposes, or it may be essential for some nutritional or other physiological research. The growing of a fungus is often a matter of considerable difficulty—indeed some parasitic fungi such as rusts and powdery mildews have not yet been grown on artificial media—and success in this is the object of the culture, for it provides the developmental stages or the required spores. When, however, nutritional studies are being undertaken, matters other than the obtaining of maximum growth are in quest. It is only in comparatively recent years that the significance of substances present in very small quantities, substances indeed of which the presence was unsuspected, has begun to be realised. There are two main aspects of this, trace elements and vitamins.

It has been known since Raulin's researches that very minute quantities of a substance may have a stimulating or a toxic effect. What is now apparent is that certain elements which are essential to the living processes of fungi, plants and animals, are required in extremely small amounts. They were previously overlooked because sufficient of them is introduced in ordinary culture work from " impurities " in water, salts used in solutions, and from the containing vessels. The amounts of these trace elements or micro-nutrients can be measured by using instruments specially designed for the purpose, the absorptiometer, the polarograph and the spectrograph. Thus in addition to the elements nitrogen, sulphur, phosphorus, calcium, potassium, magnesium, iron, salts of which are the basis of most nutrient solutions, manganese, zinc, boron, copper, molybdenum, have been proved definitely to be micro-nutrients for certain fungi, with strong evidence for gallium and some for columbium.

Elements other than those regarded as essential may be present. Thus a spectrographic examination of mushrooms by H. Ramage, 1930, showed, in addition to high potassium and low calcium content, iron (chiefly in the skin), and 1-3 per cent phosphorus in dried material, the gills containing most; that all parts contain copper (more than 0.02 per cent) and silver (more than 0.01 per cent, with not less than 0.05 per cent in the gills).

In war-time the layman had his attention called to vitamins as essential substances for the proper nutriment of his family, and knew, if he read the labels on numerous proprietory products, that the amounts needed are exceedingly small and that an alphabetical designation is adopted as nomenclature; he further knows that vitamins have to be included in or added to his diet because they are not manufactured in his own physiological processes. At the end of last century it was found that beri-beri was due to a deficiency of an essential constituent in diet, and it was rapidly learned that other human diseases had a similar origin. The term vitamin was coined to denote the definite and specific organic substances, traces of which were necessary constituents of food. They were given alphabetical symbols, for their chemical constitution was unknown, but where this has been determined appropriate chemical names have been applied.

Fungi also need vitamins for their full development, though these are usually called growth factors, growth substances, or more recently, essential metabolites. There is a vast and growing literature on these necessary, extremely active organic constituents.

Many fungi are able to grow normally on media which contain only sugars as organic food in addition to inorganic salts. This is true of *Aspergillus niger*, and was long thought to be true of all fungi, it being assumed that normal growth was dependent on a proper constitution of the medium, whether synthetic or " natural " in containing potato, malt extract or similar constituents. As early as 1871 L. Pasteur asserted that yeast could be cultivated on a synthetic medium using an inoculum " the size of a pin's head." J. Liebig controverted this, saying he had been unsuccessful in his efforts to repeat the experiment. A celebrated controversy ensued which had not been resolved when Liebig died shortly afterwards. The resolution came in 1901 when

E. Wildiers showed that success or failure depended upon the amount of the inoculum—the ill-defined size of a pin's head. Pasteur's pin must have been larger than Liebig's and he must have introduced certain unknown substances formed by the cells themselves, a substance which Wildiers called *bios*. For a quarter of a century controversy raged over the nature of bios and even over its existence. Then it was found that bios is a complex substance and components bios I, bios II, and so on, were recognised; later they were identified with known growth substances—and the numbering fell into desuetude. The constituents include inositol (Bios I); biotin (Bios IIb)—Vitamin H; aneurin* (Bios III)—Vitamin B_1; the amino-acids β-alanine (Bios IIa) and eleucine; pantothenic acid; pyridoxine—Vitamin B_6; and probably a sterol. Yeasts occurring in natural conditions, the so-called wild yeasts, thrive in vitamin-free synthetic media, whereas cultivated yeasts require the addition of growth substances, some needing all the constituents of bios, others only some, with variations depending not only on the species but on different strains.

The majority of the growth substances of fungi are identical with those of animals, though only with the water-soluble ones, particularly of the Vitamin B complex. As with trace elements these are frequently introduced into a synthetic medium as impurities, principally of sugars; in " natural " media they may be present in plant or other basis.

Apparently all fungi need aneurin (Vitamin B_1) for their metabolism. Many, such as *Phycomyces Blakesleeanus*, are able to synthesise it and require no external supply. The molecule of aneurin contains derivatives of pyrimidine and thiazole. Some fungi, as many species of *Phytophthora*, must have the aneurin supplied intact; some, like *Polystictus versicolor*, grow if the two components are supplied separately; others, for example, *Mucor Ramannianus*, synthesise the pyrimidine derivative, but must have the thiazole derivative supplied, while some, like *Rhodotorula rubra*, need only the pyrimidine derivative as they themselves produce the thiazole derivative. It is assumed that there has been a gradual loss of power to produce the vitamin or to synthesise it. Most Hymenomycetes require aneurin regardless of whether they are saprophytic (*Marasmius peronatus*), parasitic (*Fomes annosus*) or mycorrhizal (*Boletus luteus*).

For the most part the other growth factors do not prove efficient when acting alone. Biotin is sufficient for the growth of *Melanospora destruens*, though not for fruiting, which requires the addition of

*thiamin of American authors.

aneurin. Inositol is sufficient for *Ophiostoma catonianum*. Two are usually requisite; aneurin and biotin, aneurin and pyridoxine, and biotin and inositol are combinations which have been recorded so far. Three have been reported for *Ascoidea rubescens*, aneurin, biotin and inositol, and for *Trichophyton discoides*, aneurin, pyridoxine, and inositol; some strains of *Saccharomyces cerevisiae* require inositol, biotin, aneurin, pantothenic acid and other factors.*

The part played by these various substances in the metabolism of fungi is not yet clear. It has long been known that aneurin is concerned in the metabolism of carbohydrates. After absorption it forms a diphosphoric ester known as co-carboxylase, an important stage in the decarboxylation of pyruvic acid, generally considered an essential step in respiration.

There is sufficient aneurin in soil to provide for the development of most fungi needing it. The vitamins present there are either produced by the activity of living organisms or are contained in the remains of dead ones. They are more abundant near the surface than in the subsoil, a fact of importance for fungal mycelia.

In the controversy " natural manures versus artificials," which has been waged for so many years, it should not be overlooked that the former have an advantage in supplying growth factors in addition to influencing beneficially the physical properties of the soil.

How do vitamin requirements affect the general problem of fungal distribution? We know, for example, that *Boletus luteus* requires a supply of aneurin whereas *B. granulatus* does not. But in nature a fungus does not grow in splendid isolation. Though there is a welter of mycelium competing for rations and quarters, some mycelia are able to grow because of the presence of other organisms which supply the growth substance which they require.

As we have seen, however, one species may lack in one respect, a second in another. Thus *Nematospora Gossypii* requires biotin, but synthesises aneurin, whereas *Polyporus adustus* synthesises biotin but requires the pyrimidine part of aneurin. When the two are mixed in culture both grow normally. Similarly *Mucor Ramannianus* requires thiazole but synthesises pyrimidine, whereas the reverse holds for *Rhodotorula rubra*. In culture alone the *Mucor* does not grow, the *Rhodotorula* only very slightly. In mixed cultures they grow well, and

*Fungi are used as test organisms in vitamin assay; the method has many advantages over chemical estimation or animal feeding trials. It is essential that the vitamin to be assayed is one of which the test fungus requires an external supply.

Paul L. de Laszlo

Plate 7. WOOD-BLEWIT, *Tricholoma nudum*; varying in density of colour with shade and moisture. Sweet-smelling; edible

Plate 8a. Laccaria laccata; one of our commonest and most variable species. Edible *(Paul L. de Laszlo)*

b. L. laccata var. *amethystina*; varies from pale lilac, to deep violet-colour. Edible *(Paul L. de Laszlo)*

so intermingled that what is practically a symbiotic organism results. We are only at the beginning of a subject which promises to give clues to the solving of many mysteries.

As fungi do not possess chlorophyll and so do not use light for photosynthesis, it is not surprising that many, like the cultivated mushroom, develop normally in darkness. Indeed a considerable number of species are found in cellars—on stacks of firewood as well as on earth and brickwork; a sixteen years' survey of houses in St. Gallen, Switzerland, provided eighty-three species, mostly from cellars and outhouses.

The fungi of caves and mines of many parts of the world have been investigated since J. A. Scopoli described and figured seventy-five species in *Plantae subterraneae* (1772). A better known account is in F. A. von Humboldt's *Flora Fribergensis* (1793), written when he was employed as a mining engineer, though this describes only eighteen species from mines, with three figures. The strange and monstrous growths which both authors illustrated have proved a constant source of interest, far more than the normal recognisable species.

The different types of caves and mines need not be considered beyond noting that detritus is much more varied where the opening admits of currents of air and the entry of animals, and, consequently, a greater number of fungal species occur. During the 1939-45 war, when treasures were stored in caves and mines, only the driest could be used, for, where there was moisture, labels became illegible or rotten through mould attack, and, as is less surprising, wooden cases damaged or destroyed. Organic material in caves in which there is movement of air from the outside provides a crop of fungi, some even of a highly specialised type.

Many of the fungi growing on pit-props and other constructional timber of mines, are very destructive. The chief one in this country is *Poria Vaillantii* (Pl. XVII*b*, p. 242) though *Merulius lacrymans* (Pl. 35, p. 238) also occurs. Other species are *Armillaria mellea* (Pl. 11*a*, p. 110), *Trametes saepiaria, Fomes annosus, Polystictus versicolor* (Pl. 26c, p. 167), and *Lenzites abietina*, some of which are more or less restricted to coniferous wood. Enormous quantities of conifer poles for pit props have to be imported to replace losses; they are cut in lengths to correspond to the width of the coal seams, and nearly 200 different sizes are in demand.*

*2,845,750 cubic metres solid volume of pit wood were imported into the United Kingdom in the years 1935-38.

M.T.   G

Though some Agarics show no divergence from the normal, many, perhaps the majority, undergo modification. This may be merely an elongation of the stalk (a lengthening of cells rather than their multiplication) possibly due to a humid and cool atmosphere, or a lessening of the intensity of the colour, particularly in yellow and red species; such loss of colour is very noticeable in cultures in laboratories and may be seen in some species kept for a day or two in a vasculum—the common *Inocybe geophylla* var. *lilacina*, loses its violet colour after a day and regains it on exposure to light for a few hours.

A further modification is a reduction in the size of a cap, which may be little more than that of a pin head, or the cap may be distorted. Again, gills may be altered, spore production may be lacking, or no hymenium may form. Finally there may be no semblance of the normal fungus but only a sterile growth, often a monstrous apparition to one attempting its classification. One common, sterile growth appears like tufts of coarse red hair, being composed of thick-walled hyphae combined to form anastomosing cord-like strands. It is frequent in the open, on and under the bark of logs, particularly elm, and is often mistaken for some sort of moss. Formerly regarded as a distinct entity and called *Ozonium auricomum*, it is now known to belong to species of *Coprinus*; that in mines is *Coprinus domesticus*, which also grows on damp rugs, plaster and furniture; that on logs *C. radians*. Both species are much like *C. micaceus* (Pl. 18c p. 131) which, itself, occasionally develops a similar mycelium, particularly in culture.

The main interest has been in those fungi producing such abnormal growths that their identity was, and for some still is, a matter of conjecture. They are mostly species of *Lentinus* and *Polyporus*. Both *Lentinus tigrinus* and *L. lepideus* form *Clavaria*-like or branched sterile growths in darkness. The genus is characterised by being fleshy but tough, with gills which are usually decurrent, and have a toothed edge, and in growing on wood. In *L. lepideus* the cap is pale yellowish with brownish scales, the gills whitish and the stem stout, usually excentric and narrowing downwards, whitish and covered with small scales which become tinged reddish. It occurs on pine stumps but damages worked timber, causing great losses in wooden paving blocks, railway sleepers and telegraph poles*; it is very common on old railway

---

*It is to prevent the ravages of fungi that sleepers and poles are creosoted under pressure. In spite of this, replacement of railway sleepers needs an annual importation of about £2,000,000 worth of timber, chiefly because of attack by *Lentinus lepideus* which is remarkably resistant to creosote.

sleepers used as fencing. It starts as a small pad on the infected timber, from which one or more tiny papillae project at right angles to the surface. In darkness the papilla grows out into a long finger-like stem which is perfectly indifferent to the action of gravity; it may become branched. In weak light it grows towards the source. When the light is of sufficient intensity the tip reacts by flattening out and expanding symmetrically to form a normal cap. The stem now grows upright and light has no longer any effect on the direction of growth.

Several species of *Polyporus* and related genera occur in mines only in a conidial stage, which consists of a pad of densely interwoven hyphae which form conidia towards the exterior and break up into chlamydospores within. Such growths are not uncommon in the open, and often reach six inches across, showing zones of growth when sectioned. They were formerly regarded as a distinct genus, *Ceriomyces* or *Ptychogaster*.

Polyporus squamosus (Pls. 19*c*, XX, pps. 146, 259) is frequent on the boles of deciduous trees from spring to late autumn. The cap is fleshy, pale yellow, covered with large, adpressed, dark scales; the tubes are decurrent and yellowish white, with pores minute at first then becoming larger, angular and torn; the stem is thick, hard, and excentric, and whitish with a black base; it smells like uncooked tripe. It begins as a knob of firm consistency from which one or more bluntly conical processes arise, which grow straight outwards from the surface. In the light these are brown and scaly: in the dark they are white and smooth and grow into long sterile finger-like columns, usually curved and twisted and frequently flattened and branched at the ends. They grow at their tips only, and the direction of growth is not affected either by weak light or by gravity. They somewhat resemble miniature stag's horns with the old parts black like the base of the stem of normal fruit-bodies, and the tips white. A. H. R. Buller found that normal caps began to form if there was as little as one hour's stimulus of light and that the process continued in darkness.

It was an abnormal growth of *Polyporus squamosus* which John Martyn described (1744):

" In the latter Part of the Summer of the Year 1744, Mr. *Ehret* the Painter brought me a *Fungus* of a very extraordinary Shape and Size,

During the year 1932 over 1¾ million cubic feet of wood was treated with creosote before being put into use by the General Post Office, mostly telegraph poles and their necessary timbers—cross-arms, sleeper blocks and half-round guards, but also troughing for cables and the packing for cable-jointing chambers.

which had been found growing on a Piece of the Trunk of an Elm, in a damp Cellar in the Hay-Market. The whole Plant was about two Feet in Height; and, at first Sight, seemed not very unlike the Horns of some Deer, being variously branched, and covered with a thick Down. . . . The larger Branches, or rather the Tops of the whole Plant, were expanded in Form of a Funnel, smooth on the concave, and full of Pores on the convex Side."

The accompanying plate was from Ehret's drawing and is repeated in J. Blackstone's *Specimen Botanicum*, 1746, where the information is given that this " Branched Agaric, resembling the Horn of a Rein-deer," was found in a smith's cellar. Judging by the writings of the period this " elegant species " was an object of curiosity both for literary and scientific minds.* Moreover the interest continued for when the growth was cut down it " appeared again at the same time the next year, and so on for several succeeding years, as if, contrary to the nature of the generality of these plants, it had a perennial root, and grew regularly from the old stalk."

The two common species of *Xylaria* (Pyrenomycete), *X. Hypoxylon*, the Candle-Snuff Fungus, and *X. polymorpha*, also form long growths in darkness. They grow towards a source of light and can be made to twist and turn at will by moving this about. Light is necessary for the production of both conidia and spores.

Abnormal growths due to insufficient light are sometimes found on the underside of logs, in hollow trunks or under masses of leaves.

Light is of biological importance in the spore discharge of some fungi. Thus smaller stalked Discomycetes often bend over their discs to face the direction of incident light: in other Discomycetes the tips of the asci are phototropic. In some Pyrenomycetes, particularly those growing on dung, such as *Sordaria* and *Podospora*, the neck of the perithecium bends over so that it arranges itself in the direction of light. *Sphaerobolus stellatus* (pl. XIV*a*, p. 211) shoots its gleba towards the source of light. Similarly the Phycomycete, *Pilobolus*, species of which are so commonly to be seen glistening on coprophilous substrata, flings off its black cap-like sporangium for a surprising distance considering the minuteness of the organism: a sporangiophore 1 in. high can shoot the sporangium six feet vertically or eight feet horizontally. The

*James Bolton has a similar drawing in *An History of Fungusses growing about Halifax*, III, Plate 138 (1789). " A sight of this curious Fungus (Boletus rengiferinus) was procured me by Mr. Thorsby, of *Leeds*. It grew on an old log of wood in a cellar, in that town, A.D. 1788."

sporangium is borne on a stalk which has a swollen upper portion, somewhat like an inverted electric bulb. This sub-sporangial swelling acts as a lens. Light falling on it laterally converges on a spot on its opposite wall. According to Buller the protoplasm there acts as a receptive spot or eye, and transmits the stimulus down to the stalk just below the swelling, which reacts by growing more quickly on the side nearest the spot of light. Thus there is a bending and this continues until the " gun " points to the source of the brightest light and is then ready for " firing." The projectile is propelled by a squirting action resulting from the bursting of the subsporangial swelling.

All these phototropic movements have as their result the discharge of spores into space with a better chance of dispersal, for otherwise some intervening object as likely as not would be hit.

There are a number of fungi which normally develop underground. The best known of these are the truffles (see Chap. 22).

Though moisture is essential for spore germination and for further growth, an excess is detrimental for most of the larger fungi; the mycelia seem unable to grow satisfactorily if water-logged. Presumably this is on account of interference with respiration, for fungi, in common with all organisms, respire, normally taking in oxygen and giving out carbon dioxide. Few agarics grow in marshy ground, and one reason for this may be the water-sodden soil. Also in a very wet year fungi are nothing like so abundant as in a normal year, though a good crop occurs in well-drained ground. At the opposite extreme there are certain genera which grow in desert conditions.

The range of temperature at which fungi grow varies somewhat for different species. This is readily ascertained for those which can be cultured, but for agarics one must rely mostly on field observations.* Some species normally produce fruit-bodies in winter. Amongst these are *Collybia velutipes* with a bright yellow cap, with darker disc, or wholly tawny, dull yellow gills and a yellow then brown velvety tough stem, growing in clusters on old trunks, logs and fences, and sometimes acting as a weak parasite on laburnum and red currant, and *Tremella mesenterica* (Pl. 40a, p. 255) forming bright yellow jelly-like clumps on dead branches, furze, broom and ivy, while *Tricholoma nudum* (Pl. 7,

Psalliota hortensis appeared spontaneously on a year-old compost heap at Wateringbury, Kent, in August 1950, in quantities and without a break until December when " in spite of heavy frosts and deluges of rain " it continued to develop " not in ordinary numbers but compressed closely together, the upper lot of 10 or so being pushed right out of the ground by a similar batch below."

p. 82) and *T. personatum* (Pl. 6, p. 67) will continue to form fruit-bodies through a mild winter. With the spring many species appear, but it is principally the season for Discomycetes, some, like *Gyromitra esculenta*, even appearing under the snow. The closely related *Morchella esculenta* and other morels, are also spring forms. Among other large Discomycetes are *Sepultaria Sumneri* and *Sarcosphaera coronaria*. Both are at first buried in the soil, and when they emerge split into segments. The first is externally chestnut-brown, densely hairy, and with a pinkish yellow disc; the segments of the margin are irregular: it grows under cedars. The second is dirty pale blue externally downy and with a blue to purple disc; the eight or so segments of the margin are tooth-like: it grows under conifers. The beautiful *Sarcoscypha coccinea* with a bright scarlet disc and a white downy exterior and a similar stalk, arising from sticks, is common in ditches where it sometimes occurs in enormous numbers. Known in Wales as " Moss-Cups " and elsewhere as " Red-Cups " and " Fairies' Baths," it is often used with moss as a table decoration.

The St. George's Mushroom, *Tricholoma gambosum*, appears about April 23 and is accompanied by several species, mostly coprophilous. Others follow more or less in their due season, short for some, extended for others even up to the " Jan.-Dec" of books. Temperature doubtless plays a part but it is not the sole factor in determining seasons, even disregarding moisture, which is always a controlling factor. Some species require a much longer vegetative growth than others before they form fruit-bodies, which may be considered as merely the culmination of processes designed for their production.

The main fungus season begins after late summer rains in August, reaches its peak in September, and ends with the coming of frosts. *Amanita rubescens* (Pl. 3, p. 18), *Russula ochroleuca* (Pl. 14*a*, p. 119) and other *Russula* spp. are amongst the first to appear, and *Clitocybe brumalis*, *C. cyathiformis*, and *Hygrophorous hypothejus*, are late autumn forms.

The woody Polyporaceae may continue through several winters. This is especially so in the genus *Fomes*, which forms a series of strata of tubes. Normally one layer is formed annually, though it has been found that in *F. fomentarius* (and it may hold for other species) each layer may produce crops of spores for four years in succession. By counting the layers we have a rough estimate of the age of a given sporophore. As *Fomes fomentarius* is the source of amadou there is good reason why it is rarely left to attain old age, but European specimens with twenty-five to thirty layers are occasionally seen; an American specimen has been recorded with fifty, and one of the related *F. igniarius*, with eighty.

The fruit-bodies of some species revive when moistened and again begin to shed spores. This can readily be observed in *Marasmius oreades*, the Fairy-Ring Champignon (Pl. 10, p. 103). Species of leathery consistency will often revive after a year or more of desiccation.

Buller, who was particularly interested in *Schizophyllum commune*, a fungus which shows several features which he interpreted as xerophytic characters, sealed some whole and part specimens in glass tubes *in vacuo* of less than 1 mm. pressure of mercury and stored them in the dark at room temperature, to be opened at intervals. The specimens were collected in October 1909 and some put in the tubes in December 1910. In 1912 they were subjected to the temperature of liquid air (—190° c.). In the same year other specimens were sealed in very high vacuum " at about the X-ray stage." Three tubes of the first series and one of the second were recently opened, and it was found that all contained some specimens that were still living, and formed normal basidia which produced spores capable of germination—this over thirty-five years after gathering.

It is not only fruit-bodies that can withstand cold and desiccation, for many spores are able to do so in spite of showing no obvious structure that can be interpreted as an adaptive character. Paul Becquerel (1910) experimented with the spores of several common moulds (*Mucor, Aspergillus*, etc.). After being slowly dried they were placed in tubes and the air evacuated. The vacuum was maintained for a little over two years, during which time they were subjected to the action of liquid air for three weeks and liquid hydrogen for seventy-seven hours. Sown afterwards on nutrient media they germinated and produced normal growths.

When the balloon " Explorer II " made its ascent to 72,395 feet (13.71 miles) in 1935, spores of seven moulds were enclosed in small quartz tubes fastened to the outside of the gondola; the ends loosely plugged with cellulose yarn. Five of the moulds, including *Aspergillus niger* and *Rhizopus nigricans*, had their vitality unimpaired, though subjected for many hours to drying, extreme cold, strong light rays, ozone and low air pressure.

A collecting device was released from the balloon when descent began, and operated from over 70,000 feet to about 36,000 feet. Spores of five species were taken—*Rhizopus, Aspergillus niger, A. fumigatus*,

Penicillium cyclopium and *Macrosporium tenuis*—which afterwards germinated in culture.

The fruit-bodies of fleshy fungi will not withstand desiccation. Depending on their consistency, though influenced by the habitat and the weather, they may last as long as four weeks in tougher forms (*Pleurotus ostreatus* (Pl. 19*a*, p. 146), usually only a few days in membranous species, and occasionally only a few hours as in the small *Coprinus ephemerus* occurring on dung, which is so slender that a breath of air will destroy it; it develops during the night and vanishes in early morning.

CHAPTER 9

SPORE PRODUCTION
AND SPORE CHARACTERS

THE FRUIT-BODY or sporophore of a toadstool, though popularly supposed to "grow up in one night," is the culmination of a period of growth. "Pousser comme un champignon" and "mushroom growth," though expressive, are based on a fallacy. A fungus is an organism requiring certain conditions for growth and having a well-defined life-history, the climax of which is the fruit-body, which, indeed, may be regarded as the end in view, the production of spores for carrying on the species. That in mushroom-growing or in toadstool-gathering the fruit-body is also the objective, is merely of anthropocentric significance—as with wild or cultivated fruits; that they are food for man is, from a biological standpoint, pure chance.

When a spore has germinated, the mycelium grows in every direction, branching and anastomosing and so making use of all the soil or other substratum available to it. Soil is not simply an inert mass but is the seat of abundant life. The mycelium in its wanderings is not less free from the trials and tribulations of terrestrial existence than is any other organism. It may be attacked, it may be helped, it may be ignored. Just as all available surface of the soil is occupied by organisms so is its substance. There is competition for food, there is competition for space, there is competition for existence. Certain factors are necessary for the growth of a mycelium, but even when these are most favourable there is presumably a population of diverse organisms already in possession.

Fungal hyphae grow at their tips, regularly progressing in a given direction in the ideal conditions of laboratory cultures, (see Pl. 45, p. 274) but in a natural substratum, as contrasted with a homogeneous sterilised medium, growth is rarely so regular.

The fungus-mycelium in the soil is living, requiring moisture, air, warmth, mineral and organic food. Success or failure even, when all these factors are favourable, depends upon whether it is able to make use of these in the face of abundant competition with or without the assistance of other species.

A very shortened outline of the development of the fruit-body of the mushroom will serve as a focus. The spore is purple-brown, thick walled, elliptical, measuring 7-9 μ long by 5-6 μ broad, and shows a small spine-like projection (*hilum*) at the basal end, which marks the former point of attachment. It usually contains a large, highly refractive oil globule with two or three minute ones. Germination can be obtained in distilled water, dung decoction and various synthetic media in from ten to twenty days. One, two or even three, germ-tubes arise from any part of the wall, but usually at the end. The first appearance suggests an oozing out of a viscous fluid, followed by gradual enlargement to a bubble-like outgrowth until the diameter is more or less that of the width of the spore, and then an elongation to a typical hyphal growth. Branching begins early and cross walls may be formed at once, but generally are more abundant in somewhat later stages after six or more branches have been produced. The hyphae from one or from several spores anastomose apically and by lateral branches.

Mushroom-spawn consists of white cottony or string-like threads. These are not formed in culture until the surface is overrun by the filamentous mycelium. Then from the original point of inoculation, strands are formed which gradually enlarge from the centre outwards. They begin as loose aggregations of more or less parallel hyphae each elongating at its tip, but later become more compact and undergo branching. They probably serve for the more effective penetration of the substratum. After a time the fruit-body is initiated. Under cultural conditions this is often independent of the seasons. Cultivated mushrooms can be obtained all the year round because in the equable conditions of mushroom-houses and in the beds, the period from spawning to gathering can be estimated with commercial accuracy— it is cultivation which changeth the times and the seasons.

The first visible sign of the development of fruit-bodies is the formation of minute compact knobs on the spawn by the interweaving of great numbers of hyphal threads which grow out from the sides of the cords. These knots enlarge and elongate and make their way to the surface.

At a very early stage, while the outside still shows no sign of differentiation, the first indication of gill-formation appears. In a longitudinal section two deeply staining areas are seen, one at either side in the upper portion some distance from the centre—portions of an annular area. As this area increases many slender and pointed hyphae push their way into it from above to form the primordia of the gills. Meanwhile the ground tissue below either ceases or slows down growth, and a cavity, the gill cavity, results through mechanical tearing. The stem and cap primordia are thus also differentiated.

The internal (endogenous) origin of the gills is confined to those genera with a ring or a volva. They arise on the surface (exogenous) of the developing fruit-body in species not so provided, and are then usually protected during development by the edge of the pileus gradually arching towards the stem.

The gills of a mushroom are not all of the same length, but can be classed roughly as long, intermediate and short; they are so arranged that they occupy the whole of the lower surface of the cap. There are about four hundred of them in a Field-Mushroom with a cap 3 in. across; in the Cultivated Mushroom there are slightly more. The covering over of the gills by the marginal veil during development provides them with an even temperature and moisture.

The gills are narrowly wedge-shaped in section. The central portion (*trama*) is composed of chains of large elongated cells running more or less parallel to the outer surface. Next there are several layers of rounded or oval cells (*subhymenium*), and on the outside the spore-bearing layer (*hymenium*). The shape of the gills enables a greater amount of hymenium to be formed than if it were on a flat surface; Buller calculated that there is about twenty times more and that a mushroom with a cap of 4 in. diameter has a hymenial surface of about 1.33 square feet.

The hymenium is composed of serried ranks of club-shaped basidia interspersed with sterile paraphyses. The swollen outer end of the basidium has four curved pointed projections (*sterigmata*) each of which bears a spore above the general surface of the hymenium. The spore arises as a colourless swelling at the tip of the sterigma and takes half an hour or so to reach full size. After about two hours more the wall begins to pigment and reaches its final colour in a further two hours. It remains in position for another three hours—about eight hours in all from its inception to its discharge.

A few seconds before the spore is shed the small projection by which the spore is attached (hilum) exudes a drop of water. The spore is then violently shot off about 0.1 mm. into the space between the gills carrying the drop with it, and then falls at a rate of 0.13 cm. per second. The remaining spores are shot off in succession at short intervals. No reasonable suggestion of the mechanics of this process has yet been put forward. It ensures that the spore is enabled to get free from the sporophore to be wafted away by air currents. The rigidity of the stem and the horizontal orientation of the cap keep the gills upright; if by any chance they veer from that position they are righted by the action of gravity. In slender fungi where there is no such rigidity the stem is also sensitive to gravitational stimulus.

The gills when first formed are almost white but change colour with age. Part of this change is due to the darkening of the pigmented sap of the cells, probably by enzyme action. As the spores begin to mature the surface of the gills appears mottled. This is because the basidia ripen in patches—an area of mature spores showing dark, one of developing spores lighter—and as successive generations pass through the stages the areas change position. Spore-production continues for five or six days.

The number of spores produced by the mushroom can be estimated in various ways. One is by counting the basidia in a given area and then calculating the number on the measured total gill-surface. A square millimetre gave 33,265 basidia, which would produce 133,060 spores; a square inch would therefore produce approximately 83,162,500 spores and the 1.33 sq. ft. of a specimen with a 4 in. cap, 16,000,000,000 spores. As these are discharged in five or six days there is an average fall day and night of over 100,000,000 an hour.

Gills of other fungi differ in details of structure, but have essentially the same general pattern, except in the genus *Coprinus*, the inky caps, a name given because of the gradual dissolving of the cap into a black liquid. Some of the large forms like *Coprinus comatus* (Pl. 22*a*, p. 151), *C. atramentarius* (Pl. 22*b*, p. 151) and *C. picaceus* (Pl. 21, p. 150), have caps which remain conical during spore-discharge, whereas others, such as *C. micaceus* (Pl. 18*c*, p. 130) and *C. plicatilis* (Pl. 38*c*, 247), have their caps expanded. The gills are more or less parallel-sided and not wedge-shaped, and they do not react to gravity. In the species in which the cap does not spread out there are devices for keeping the gills apart. This is accomplished in *C. comatus* by flanges at the edges of the gills. In other species it is by long sterile outgrowths (*cystidia*) projecting from the hymenium; this is best seen in *C. atramentarius* where the cystidia are attached by their ends to the opposite gill.

In the mushroom the spores ripen over the whole surface of the gills at the same time: in *Coprinus* the spores form, ripen and are shot off from below upwards, the flesh of the cap undergoing self-digestion (autolysis) following spore-discharge. Thus the cap gradually becomes converted into a black liquid, which owes its colour chiefly to the spores it contains. An intensely black ink can be made of it, as first pointed out by P. Bulliard in 1784, who named the species he found best for the purpose *l'Agaric atramentaire*, the Inky Agaric. It has been suggested that as the contained spores of different species of *Coprinus* give a specificity to the ink it should be used for documents where forgery might be attempted.*

The zone of spore discharge is comparatively narrow. Within it there are two or more waves of development owing to the fact that the basidia are of at least two different lengths. Usually they are dimorphic, but in *C. plicatilis* they are trimorphic, and in *C. micaceus* tetramorphic. The different sized basidia are intermingled in the hymenium; they ripen and discharge their spores in the order of descending length.

All fleshy species of *Coprinus* " deliquesce." In membranous species, which are usually very small, the gills merely dry up: *C. plicatilis* (Pl. 38c, p. 247) is exceptional in its size but the general structure of its gills and the character of its spores, place it in the genus despite the fact that it has lost or maybe never had what may be considered its hall-mark.

The method of development in Agarics leads to differences in the structural relations of cap and stem. The genera in which the gills develop endogenously have the flesh of the cap distinct from that of the stem; there is no real continuity and the two readily come apart without tearing. In exogenous forms the flesh of the cap and stem run into each other: where the stem is fleshy as in *Clitocybe* and *Tricholoma* both have the same anatomical structure; where it is fibrous or cartilaginous as in *Collybia* and *Mycena* the structure is different but the two cannot be separated without tearing.

Differences in internal structure are of importance in classification. Some of them gain expression in external form and texture and give characters which have always been used by systematists, with the result that new systems of classification have much in common with the old. One may say that the general plan gives the larger divisions and the

*An Australian suggestion is for police to carry " pistols " containing Indian ink impregnated with the spores of different species. A stain on clothing, made during a mêleé, would be recognised as of police origin " fired " by a particular pistol.

special plan the genera; specific differences are more usually displayed by modifications of measurements.

While the general anatomy of gills follows the pattern in *Psalliota*, where the trama is composed of regular parallel hyphae, others have a trama of interwoven hyphae (*Lentinus*), some a narrow median band of parallel hyphae from which large elongated cells pass obliquely (*Amanita*), or there may be no median layer and the elongated cells appear to originate in the subhymenium (*Pluteus, Volvaria*).

The presence or absence of cystidia in the hymenium is of systematic importance. These sterile cells are usually large and project above the general surface. They have often a characteristic shape and frequently have crystals of calcium oxalate on their walls, particularly at the tips, possibly due to their acting as excretory organs.

The surface of the cap also shows important differences. The cells may be hardly different from the underlying tissue or a little more dense; the cuticle may be composed of elongated, globular or club-shaped cells arranged vertically; or there may be several distinct layers of structurally different cells.

Shape, texture, colour, smell and taste are the characters which, being obvious, receive most attention. Shape, texture and sometimes colour are closely related as are smell and taste; all entered largely into the old classifications and all play a part in modern taxonomy, though it may be very small.

Shape is the outward and visible sign of inward physiological development in equilibrium with the factors of the environment. The fact that a fungus has gills is a sure token that its spores are borne on basidia. The manner in which the gills are attached is an important generic character: they may run down the stem as in *Clitocybe* and *Cantharellus* (decurrent); they may join the stem more or less at right angles as in *Russula* (adnate), or just join it as in *Panaeolus* (adnexed); before they reach the stem they may form a small upward curve as in *Tricholoma* (sinuate); or they may not join on to the stem but to the flesh of the cap as in *Lepiota* (free).

The typical basidium, club-shaped and crowned with four sterigmata bearing the spores, characterises other groups as well as the mushroom (agarics). It is found where there are tubes in place of gills: in *Boletus* with fleshy cap and stem; in the hard bracket-shaped *Polyporus, Polystictus* and the perennial *Fomes*; in *Trametes* and *Daedalia* with tubes of different lengths, having elongated openings in the former and labyrinthine in the latter; in *Merulius* with very shallow gyrose pores and a fleshy fruit-body of no predestined shape.

Typical basidia occur also in *Hydnum* and its allies where the hymenium surrounds spine-like structures; *Hydnum* itself may have a cap and stem or these may both be absent. Many forms where the hymenium covers a smooth or slightly rugulose surface as *Craterellus*, *Thelephora* and *Stereum*, and the fairy clubs, *Clavaria* (Pl. 28, p. 175) where it covers a single club-shaped structure or a branched one, have also this type of basidium. With all these forms and shapes it is possible to be certain at a glance that the spores are borne on typical basidia, except with the club-shape, for this is also found in Ascomycetes (Discomycetes and Pyrenomycetes). Even in Basidiomycetes there is a genus *Calocera* which appears to differ from *Clavaria* only in being gelatinous and not fragile—the orange-coloured *C. viscosa* forms tufts on pine-stumps—but when examined microscopically is found to have basidia with two large pointed sterigmata; the same type of basidium occurs in *Dacryomyces*, the commonest species of which, *D. deliquescens*, forms small gelatinous yellow pustules on dead wood. In the Jew's Ear, *Hirneola auricula-Judae*, (Pl. III*b*, p. 50) the basidia have transverse septa and the sterigmata, one from each segment, are of different lengths so as to reach the general surface for spore production and liberation. Other gelatinous forms such as *Tremella* (Pl. 40*a*, p. 255), have basidia with two longitudinal septa so that they are cruciately divided; they have long sterigmata. The main outlines of the families having these four different types of basidia were reached before microscopic examinations revealed them; exceptions were *Calocera*, which was associated with *Clavaria*, and *Tremellodon* which, because of its spines, was classed with *Hydnum*, though it was regarded as anomalous because of being gelatinous; it has basidia of the *Tremella* type. It is remarkable that the great majority of the larger fungi with atypical basidia are more or less gelatinous, swelling with moisture and becoming horn-like when dry. This particular texture and the various external forms are certain guides for their identification.

All these different types—Agaricaceae, Polyporaceae, Hydnaceae, Clavariaceae and Tremellinaceae of the older classifications—have their hymenium either exposed from the first or during development; as the spores ripen they are discharged. They are *Hymenomycetes*. The other main division of Basidiomycetes, *Gasteromycetes*, includes the Stink-Horns (*Phallus*, see Chap. 16,), the Puff-Balls (*Lycoperdon*, see Chap. 15), Bird's Nest fungi (see Chap. 21) and others in which the hymenium is enclosed by a sterile covering of hyphae until maturity; the spores are liberated *en masse* and not in succession, and are not violently discharged from the basidium; most frequently they are borne directly on the basidium without intervening sterigmata and not invariably to the number of four.

Many fungi have a characteristic smell, though probably this is never specific. As there is no scale denoting either the nature of odour or its intensity, recourse has to be made to analogy. Some comparisons are both sufficiently homely, and exact, to be of real use in descriptions and are repeated in most books; others, however, are somewhat bewildering. Fries, for example, describes *Stereum* [*Corticium*] *odoratum* as " Odor forte peregrinus." What is the smell perchance emitted by foreigners or travellers? Can it be " nach Fussschweiss oder käseartig" which J. Schaeffer gives for eleven species in his monograph on the genus *Russula*! Association of smells is as perplexing as association of ideas. If it were not already known it could be deduced from mycological floras that the sense of smell is very deficient in some people; others detect the nuances but their olfactory memory does not always provide the same analysis. Fries in *Hymenomycetes Europeae* gives little information about odours, and it has been suggested that he often failed to notice or recognise them because he was excessively fond of snuff. His fellow countryman, Linnaeus, would have strongly supported this view, for after saying that scent is never a clear distinguishing character of a flowering plant species, he adds:

" Unless scent, taste and touch come in and that very obviously, a botanist is of no account. For this reason I am sorry for those nations which a dread disease, called *Pica* or *Malacia nasi*, has so infected with the contagious poison of tobacco, that it has not only weakened their sense of smell: it has even covered their olfactory nerves with a thick callus, so that there no longer remains to them the faculty of smell."

He comments on the difficulty of determining the significance of the usual expressions pleasant, unpleasant, faint and strong

" For a scent which is disgusting to a boy is most pleasing to a hysterical woman. A countryman entering a drug-store turns faint with the scent of the perfumes, but recovers when a heap of cow-dung is presented to his nostrils."

The point was put to the test by A. F. Blakeslee at the International Flower Show, New York, in 1936. In over 8,000 visitors he found that a strong scent for one person might be a weak scent for another, but the reactions might be reversed for a different flower. A woman unable to detect any scent in one bowl of *Freesia* described the second as being " a perfectly heavenly odour "; a man called the scent of the first strong, and of the second he said, " These stink, they stink like hell."

In spite of this there is general agreement in the description of most fungus smells, though judging from Floras a particular species occasionally arouses a multiplication of olfactory similes.* A point to be stressed, moreover, is that the smell sometimes changes as a fruit-body passes through the stages from youth to old age.

French mycologists have always given much attention to odours, probably because many have been pharmacists and consequently interested in perfumery, but they are not averse to unsavoury similes. Recently there have been attempts to make an olfactive scale by matching the odours in the laboratory, but as the ingredients are for the most part organic chemicals not commonly known, these reconstituted odours are not likely to be of practical use even when they are much more precise than at present.

The commonest odour is what is usually called a fungus smell— and this defies further definition. In some species, however, it is very feeble or absent. A very common smell is one resembling that of new meal: this occurs in *Tricholoma gambosum, Entoloma lividum, Clitopilus prunulus.* Several species contain a small amount of hydrocyanic acid and smell of bitter almonds; such are *Marasmius oreades, Clitocybe infundibuliformis.* Amongst sweet smells are Anise; *Clitocybe odora, Lentinus cochleatus, Trametes suaveolens*†: Musk; *Lactarius helvus, Polyporus benzoinus*: Scented soap; *Poria xantha*: Coco-nut toffee; *Lactarius glyciosmus*: Honey; *Russula melliolens*: Fruits; Pear, *Hebeloma sinuosum*: Apple, *Pholiota aurea*: Mirabelle plum, *Cantharellus cinereus*: Apricot, *Cantharellus cibarius*: Peach, *Russula amoena*: Flowers; Jasmine, *Inocybe pyriodora*; Rose, *Russula maculata*; Geranium, *Cortinarius paleaceus.*

*Thus *Tricholoma suphureum* is given as smelling of Jasmine, *Narcissus*, Hyacinth, *Hemerocallis flava*, Lilac, *Tagetes*, decayed Hemp, coal gas, coal tar—and fetid, or nauseous.

†" The Lapland youth having found this Agaric, carefully preserves it in a little pocket hanging at his waist, that its grateful perfume may render him more acceptable to his favourite fair-one. O whimsical Venus! in other regions you must be treated with coffee and chocolate, preserves and sweetmeats, wines and dainties, jewels and pearls, gold and silver, silks and cosmetics, balls and assemblies, music and theatrical exhibitions: here you are satisfied with a little withered fungus! " Linnaeus, *Flora Lapponica.*

M.T.   H

Other odours resemble those of vegetables: Radish; *Hebeloma crustuliniforme* and many other species: Potato; *Amanita mappa*: Onion; *Marasmius alliaceus*, *M. scorodonius*. Of animal smells there is fish; *Naucoria cucumis*: crab, *Russula xerampelina*; Goat moth, *Hygrophorus cossus*. *H. russocoriaceus* smells of Russian leather.*

Some smell of gas tar, *Tricholoma bufonium*; chlorine, *Mycena rubromarginata*; ammonia, *Mycena ammoniaca*; acetylene, *Cortinarius prasiosmus*. *Tricholoma saponaceum* and *Collybia butyracea* smell of soap; *Collybia rancida* of rancid oil; and there is a fetid odour in *Marasmius foetidus* and *Hygrophorus foetens*, but it is most characteristic in *Phallus*, *Mutinus* and *Clathrus*.

Taste has much in common with smell and it is probable that there is often confusion between them. Few species have what may be termed a characteristic flavour though some species of *Russula* taste of nuts.

Some fungi have a bitter taste, for instance, *Boletus felleus* and *Armillaria mellea*, while some are acrid, *Russula drimeia* and *Lactarius rufus* being examples of species which are extremely hot to the taste. Whether a *Russula* is mild or peppery forms an essential part of the description, and indeed the character has been regarded by some mycologists as of sufficient importance to use in dividing up the genus. The character is probably associated with the presence of resinoid or phenolic substances and it is unscientific to assume that their systematic importance, if any, can be ascertained by taste. While there is never any doubt about the almost strangling effect of chewing a small piece of *Russula drimeia*, the " mild then acrid " of some species often defies detection, for tastes differ. How much they may do so is shown by the fact that phenyl thio-carbamide is bitter for some people and nearly tasteless for others—and, moreover, this palatal sensitiveness is hereditary† acting as a Mendelian dominant character.

An acrid or bitter taste may be restricted to the gills, the pellicle of the cap, or some other part of a fungus.

Colour in fungi is important in the characterisation of species, and it is probable that when the chemical significance of the various pigments is understood we will be provided with valuable data both of physiology and of taxonomy.

Though colour is at present chiefly an important character in

*Specimens collected in 1877 (Herb. M.B.) still retain the odour.
†Flavours (e.g. of bitter almonds) and tastes (e.g. of bitters) regarded as pleasant by most Europeans, nauseate most Indians.

specific differentiation it plays a large part, certainly too large, in the customary grouping of genera in the Agaricales. J. B. von Albertini and L. D. von Schweinitz in 1805 remarked on the constancy of the colour of the spores deposited by a given species of the old genus *Agaricus* and questioned whether the colour of the spores, white, pink, black, etc. could not be used for dividing up the genus. This method was adopted by Fries in 1821 and he continued to use it: in its final form in 1874 there were five series—white, pink, brown, purple, black. Though some of his names have been changed these divisions are still in general use for the main sections of Agarics. A method which has been consistently adopted for more than a century might be assumed to be intrinsically sound. This cannot be upheld, however, for it is a purely artificial division and widely separates genera which by their development and structure are obviously closely related. Moreover, in some genera there is a range of spore colour which cannot be taken into account by rigid adherence to these main divisions—even indeed to fit them in. Perhaps the best example of this is the genus *Lepiota*. We have in our flora *L. echinata* with dull green spores, changing rapidly to reddish brown and then to red, *L. Georginae* with pink spores, and *L. Eyrei* with green spores; the last has been placed in a separate genus *Chlorospora* or *Glaucospora*, and additional series created for this and two other genera. In recently discovered tropical species although the spores are mostly white they may be cream-colour, pink, clay-colour, olive, greenish, grey, or show ranges such as from white to dark red, grey-green to bistre, yellow to purple. The pigment may be in the membrane, in the cytoplasm, or both. The facts suggest that *Lepiota* might well be connected up with *Pholiota aurea* (for which the genus *Phaeolepiota* has been proposed), and so on to *Psalliota*. It appears certain that future classification will pay diminishing regard to the time-honoured divisions which were founded on spore colour, though, as the essential chemistry of the colouring matter and its location are ascertained, it will become even more important in the delimitation of genera and the determination of species.

Though the majority of fungi are somewhat drab there is an abundance of bright spectrum colours. The amount of pigment present is usually very small which makes chemical analysis difficult. The intensity of some colours is due to water in the intercellular spaces making the tissues transparent. In the so-called hygrophanous species, imbibed water accumulating between the cells of the cuticle renders them translucent and strongly coloured, and with its loss they become pale, to darken again with added water. A well-marked example of this is *Hypholoma hydrophilum* which forms clusters on stumps. When moist this has date-brown caps which turn tan-colour as they dry, much to the bewilderment of a beginner sorting out his finds at the end of a day's collecting.

The pigments may occur in the cell interior either in the form of granules dispersed in the cytoplasm (or impregnated in the cytoplasm) or in the vacuoles, generally as a fluid but often precipitated with age; they may be present in the membranes, fine particles of colour being evenly distributed on a colourless base; or they may accumulate in the air spaces between the hyphae and may be deposited on the outer surface.

Some pigments, more especially reds and purples, are soluble in water or destroyed by strong sunlight. Many species of *Russula* show this well: the common *Russula emetica* (Pl. 14*b*, p. 119) often loses its bright red and becomes completely decolourised. Yellows are usually more permanent and a cap in which there is a mixture of it with red or purple will gradually become more or less wholly yellow as in *Russula amoena*.

Similarly with one of the few green species, *Stropharia aeruginosa*, which has a bright verdigris-coloured cap and stem, with scattered white patches. The colour resides in the skin which can be readily peeled off. The green is soluble in water and is washed out by rain, so that specimens are commonly found with a yellow cap. This is decolouration, not discoloration.

The chemistry of pigments is a highly specialised study and has hardly been studied in the larger fungi, though much more so in micro-fungi. Similarity in colour does not imply similarity in chemical constitution or *vice versa*. Within the molecular structure of a pigment (or chromogen) is a special group, the chromatophore ($C=O$, or $-NO_2$, or quinone) which suffices for coloration; other groups ($-OH$, $-OCH_3$, $-CO_2H$, NH_2), known as auxochromes, modify this basal colour in various ways. Thus the yellow-orange pigment muscarufine present in the pellicle of the cap of *Amanita muscaria* has a quinone nucleus as a chromatophore and $-OH$ as an auxochrome.

Two other chemically related pigments (being also derivatives of di-phenyl-benzoquinone) are polyporic acid and atrotomentine. It has long been known that when ammonia solution is applied to the flesh of *Polyporus nidulans* a violet colour immediately results—a phenomenon which led to the synonym *Polyporus purpurascens*: the

Plate 9a. Collybia radicata; the stem extends underground as a tapering " root," the length of which depends upon the depth of the underground tree-root or wood from which it grows *(Paul L. de Laszlo)*

b. Collybia dryophila; sometimes placed in the genus *Marasmius;* frequently under oaks *(Paul L. de Laszlo)*

Plate 10. FAIRY-RING CHAMPIGNON, *Marasmius oreades;* very common in lawns, reviving with rain after drying. Edible. (*Photographs by Paul L. de Lazlo*)

pigment is polyporic acid. Atrotomentine is a brown pigment present in *Paxillus atrotomentosus*.

Increasing use is made of the reactions of the flesh to various chemicals in distinguishing between species. Ammonia, soda, potash, sulphuric and nitric acids, iron salts and various organic reagents are the most usual. Thus with sulphuric acid the flesh of *Amanita pantherina* becomes dark brown, *A. phalloides* lilac-colour, *A. muscaria* light brown, *A. virosa* light pink, while *A. rubescens* is unchanged.

Possibly of greater significance is the action of iodine on the membranes of the spores of white-spored Agarics. In some genera, e.g. *Hygrophorus* and *Lepiota* there is no effect; in others, e.g. *Russula* and *Lactarius*, the membranes become grey, blue or blackish; but in *Amanita* and *Mycena*, for example, only some species react, and the difference does not seem to be related to other characters.

In woodlands one often comes across pieces of bright green wood and occasionally small stalked cup-shaped fruit-bodies of *Chlorosplenium aeruginosum* are found upon it. Oak, ash, beech, birch, hazel and other deciduous wood may be infected, but in this country are commonly known as " green oak," for it was this which was formerly used in the manufacture of Tunbridge ware.* The pigment is xylindeine, a phenanthrene (quinone) derivative. Another derivative is thelephoric acid which gives the brown colour to many species of *Thelephora* and some species of *Hydnum*.

There is a series of species of *Cortinarius* which are bright red. *Cortinarius sanguineus*, common in coniferous woods, contains two pigments derived from anthroquinone—about 3% of orange-yellow emodine and 0.2 to 0.4% red dermacybine.

In common with other groups, both plant and animal, fungi of all kinds are provided with carotenoids; thus they occur in *Peziza aurantia* (Pl. 42*c*, p. 263) and *Tremella mesenterica* (Pl. 40*a*, p. 255); *Cantharellus cibarius* (Pl. 20, p. 147) contains mainly β-carotene (orange), but also small amounts of α-carotene (orange-yellow), and γ-carotene (orange-red) and very little lycopene (dark red).

The change of colour in the flesh of some species of *Boletus* and

*In preparing Tunbridge ware thin strips of differently coloured woods are assembled into a block, so that their ends display the desired pattern or picture. They are then glued and bound together under pressure and the mass is cut transversely into thin strips with a circular saw. This " veneer " is glued on to the table, box, or other article to be decorated, then carefully smoothed and polished.

Proposals have been made to produce the attractive green wood by artificial inoculation with the fungus, and even a patent applied for.

other genera when exposed to the air, has been referred to earlier (p. 56).

The problems which arise in studying pigmentation are many and varied. Thus there is a direct connection with vitamins, for β-carotene is protovitamin A, which by the splitting of its molecule produces the vitamin; lactoflavine (vitamin B2) gives the yellow colour to the yeast *Ashyba Gossypii*, as well as to some toadstools. Further it is believed that pigments play an important part in metabolism and more particularly in intracellular respiration.

For defining colour sufficiently precisely for descriptive work it is necessary to use a colour chart. Many of these have been compiled, but the older ones were never in general use because of their incompleteness and the more recent ones, chiefly horticultural and ornithological, lack some of the ranges of colours met with in toadstools.

CHAPTER 10

SEX

W
HEN IT WAS REALISED that toadstools and other fungi reproduce from spores the search began for organs of sex, for it was assumed that fertilisation must precede fructification. Naturally what was sought was anything resembling the stamens and pistils of flowering plants, and, over the years, imagination helped to homologise these with various structures seen imperfectly through primitive microscopes. Flowering plants were called Phanerogams (*phaneros*, visible; *gamos*, marriage) by Linnaeus because he thought that the sexual process in them was obvious, and the flowerless plants he called Cryptogams (*kryptos*, hidden) because their sexual process was concealed. These names are still in use, though their descriptive significance does not hold: Linnaeus in spite of his certainty about sex in plants and his sexual system of classification, was dealing merely with the stamens and carpels and not with the complicated fertilisation process, the details of which were not fully made out until modern cytological methods made it possible about fifty years ago. Meanwhile, when reasonably powerful microscopes became available, the simpler Cryptogams soon revealed their secrets, and nowadays elementary students of botany are accustomed to study the course of events. Phanerogams and Cryptogams are distinguished by the results of fertilisation regardless of whether the process would formerly have been classed as manifest or clandestine: Phanerogams reproduce by seeds, Cryptogams by spores.

Though Phycomycetes do not come within the scope of this book, and Ascomycetes only in so far as some of them are of a size comparable to that of toadstools, passing reference must be paid to their sexuality. The simplest Phycomycetes, the Chytridiales, are a complex group often classed as a separate cohort. They are microscopic, mostly unicellular organisms usually occurring in an aquatic habitat, frequently parasitic on green algae. Many of them reproduce vegetatively by motile spores (*zoospores*). The sexual cells (*gametes*) in some genera are also motile, later fusing in pairs. It is usually impossible to distinguish between the gametes—there is no male and female. Such isogamy (*isos*, equal), as it is called, is regarded as the beginning of sex, and it has been held that fusion originally took place because of shortage of food. On this view sex began as a hunger phenomenon!

Chytridiales show a range from isogamy to oogamy, that is from the fusion of gametes in every way indistinguishable, to a clear differentiation between the two cells, one motile, the male, the other stationary, the female; the resulting fusion-product (*zygote*) becoming surrounded by a thick wall, is capable of resting over an inclement period.

Chytridiales show many resemblances to simple, motile Protozoa (Flagellates). Of the views about the origin of fungi, that which regards the Chytridiales as having arisen along several lines from Flagellates and that from them the other groups were eventually derived, has most support among modern mycologists. If fungi originated from colourless Flagellates it follows that they never possessed chlorophyll, indeed that they never had any connection with green plants, which themselves are believed to have developed along several parallel lines from green Flagellates. It should be remarked, however, that the " phylogenetic trees " of botanical text-books usually represent different groups of fungi as derived from algae at different levels by loss of chlorophyll; regarding them indeed as degenerate algae but disregarding the fact that the presumed decadence is so successful as to have led to overwhelming superiority not only in the number and variety of forms, but also in the number of individuals.

In Phycomycetes proper, that is the filamentous forms, we have two main groups, Oomycetes and Zygomycetes. The Oomycetes have differentiated male and female organs: in the majority a male gametangium (*antheridium*) becomes applied to a female gametangium (*oogonium*), the gametes being reduced to little more than the essential nuclei which fuse in pairs. The ancestral type is, however, still seen in *Allomyces* where motile male and female gametes are formed, though there is a difference in size, the female being larger. In *Monoblepharis* a further step occurs, for though the male gamete is motile, the female is a stationary oogonium. Both genera also reproduce vegetatively by zoospores. Such motile zoospores are also found in aquatic forms like *Saprolegnia*, well known as " fluff " on fish in aquaria and on diseased salmon. This motility is gradually lost in terrestrial forms; conidia-producing zoospores occur in some, for example, *Phytophthora infestans*, the cause of the destructive Potato Blight; the film of moisture on the plants is ample for the zoospores to progress, a progression that has often brought about financial disaster and famine. A further stage is for the conidia to produce ordinary mycelium—the transition from zoospore-formation to mycelial production, is seen in the different species of some genera, occasionally even in the same species, the one or the other occurring according to the environmental conditions.

In the other main division of the Phycomycetes, the Zygomycetes, there are usually no morphological distinctions between male and female gametangia. These are cut off from two hyphae which approach one another and fuse end to end to form a thick-walled zygote. It was in this group that the phenomenon of *heterothallism* was discovered, a phenomenon which has revolutionised our ideas of sex in fungi.

The common mould on bread, *Mucor Mucedo*, appears usually in its asexual or vegetative stage. This has roundish black heads surmounting upright stalks. The heads (*sporangia*) contain large numbers of spores. When these spores germinate they again give rise to mycelia which bear sporangia.

For very many years it had been known that some of the Mucoraceae formed zygospores readily, whereas others did so rarely. Thus *Sporodinia grandis*, which is frequent as a grey felt on *Boletus* and other toadstools, always forms abundant zygospores—they were first described for this species—but *Mucor Mucedo* rarely does. It was thought that these differences were due to growth conditions, and much research was undertaken to ascertain the chemical or physical factors influencing them. All was unavailing—and the reason was found by Blakeslee in 1904. *Sporodinia* will react to environmental conditions because all the spores give rise to the same kind of mycelium, able to form gametangia which fuse to form zygospores. Fungi with only one kind of mycelium are said to be *homothallic*. In *Mucor Mucedo* on the other hand, though all the spores in a given sporangium are of the same kind, no intermingling of the mycelia formed by them will produce zygospores. If, however, spores from several sporangia are grown the mycelia prove to be of two kinds; both are necessary for zygospore production, and no amount of culture or torture will induce this in either alone. The mycelia are designated(+) and (−)and usually spoken of as strains. Fungi with (+) and (−) strains are said to be *heterothallic*. Some form of heterothallism is now known in all groups of fungi.

Turning now to Ascomycetes there are some simpler forms with undifferentiated gametangia. Others have well-marked sexual organs, the best known being *Pyronema confluens*, a Discomycete which forms a salmon-pink layer on burnt ground: I have seen it carpeting an area of a quarter of an acre. The large female ascogonia (oogonia) and male antheridia form clusters, and each organ contains a number of nuclei. The male nuclei enter the ascogonia, but the precise details of fertilisation are still in question, though " much ado there was, God wot! He would love and she would not," indeed was the conclusion reached by a French observer. From the fertilised ascogonium hyphae grow out and the nuclei pass into them. The ends of these ascogenous hyphae bend over as hooks and, through septation, the cell at the bend of the hook is binucleate. It is from this cell that the young ascus grows out. The nuclei fuse and the fusion nucleus undergoing three successive divisions forms the eight nuclei which surround themselves with walls and become the eight spores characteristic of an ascus. As the more highly organised members of the group are reached there is first a disappearance of the antheridium, then of the ascogonium until finally there is no trace of either.

When we come to the main groups of Basidiomycetes (excluding the Rusts and the Smuts) all trace of sexual organs has disappeared. Early observers were deceived by odd swollen cells or by projecting processes which appeared to emit their granular contents, into thinking the first to be oogonia, and the second antheridia and spermatia. It did not seem to matter where and when the structures occurred in the life-history of the fungus, but most commonly they were located either in the young mycelium shortly after spore-germination, or on the gills in connection with spore-formation. The introduction of cytological methods completely changed the picture. It was then found that the young basidium has two nuclei, and that as the basidium grows the nuclei fuse. The fusion nucleus divides, and then the daughter nuclei, the four resulting nuclei passing into the developing spores. Nuclear fusion followed by reduction divisions clearly is the culmination of a sexual act and the problem was to discover how the nuclei became associated. It was soon found that in most species the young basidium was only the end of a series of binucleate cells, the nuclei dividing simultaneously during growth and segmentation of the hyphae, but keeping apart until the fusion in the basidium. Such conjugate nuclei, as they are called, occur also in Rusts and Smuts and apparently, though to a much less extent, in Ascomycetes. Indeed they may be said to be characteristic of fungi.

The puzzle, however, still remained, merely having been pushed back to an earlier stage of development. When M. Bensaude in 1918 discovered that *Coprinus fimetarius* is heterothallic, a great step was made, but there are still many problems awaiting solution, though the subject is too complex for any but the barest outline to be attempted here. It is now known that heterothallism is prevalent in Basidiomycetes, homothallism apparently rare.

The individual spores of a homothallic species as, for example, *Coprinus stercorarius*, when germinated give rise to a haploid mycelium, that is a mycelium in which the segments formed by the numerous transverse walls each contain a single nucleus. After a few days each haploid mycelium passes spontaneously into the diploid condition, that is the segments become binucleate. The diploid mycelium later gives rise to fruit-bodies. In other homothallic species as in *Corticium terrestre* and many Gasteromycetes the nucleus of the developing spore divides and the mature spore is consequently binucleate and produces a diploid mycelium on germination.

In the simplest expression of heterothallism, as in *Hypholoma fasciculare*, the four spores of a basidium give rise to two different kinds of mycelium (+) and (−). These, grown separately, do not produce normal fruit-bodies; for this, fusion between the two is necessary.

The primary (+) and (−) strains have uninucleate segments; they are haploid. When opposite strains are grown together they fuse by means of side branches, and the nucleus from a segment of one hypha passes over to a segment in the other hypha, and so there arises an association of (+) and (−) nuclei which divide conjugately until their long delayed union is accomplished in the basidium. This secondary mycelium is diploid. Contrary to all expectation this bipolar arrangement has been shown to be somewhat exceptional. Much commoner is a tetrapolar arrangement in which the four spores of the basidium give rise to four different strains, as it were two (+) and two (−), for they are not all compatible with one another but each with its opposite. If the differences are regarded as sexual then in bipolar species we have two sexes, which is simple to comprehend, but in tetrapolar species four, needing an unlooked for extension of current theory to accommodate them. It is probable, however, that the explanation lies in sterility factor mechanisms.

Assuming a Mendelian explanation, bipolar species such as *Coprinus comatus* are governed by one pair of factors (Aa) and the four spores are A, A, a, a. The resulting cross is (A) × (a).

In tetrapolar species such as *Coprinus fimetarius* there are two pairs of factors (Aa) and (Bb). The possibilities of the distribution of these in the four spores of a basidium are

(AB)(AB)(ab)(ab)
(Ab)(Ab)(aB)(aB)
(AB)(ab)(Ab)(aB)

The only successful matings are (AB) × (ab), and (Ab) × (aB), each giving (Aa)(Bb); thus, all four factors are brought together in the fusion nucleus of the basidium. Mycelia with factors in common do not interact sexually. Fusions may occur between other hyphae, but the nuclei do not become associated. A secondary or diploid mycelium may have buckle-shaped connections on its transverse walls. These so-called *clamp-connections* are invariably associated with the binucleate condition, but they do not always occur, and, when they do, are often restricted in their distribution—sometimes being confined to the mycelium, or to a part of the fruit-body. Where they are present they are definitely related to the conjugate division of the nuclei.

Near the growing tip of the hypha where a septum is to be formed the wall grows out and bends backwards in a hook-like manner, and one of the nuclei passes into it. Conjugate division of the nuclei takes place and the septum is laid down across the main hyphae at the level of the middle of the hook. A septum is then formed across the top of the hook and temporarily imprisons one of the daughter nuclei of the division. The tip of the hook fuses with a small peg-like out-growth from the main hypha and the nucleus which was imprisoned passes through the opening. Thus the terminal and the penultimate segments are both binucleate. The formation of these clamps can readily be observed, for the whole process usually takes less than half an hour. Why this strange performance is gone through lacks reasonable explanation, for those which have been proffered fail to explain why it should accompany conjugate divisions in some species and not in others.

Another interesting fact is the occurrence of what have been called geographical races. Having sorted out the two or four strains of mycelia in a bipolar and tetrapolar species respectively, it would normally be assumed that corresponding strains from the same species in other districts or regions would behave towards them in precisely the same manner. They sometimes do, but it has been found in some species that all the strains are fertile with one another. Thus if three fruit-bodies of a bipolar species be analysed and the spores labelled

Plate 11a (above left). HONEY-TUFT, *Armillaria mellea*; very destructive to trees and shrubs. Edible. *(Paul L. de Laszlo)*; *b (above right)* FALSE CHANTERELLE, *Clitocybe aurantiaca*; formerly placed in the genus *Cantharellus*, but the gills are not vein-like. *(Paul L. de Laszlo)*; *c (below left) Pholiota spectabilis*; in clusters on trunks or stumps of deciduous trees. *(Paul L. de Laszlo)*; *d (below right) Pholiota marginata*; on stumps and twigs, usually in coniferous woods *(Paul L. de Laszlo)*

Paul L. de Laszlo

Plate *12.* *Hygrophorus puniceus*; the base of the stem is white, the cap blood-red when young, and viscid

(A), (a), (A^1), (a^1), (A^2), (a^2), then mycelia (A) will fuse with mycelia (A^1), (A^2), as well as with (a), (a^1) and (a^2). Similarly with the mycelia produced by the four spores of heterothallic species. Thus we may have any number of " distinct sexual groups "—H. Brunswik obtained twenty-seven in *Coprinus fimetarius*; W. F. Hanna, twenty-four.

Occasionally in culture a monosporous haploid mycelium gives rise to fruit-bodies. These often differ in size, and some have basidia bearing only two spores instead of the normal four. This is of interest as bi-spored " varieties " often occur in nature and herein may lie the explanation for some of them. In some species, as in *Galera tenera*, the normal form has four uninucleate spores and is heterothallic, whereas the variety has two binucleate spores and is homothallic.

Matters are not always so simple however. Thus *Corticium coronilla* is considered to be a well-defined species by some mycologists, whereas D. P. Rogers in 1935 concluded that the specific concept should include three other described species of *Corticium* and a *Grandinia*, basing his opinion chiefly on their possession of a special type of basidium (coronate uniform, i.e. urn-shaped with a definite crown of (usually) eight slender sterigmata). R. Biggs in 1937 grew spores of the fungus from several localities, and distinguished four well-defined groups which differed in their cultural characters and also in their " sexuality": one was homothallic, the others heterothallic, both bipolar and tetrapolar. None of these agreed with any of the previously distinguished species. The conclusion reached was that *Corticium coronilla* is a collective entity made up of innumerable different and more or less constant genetic strains.

Robert Browning's pedant, Sibrandus Schafnaburgensis, about whom he asked, " Did he guess how toadstools grow, this fellow? " certainly had no idea of the complexities of their nutrition, development and sex-life!

CHAPTER II

FAIRY RINGS

F EW PEOPLE have not noticed the rings or lines of darker coloured grass in pastures, which, in this country, are usually now known as fairy rings, though formerly they were also called fairy (or fairies') dances, fairy courts, fairy walks, fairy grounds: in Sussex the old name was hag tracks.

Though belief in the existence of fairies is now more or less restricted to an age which gleefully shouts an answer to Peter Pan, it was not always so:

> " *In tholde dayes of the King Arthour,*
> *Of which that Britons speken greet honour,*
> *All was this land fulfild of fayerye;*
> *The elf-queen with hir Joly companye*
> *Daunced ful ofte in many a grene mede;*
> *This was the olde opinion, as I rede.*"

The circles of darker green grass, " more fertile fresh than all the field," often with an enclosed bare zone of compacted soil, have attracted the notice of poets of many nations—with us, Shakespeare, Pope, Dryden, Cowley, William Browne, Tennyson, Kipling, as well as Chaucer; only the first, however, mentions " midnight " mushrooms, though in modern children's stories they form fairies' tables, or, more usually, suitable seats for the musicians or the tired dancers. In some fancies the fairies dance under moonlight, or, if in the dark, with a glow worm for a lamp and a drone beetle or grasshopper for musician. It should be noted, however, that fairies were not necessarily diminutive creatures.

Though, as acted, Shakespeare's fairies are of human size, from their own description they were " demipuppets," but not " rude, coarse and earthy," as writers immediately before this time regarded them. *A Midsummer Night's Dream* may have owed something to a contemporary chap-book, *Robin Good-fellow, his mad prankes and merry jests*, which was probably written far earlier than 1628, the date of the first known edition.* " There were with King *Oberon*† a many faryes, all attired in greene silke. . . . *Oberon* tooke *Robin* by the hand and led him a dance, their Musitian was little *Tom Thumbe*, for hee had an excellent Bagge-pipe, made of a Wrens quill, and the skin of a Greene-land louse: This Pipe was so shrill and so sweete, that a Scottish Pipe, compared to it, it would no more come neere it, then a Jewes-Trumpe doth to an Irish Harpe . . ."

> " *When ere you heare my piper blow,*
> *From thy Bed see that you goe,*
> *For nightly you must with us dance,*
> *When we in circles round doe prance.*"

Rings differ in appearance at different seasons of the year and there are several types. That in which there are three concentric circles, an outer and an inner zone of darker coloured grass and a middle bare one, has attracted most attention, for obviously the bare part of the ring needed explanation. As Conan Doyle said, " It might be asserted and could not be denied that the rings once formed, whatever the cause, would offer a very charming course for a circular ring-a-ring dance."

But in addition to the bare circle, which was strong evidence of pattering feet, support was given by the evidence of eye-witnesses, usually some belated peasant whose sight was " ethurielised "—it may be by moonlight or possibly by the cause of his belatedness:

> " *Faerie Elves,*
> *Whose midnight Revels, by a Forrest side*
> *Or Fountain some belated Peasant sees,*
> *Or dreams he sees, while over head the Moon*
> *Sits Arbitress, and neerer to the Earth*
> *Wheels her pale course, they on thir mirth and dance*
> *Intent, with jocond Music charm his ear.*"

The miscellaneous Wiltshire collections of John Aubrey, preserved in the Ashmolean Museum at Oxford, gives a fair sample of the evidence:

*The earliest copy of this rarity in the British Museum (1639), has a note " Reprinted from a black letter copy in 8vo published soon after the year 1600."
†Oberon, King of the Fairies, is a borrowing from the French; the German is Albrich (elf-king): " he is of heyght but III foot and crookyd shoulderyd."

" In the year 1633-4, soon after I had entered into my grammar at the Latin School at Yatton Keynel, our curate, Mr. Hart, was annoyd one night by these elves or fayries comming over the downes, it being near darke, and approaching one of the faery dances as the common people call them in these parts, viz., the greene circles made by those sprites on the grasse, he all at once sawe an innumerable quantitie of pygmies or very small people dancing rounde and rounde, and singing and making all maner of small odd noyses. So being very greatly amaz'd, and yet not being able, as he says, to run away from them, being as he supposes kepte there in a kinde of enchantment. They no sooner perceave him but they surrounde him on all sides, and what betwixt feare and amazement, he fell downe scarcely knowing what he did; and thereupon these little creatures pinch'd him all over, and made a sorte of quick humming noyse all the time; but at length they left him, and when the sun rose he found himself exactly in the midst of one of these faery dances. This relation I had from him myselfe a few dayes after he was so tormented; but when I and my bedfellow Stump wente soon afterwards at night time to the dances on the downes, we sawe none of the elves or fayries. But indeed it is saide they seldom appeare to any persons who go to seeke for them."

The rings were attributed to fairies also in Denmark, Sweden, France and the Philippines: thus Olaus Magnus in his *History of the Goths* (1628) says that elves " make so deep an impression on the earth that no grass grows there, being burned with extreme heat." In Denmark:

" the women are most frequently to be seen by moonshine: then they dance their rounds in the high grass. . . . It is also necessary to watch cattle, that they may not graze in any place where the Elle-people have been; for if any animal come to a place where the Elle-people have spit, or done what is worse, it is attacked by some grievous disease, which can only be cured by giving it to eat a handful of St. John's Wort, which had been pulled at twelve o'clock on St. John's night."

In Germany the rings were attributed to the assembling of witches on Walpurgis night (May 1st) to perform their famous dance. In the Tyrol it is a winged dragon which at the epoch of Pegasids (10 August) and Martinmas (11 November) passing over the field scorches them with his tail of fire; wherever he passes the grass is burnt and does not revive until seven years later, being then preceded by circles of toadstools. The dates seem to be connected with Celtic worship, which was centred round the four days in the year marking the rise, progress and decline of the sun and consequently of fertility in crops and flocks.

This connects with the opinion " that the fairy tradition is to a large extent the ·broken-down folk-memory of a definite and far-reaching cult or system of worship." Elsewhere, a fiery dragon scorches the grass when he rests after his nocturnal exploits. In Holland the bare ring is where the devil's churn has rested. But however formed they are always magic circles. It is lucky to have several in a field adjoining a house, though to step inside one might bring about ill-fortune: in France enormous toads with bulging eyes abound within the ring, and any but unintentional entry brought its retribution. Superstitions vary, however, and in some districts of England it is lucky to enter a ring. The dew from the darker grass of the ring has been used by country girls for their complexions or in the equally serious matter of a love potion. It is not thought proper to do anything that will interfere with a ring. The old Scottish rhyme:

> " He wha tills the fairies' green,
> Nae luck again shall hae;
> And he wha spills the fairies' ring,
> Betide him want and wae;
> For wierdless days and weary nights
> Are his to his deein' day! "

puts the penalties in direst form. Whereas:

> " He wha goes by the fairy ring
> Nae dull nor pine shall see:
> And he wha cleans the fairy ring
> An easy deeth shall dee."

The history of the belief in fairies, goblins, elves and suchlike, provides much of interest to many branches of knowledge. From a theological point of view it was illogical to have the earth infested by a horde of beings which were neither material nor spiritual, though witches were sufficiently corporeal to ensure belief in their existence, and the evidence for their peculiar powers was not to be lightly cast aside. W. Fulke, so early as 1563, in his *A goodly Gallerye with a most pleasaunt Prospect, into the garden of naturall contemplation, to behold the naturall causes of all kynde of Meteors*, in which, combining the offices of priest and meteorologist, he attributed the formation of " those round circles that ignorant people affirm to be the rings of the Fairies dances " to the effects of lightning. The scorched appearance seen in the commonest forms of ring would suggest some natural source of burning if a supernatural or semi-supernatural cause was discarded, and lightning was the obvious if not the only agent capable of causing burning.

Robert Plot, in *The Natural History of Stafford-shire* (1686), enters very fully* into

> " the nature and efficient cause of those *Rings* we find in the *grass*, which they commonly call *Fairy circles*: Whether they are caused by *Lightening?* or are indeed the *Rendezvouzes* of *Witches*, or the dancing places of those little *pygmy Spirits* they call *Elves* or *Fairys?* . . . Now that *Wizards* and *Witches* have sometimes their field *Conventicles*, and that they dance in such *rings* we have ample Testimony from divers good *Authors*."

He also believes in " dwarf spirits " but

> " Not that there are any Creatures of a *third kind* distinct from *Men* and *Spirits* of so small a stature, as *Paracelsus* fancied, which he was pleased to stile *non-Adamical* Men. . . . For my part though my faith be but weak in this matter, (notwithstanding it cannot be deny'd but the bad as well as good Angels may be Ministring spirits and converse with Mankind) yet if I must needs allow them to cause some few of these *Rings*, I must also restrain them to those of the *first* kind, that are bare at many places like a *path-way*; for to both the others more *natural causes* may be probably assigned."

Plot was an excellent observer and a prominent scientist of his time, Professor of Chemistry at Oxford and first keeper of the Ashmolean Museum. He gives several pages to discussing the evidence for the occurrence of the hierarchy of other beings and finds it too strong to disregard. Every statement in the ancient writings, every assertion by travellers to the newly-discovered lands were accepted in those days as truth no matter how unlikely; truth was known to be strange. It was only when confirmatory evidence was sought that it became possible to distinguish between facts and fictions.

How did Plot fare with the more natural explanations which were evidently much more to his liking? Lister, in 1674, had reported on a letter he had received, in which it was stated:

> " Mr. *Walker*, a Man not only eminent for his skill in *Geometry*, but in all other Accomplishments. . . . It was his chance one day, to walk out amongst some Mowing-grass (in which he had been but a little while before,) after a great storm of Thunder and Lightning, which seemed by the noise and flashes to have been very near him. He presently observed a round Circle, of about four or five yards diameter, the rim whereof was

*Chapter 1. Of the Heavens and Air.

about a foot broad, newly burnt bare, as the colour and brittleness of the Grassroots did plainly testifie. He knew not what to ascribe it unto but the Lightning, which, besides the odd *capricios* remarkable in that fire in particular, might without any wonder, like all other Fires, move round, and burn more in the extremities than the middle. After the Grass was mowed, the next year it came up more fresh and green in the place burnt, than in the middle, and at mowing time was much taller and ranker."

Lister, however, according to Plot, also held the opinion

" that at least some of them may be occasioned by the working of *Moldwarps*, which however for the most part irregular they may be, yet may have a time when perhaps by instinct of nature they may work in *Circles*; as 'tis certain *fallow Deer* do in the time of *Rutting*, treading the same *Ring* for many days together: indeed the strange fertility of these green *Circles*, even upon the most barren Heaths, beyond any place else about them, doth argue some extraordinary dung or compost, which he supposes to be the Excrements of *Moles*, or *Moldwarps*: others have fetcht their Origin from the *dung* and *urin* of *Cattle* fed in winter time at the same *pout* of hay, for their heads meeting at the *Hay* as the *center*, and their bodies representing as it were so many *radii*, has made some imagin that such *Circles* are described by their *dung* and *urin* falling always from them in due distance, and *fertilizing* the ground in a more than ordinary manner by the largeness of the quantity. Others again have thought them described by the *water* and some of the *Hay* it self, falling plentifully in wet weather from the *Eaves* of round *hay-stacks*, that have been situate within them, which rotting into dung thus fertilizes the Earth in a *circular* manner; and indeed 'tis possible that some of them may be made either of these ways."

These explanations, however, could not account for rings of fifty yards in diameter, or for some of them running through hedge and ditch, and, being at a loss for obvious causes, Plot examined the rim of the rings. Here he found the ground

" much *looser* and *dryer* than ordinary, and the parts interspersed with a white *hoar* or *vinew* much like that in *mouldy* bread, of a musty rancid smell, but to tast insipid, and this scarce anywhere above six inches deep, the *earth* again below being of its due consistence and genuin smell, agreeable to the rest of the *soils* thereabout,"

but did not comment further on the fact. Finding no explanation " either from any thing under or upon the ground; it remained that

I should look for some *higher principle*." After long and mature delibera-
tions he concluded " that they must needs be the effects of *Lightning*,
exploded from the *Clouds* most times in a *circular* manner." The
hypothesis is fully explained in the science of the time; the mycelium
was taken to be " the *faeces* of both *sulphurs*." The lightning singes the
grass but, the year following, this becomes of a dark luxuriant green:

> " the earth underneath having been highly improved with a fat
> sulphureous matter (received from the *Lightening*) ever since it was first
> striken, though not exerting its fertilizing quality till some time after."

The growth of the rings is theoretically accounted for:

> " The *Explosion* of *Lightening* when it first breaks the *Cloud* presses
> equally outward on every side, so 'tis like it may retain the same tendency
> after it has striken the *Earth* in such *Rings* as are intire, such being
> supposed to be made by streams of lightening . . . which possibly too
> infecting the *Earth* (for I look on them as a disease) with some noxious
> quality that may have somewhat of the nature of the *Herpes* ἐσθιόμενος,
> a sort of *Shingles* . . . *i.e.* a Disease that creeps on in the out parts, the
> middle growing well; these *Circles* I say being infected thus at first from
> the *Clouds* with something of this nature, may continually perhaps extend
> themselves in the like manner."

Here again we have lightning as a cause; when later it was
proved to be an electrical discharge its prestige was enhanced and the
ability to form rings in grass was one of its very minor achievements.
The hypothesis is chiefly associated with the name of Erasmus Darwin
who popularised it. A couplet in his *Botanic Garden* (1790) is often
quoted: " So from dark clouds the playful lightning springs, Rives
the firm Oak, or prints the Fairy rings." It has continued to be the
most popular explanation; it was frequently detailed in magazines
of the later years of the eighteenth and the first half of the nineteenth
centuries, often with complicated explanations of how the various
phenomena fitted in with electrical theories; moreover, there were the
inevitable eye-witness accounts of these manifestations, which added
verisimilitude and confusion.

Bradley gives his explanations of fairy-ring formation in *New
Improvements of Planting and Gardening* (1718). He had the usual
difficulties about fungi; " The Observations I have made concerning
the natural Produce of *Mushrooms*, seem to discover that they are
produced by some Putrifaction in the Earth, or in those Bodies they
are apt to grow upon." The rings of mushrooms called by the country

Plate 13a (above). Hygrophorus coccineus; at first bright scarlet but later becoming golden yellow. (P. L. Emery); *b (below) Bolbitius vitellinus* ; a variable, coprophilous species ; the cap usually liquefies after spore-discharge (S. C. Porter)

Plate 14a. Russula ochroleuca; the cap is ochre-yellow of various tones, the white stem becomes grey except in very dry weather

b. SICKENER, *R. emetica*; the pine-wood form of this very common species. Poisonous *(Paul L. de Laszlo)*

people Fairies Dances " are not always of one Sort of *Mushroom,* but various, according to the Soil that produces them. It is observable, that the Grass is always much greener and ranker in the Line where those *Mushrooms* appear, than in other Places of the same Grounds, which I have often wonder'd at, as well as the exact Figure of a Circle they have represented." When he inquired into the reason of this strange production, he described two things under observation:

" The first was, that just under the Turf where the *Mushrooms* were growing, was a Tract or Path made by *Pismires* [Ants], which was not only hollow in many Places at that Time, but the very Covering of that Passage was made of Earth extreamly fine, which those Creatures had flung up: The Fineness of the Earth wrought by those laborious Animals might very reasonably contribute to the extraordinary Vegetation of the Grass growing upon it, and the Hollowness of the Ground underneath might produce that Moldiness within it, which afterwards might be formed into *Mushrooms;* for it has always been my Opinion, that if Earth is made extreamly fine, and by that means the *Salts* of it more at liberty to act, whatever grows upon it will be much more vigorous. Again, we find by Experience, that in such Places where the Ground lies hollow near the Surface, it always turns musty and moldy.

But *2ndly,* Garden-Snails, the large black *Dew-Snails,* and others without Shells call'd Slugs, when they couple, always make choice of short Grass to creep upon: It is their manner, when they generate, to take a large Compass upon the Ground, and meet one another: Thus I have seen them creep into a Circle for more than half an Hour, going over the same Ground at least twenty times before they could join, leaving upon the Grass where they crept, a viscous shining Matter. So that it may be, that Slime, when it putrifies, may produce the *Mushrooms* we find growing in Circles upon Commons; and I am the more apt to believe it so, because I have more than once observ'd, that where a *Snail* has left such a Tract upon the Grass, a few Days afterwards I have found *Mushrooms* to come up: But it must be observ'd, that such as come up in this manner are not fit to eat."

Several other " natural explanations " were propounded, some of them as well argued as those of Plot and Bradley. Often the logic was not faulty but the premises were invariably awry. As Bruno said: " If the first button of a man's coat be wrong buttoned, then the whole will be crooked."

Later, Aubrey, in his *Natural History of Wiltshire,* written between 1656 and 1691, discarded the fairies of his schooldays:

" As to the green circles on the downes, vulgarly called faiery circles (dances), I presume they are generated from the breathing out of a fertile subterraneous vapour. (The ring-worme on a man's flesh is circular. Excogitate a paralolisme between the cordial heat and ye subterranean heat, to elucidate this phaenomenon). Every tobacco taker knowes that 'tis no strange thing for a circle of smoke to be whiff'd out of the bowle of the pipe; but 'tis donne by chance. If you digge under the turfe of this circle, you will find at the rootes of the grasse a hoare or mouldinesse. But as there are fertile steames, so contrary wise there are noxious ones, which proceed from some mineralls, iron, &c.; which also as in others, *caeteribus paribus*, appear in a circular forme."

If Aubrey had realised that ring-worms are due to fungi (species of the mould *Trichophyton* and its allies) he might have got a little nearer elucidating the phenomenon.

Gilbert White, in his Journals,* 15 Oct. 1780, is more simple and nearer to facts:

" The cause, occasion, call it what you will, of *fairy-rings*, subsists in the turf, & is conveyable with it: for the turf of my garden-walks, brought from the down above, abounds with those appearances, which vary their shape, & shift situation continually, discovering themselves now in circles, now in segments, & sometimes in irregular-patches, & spots. Wherever they obtain, puff-balls abound; the seeds of which are doubtless also brought in the turf."

J. L. Knapp, in his anonymous *The Journal of a Naturalist* (1829), although he mentions the crops of *Marasmius oreades* produced by the rings, attempts no explanation; " we will leave them as we find them an *odium physiologicum.*"

The old ideas—moles, ants, lightning and so on—continued to be put forward, often as new. Horses, usually stallions, running in circles, tethered goats, starlings and such like, indeed anything that moves or sits in circles was at one time or another observed to produce the rings by its actions. Nothing even remotely possible seems to have been omitted, though little real observation was needed to show that some at least of the rings occurred in places where the explanation could not possibly account for them. James Hutton, in 1790, published the first really scientific observations. Fourteen years previously he had had his attention called to a particular appearance on the hill of Arthur's Seat, " something, which, at a distance, resembled the altered grass

*White left a series of yearly books containing his daily observations from 1768 till his death in 1793. From these he had extracted the material for his *Natural History of Selborne* (1789).

of a footpath, but which traversed a shoulder of the hill in such a direction as corresponded to neither sheep-track nor footpath." The track was a hundred yards or so long, but there were smaller rings. The dark green borders to the bare portion were noted and by attentive examination five or six successions were distinguished which showed clearly that the rings were extending outwards. The appearance he would have attributed to thunder " were it not for the regular annual progression, which, if the effect of thunder, must follow rules not yet investigated, either in electricity, vegetation or the mineral system." The next conjecture was that the death of the grass was due to insects. His comment on deductions to be drawn from observations is worth noting:

> " The difficulty of this task is much increased by an ambiguity which occurs on certain occasions, where the breeding of insects in consequence of the death of plants, may be mistaken for the death of plants in consequence of insects. . . . The apparent production, or rather the multiplication of some species of animals, in consequence of a certain destruction of the vegetable turf, is a thing easily to be conceived, like what happens in . . . the second year, when I have seen an abundant crop of a certain species of mushrooms in the track."

It was the abundance of ants, and the frequency of slugs which misled earlier observers, but Hutton was satisfied that ring-formation is " a piece of natural history worth recording, and for which a theory is wanted."

William Withering, in the second edition of *Systematic Arrangement of British Plants* (1792), was the first to attribute the formation of fairy rings to a fungus. After describing *Agaricus oreades* (wrongly written *orcades*), he writes, " I am satisfied that the bare and brown, or highly clothed and verdant circles, in pasture fields, called Fairy Rings, are caused by the growth of this Agaric." He mentions that the rings are of several sizes, the largest eighteen feet in diameter, and about as many inches broad in the periphery where the fungus grows. Spawn of the fungus occurred under the surface of the soil where the ring is brown and almost bare, " but where the grass has again grown green and rank, I never found any of the spawn existing." Withering's opinion soon came to be generally accepted by botanists, though he had not provided the theory that was wanting to explain how the fungus acted.

W. H. Wollaston attempted this in 1807. He was struck by the fact that if examined at the proper season the circles always bore a crop of fungi and that these occurred solely at the exterior of the margin of the dark ring of grass. This led him to conjecture that progressive increase from a central point was the probable mode of formation. He thought it not improbable that the soil which had once contributed to the support of the fungi might be so exhausted of some peculiar pabulum necessary for their production as to be rendered incapable of producing a second crop; the next crop would consequently appear in a small ring surrounding the original centre of vegetation. At every succeeding year the defect of nutriment on one side would necessarily prevent the mycelium from growing in that direction and would occasion the circle continually to proceed by annual enlargement from the centre outwards. The darker green grass results from the soil at the interior of the circle being enriched by the decaying mycelium of the preceding year's growth. During growth the fungi so entirely absorb the nutriment from the soil that the herbage is for a while destroyed. Adjacent rings do not cross as the exhaustion caused by each obstructs the progress of the other, and both are starved. He made measurements of the progress of various circles and found that over three or four years it varied from eight inches to as much as two feet. He recorded that mushrooms, *Agaricus terreus* (*Tricholoma*), *Agaricus procerus* (*Lepiota*), and the Giant Puff-Ball also form rings.

In the century and a half since the acceptance of the fact that fungi are responsible for the rings, there have been many attempts to explain how this is brought about. These can be grouped into chemical, physical, and biotic: the fungus takes something from the soil which is necessary for the growth of green plants or it exudes an enzyme or other substance poisonous to them; it acts physically on the soil making it impervious to water; it is parasitic on roots of grass and other plants.

Certain facts are of importance in judging between these hypotheses. The first is often overlooked; it is that hundreds of fungi grow in circles. Mycelial growth radiates from a centre as is obvious in any culture whether it be of a mushroom or of a mould (cf. Pl. 45, p. 274). *Marasmius oreades* (Pl. 10, p. 103), the Fairy-Ring Champignon, has a yellow-brown hemispherical cap which becomes flattened, but usually retains a central boss, giving it a shape which accounts for its old name, Scotch Bonnets; the gills are free, yellowish white and widely spaced, alternately long and short; the stem is coloured like the cap, slender, but tough and pliable, usually downy especially at the base. The genus

Marasmius, when dry, shrivels and does not become putrescent but revives again with rain and continues to produce spores. The structure of the central part of the cap of *M. oreades* allows of the easy absorption of water. It is common in pastures and the unsightly effect it produces in lawns is well known, as it forms " classical " rings, that is, bare circles bordered by grass darker in colour and more vigorous in growth than the rest. Rings of other common species such as the Parasol-Mushroom (*Lepiota procera*) are dark green but with no bare portion. Still others, for example, that of the Common Puff-Ball (*Lycoperdon perlatum* (Pl. 31*a*, p. 190), and the Field-Mushroom (*Psalliota campestris*), have no apparent effect on the turf. Fungi in woods also often grow in circles; sometimes the ring is small, complete and obvious; sometimes large and broken so that there is difficulty in tracing it. Indeed, one is driven to the conclusion that most of the larger saprophytic fungi form rings. The significance of this is that there must be a perennial mycelium, continuing its growth outwards and dying off behind; that the majority of the fruit-bodies do not arise from mycelium produced directly from spores; that this extensive vegetative reproduction has to be taken into account when assessing the significance of the enormous numbers of spores produced and the marvellous devices for their liberation and dispersal.

A further point is that the mycelium in the soil lives on the nutriment it obtains there. In doing so it brings about various changes in the soil, both chemical and physical, a fact so obvious that it is frequently overlooked. The mycelium starting from a centre radiates in all directions and if there be no obstructions, advances in a circular manner, like, as one writer says, the flame from a match dropped in dry grass on a calm day. Each year the mycelium advances, the distance depending upon the season, that is, on moisture and temperature, but also on the nature of the soil; moreover, it differs according to the kind and density of the mycelium of the particular fungus. Growth takes place towards the tip, the older portion dies off. Thus we have a fringe of advancing mycelium, the hyphae of which are not necessarily organically connected and must therefore often be in competition; indeed there must be invasions of territory and combat, but, on the whole, there is balance and an ordered advance. In their due season the mycelium forms fruit-bodies if climatic conditions are favourable and there may be more than one crop in a year; if unfavourable none appears, and with species which are nice about their appearance, none may occur for several seasons, though the mycelium survives—a ring of *Clitocybe maxima* is recorded as having produced fruit-bodies only once in fifty years. The advancing mycelium acts upon the organic substance of the soil. Carbohydrates are consumed and proteins are partly absorbed and partly changed into amino-acids and into ammonia. This ammonia may combine to form ammoniacal salts or be converted by bacteria to nitrites and later into nitrates. Nowadays the fertilising effect of nitrogenous material on plant growth needs no special comment: the grass and other plants on the exterior are stimulated and become larger and greener. In typical fairy rings the inner darker green zone is due to the same cause. The source of the increased available nitrogenous material is, however, different. The mycelium as it dies off, the old toadstools, the dead grass, are subjected to bacterial activity, ammonia results and may later be built up into nitrates.

The origin of the bare zone continues to be a matter of controversy. How is the vegetation killed? We may eliminate the suggestion that the fungus denudes the soil of food-stuffs necessary for the growth of green plants. The remaining hypotheses can then be boiled down to two. The first of these is that the fungus attacks the young roots, kills them by means of some toxic substance* and gradually destroys the whole plant except the fibrous portions. Though this explanation might seem obvious there are some difficulties in accepting it. The roots of grasses taken from just without the bare zone certainly show fungal infection, but this, I believe, is because of an incipient weakness and not the cause of it. Further, all plants that happen to be in the bare zone die, which means that if the fungus is truly parasitic it is an omnivorous parasite of herbaceous species; moreover, several species form such rings and must have the same somewhat unusual characteristic. The regular advance in a ring also seems inconsistent with behaviour as a parasite, for an occasional burst of activity of the type that leads to epidemics might reasonably be expected. The other, and more likely explanation, is physical. The mycelium of the fungus masses behind the advancing peripheral hyphae and permeates the soil, filling the air-spaces between the particles, or entangling the air, and so preventing the absorption of water. Walking along a field-path

*A. C. Hollande, 1945, observed that in rings of *Clitocybe gigantea* f. *candida* growing in alpine meadows at 900-1400 metres the plants in the dead zone which he assumed were killed by the fungus, did not putrefy. He thought this must be because the mycelium developed something which inhibited bacterial growth. He extracted a substance which he called *clitocybin* which was found to produce lysis in Koch's tubercle bacillus. (Cf. Chap. 23: Penicillin.)

after heavy rain one notices water standing on the bare portions of the rings just as it does on the path: the rain does not penetrate because of lack of porosity, in the one due to the air-spaces being filled with mycelium, in the other to their being expressed. If the bare area is dug up, white mycelium, sometimes thread-like, will be found to a depth of several inches, sometimes, as in *Marasmius oreades*, to well over a foot. This massing of mycelium is progressive and there is invasion of the surrounding vegetation. This has already been stimulated to great activity by the chemical changes brought about by the advance of the hyphae and is consequently making heavier demands upon the soil moisture. There ensues a physiological drought, for the available water decreases rapidly; the inevitable result is that the plants die.

As the circumference of the ring extends, grass and other plants invade the bare zone. In uncultivated areas there is frequently a marked succession in the type of plants which colonise the denuded circle, beginning with various flowering plants followed by an intermediate grass stage and finally the normal perennial grass type, a succession which is paralleled on bombed sites. In cultivated ground there is usually no such well-marked succession.

As has been said, the amount by which the mycelium advances each year varies for a particular fungus according to atmospheric conditions. J. S. Bayliss found a range of from five to thirteen and a half inches in a year for *Marasmius oreades*. Though there is no regulated annual increment the average can be taken over a number of years and the approximate age of the ring estimated by dividing this into the radius. H. L. Shantz and R. L. Piemeisel calculated that certain rings in Colorado were at least four hundred years old and others, if part of an original ring, about six hundred and fifty years. These American records are surprising but would be more so if they were unique. Bayliss thought that rings of *Marasmius oreades* might continue to extend " for fifty or even a hundred years "; G. Becker estimated the age of a circle of *Clitocybe geotropa* near Belfort as almost seven hundred years. The largest rings known to me are on the South Downs formed principally by the St. George's Mushroom (*Tricholoma gambosum*). Many of them are several centuries old. They show up well in aerial photographs (Pl. VII, p. 142), and lend themselves to easy measurement. The difficulty is to decide whether some of them are single or compound, for rings often intersect, and by further growth the place of junction is masked. The elimination of the portions of the rings where they join is doubtless owing to the alteration in the soil, which prevents growth either because of lack of appropriate nutriment or by the presence of staling or other substances. This alteration similarly prevents the turning back of the mycelium in its tracks if there is any obstruction to its advance.

When rings grow in cornfields, not infrequent when all available land is put under the plough, their presence is shown by a circular wave in the level of the ears, crests of stimulation and troughs of depression.

Occasionally smaller rings grow within larger ones, either of the same or other species. I can recollect only once, however, seeing a ring of *Marasmius oreades* within an outer ring. This was on a bowling green which was riddled and ruined by this fungus, whereas rings of Horse-Mushroom and Common Puff-Ball hardly affected the turf.

S. C. *Porter*

Plate 15. YELLOW-STAINING MUSHROOM, *Psalliota xanthoderma*; all parts turn bright yellow where touched and the flesh at the base of the stem when cut. Poisonous

Plate 16. HORSE-MUSHROOM, *Psalliota arvensis*; young specimens. The skin tur
yellowish or brownish when handled. Edible

CHAPTER 12

RHIZOMORPHS AND SCLEROTIA

A REMARKABLE property of fungal hyphae is their ability to with-stand inclement conditions. The perennating mycelium of a species parasitic on a tree trunk, putting forth its fruit-bodies in due course, appears to be well protected against cold and drought, but mycelium growing in the ground has no protection beyond that provided by the soil, and, moreover, has no structural device which would lead one to suppose that it could be as enduring as it often undoubtedly is. In dry conditions the mycelium may divide into segments by numerous cross walls, and less often these " oidia " become " chlamydospores " by acquiring a thick internal wall. These structures are probably best regarded as reproductive.

There are, however, modifications of the ordinary mycelium which appear to be adaptations for enabling more effective extension, and which, in their most complex forms, also provide for the conduction of food materials to the growing parts: presumably they are more able to withstand desiccation than are single mycelial hyphae. The commonest modification is the formation of threads readily visible to the naked eye which are composed of a number of hyphae running side by side with their lateral walls closely applied. The " spawn " of the cultivated mushroom is the best known example, but is also seen in the Field-Mushroom, particularly when it is growing in loose sandy soil. There is no definite organisation, no separation into an outer cortex and an inner pith, though there may be some slight difference in the hyphal cells, those on the outside being wider and shorter. It is by means of such threads that the mushroom can sometimes spread to unexpected places*. Similar cotton-like threads are produced by

*The mushroom usually seen on paths and between paving sets is *Psalliota edulis* (*P. Rodmanii*, *P. bitorquis*), the " champignon des trottoirs." It is closely related to the Field-Mushroom but can be distinguished by its double ring on the stem, the lower one sometimes so placed that it looks at first sight like a kind of volva.

127

many species; they are well shown in *Collybia dryophila** (Pl. 9*b*, p. 102), *Stropharia aeruginosa* and *Pholiota praecox*. They are abundant in leaf-mould after rains, and this "running" is often noted by field mycologists as an indication of the crop to be expected. They are also common amongst species growing on wood, as in *Hypholoma fasciculare* (Pl. 17, p. 130), *Paxillus atrotomentosus* and *Clavaria stricta* (Pl. 28*d*, p. 175).

The older botanists, unaware of the nature of these threads, regarded them as separate entities and gave them names according to their mode of growth, colour, thickness: such were *Byssus*, *Himantia*, *Fibrillaria*, *Racodium*† and *Ozonium*.

It is not usually realised how frequently the mycelium at the base of the stems of agarics is in strings or threads: these may be readily seen if the fungus is dug up together with the surrounding soil. This doubtless was what Theophrastus referred to when he said:

> "The real mushrooms have, as the beginning by which they adhere to the ground, a stalk of some length, and they put forth fibres from that stalk."

Though sometimes the presence of fruit-bodies on hard substances can be explained by the passage of hyphae or mycelial strands through cracks, at other times the fruit-body itself obviously bursts through the hard layer. Thus *Coprinus atramentarius* (Pl. 22*b*, 151) is often seen on asphalt or on hard tennis courts, sometimes in considerable quantity, causing damage by breaking up the surface as it emerges. One such specimen was noted "still bearing, like a mortar-board, the piece of asphalt that it had broken and pushed up." There are many accounts of such phenomena. Andrew Knight, the famous horticulturist, passing along a turnpike road in autumn after a long drought had made the earth extremely hard, found that a mushroom several inches under the surface had raised and fissured it, though it had not yet forced its way through as he believed it would have done. It is difficult to understand how so great pressure can be exerted by such comparatively tender structures. Buller found that a fruit-body, *Coprinus sterquilinus*,

---

* The strands of this fungus have been reported to have damaged paeonies in France and black mulberries and gooseberries in U.S.A. I have seen them affecting cultivated roses in this country.

† This genus is still retained for the sterile *Racodium cellare* which grows in vaults and cellars, covering casks and bottles with a dull yellowish or pinkish, soft, woolly coat which gradually develops into an olive-black, thick felt. It often hangs down in festoons of a foot or more from the roof.

exerted an upward pressure of nearly half a pound. This species is very fragile with a slender stem about ¼ in. thick. Obviously more robust forms, especially if growing in clusters, can exert a much greater pressure.

Coprinus comatus (Pl. 22*a*, p. 151) is often found growing on cinder paths, its mycelium developing on rubbish as much as three feet below the surface. The pressure exerted by a fruit-body may well be sufficient to explain its eventual passage through a layer of cinders, but it hardly accounts for the example most often referred to. At Basingstoke in 1819 or 1820 a paving stone about 30 × 24 in. was gradually raised about 1½ in. above the level of the other pavement in about forty-eight hours. Under the stone " near the centre was a very large mushroom about the size of a tea-saucer,* much flattened at the top." At an earlier period other paving stones in the same street " were upturned, and on taking them up mushrooms were found to be the cause, so troublesome did it become that part of the mould was removed and fresh substituted to get rid of the spawn." In former days mushrooms often sprang up in foundries, supposedly from horse-manure used in preparing " loam " for casting. It was reported that many instances have occurred of these mushrooms apparently lifting heavy castings from the horizontal position.

If several hyphae interweave and fuse, some slight protection against desiccation results. Probably most fungal hyphae can revive and continue their growth after a short period of drying, but their massing together will tend to reduce the rate at which water is lost, and consequently lengthen the time during which they can remain active.

Mention is rarely made of the mycelium except when it is brightly coloured, as, for example, yellow in *Tricholoma orirubens, Boletus luridus* and *B. piperatus*, blood-red in *Cortinarius Bulliardii*, reddish in *Boletus tridentinus*, pink in *B. bovinus* and blue in *Mycena amicta.* The reddish orange threads of *Coprinus domesticus* and *C. radians,* form dense mats on elms and other stumps, under the bark of old logs and sometimes an inch or two below the ground; they are also common on damp walls and in mines. The mass is usually well-developed and sterile, and in this state was formerly known as *Ozonium auricomum* and *O. stuposum.* A similar *Ozonium* is formed by *Psathyrella disseminata* (Pl. IV, p. 51). This fungus occurs in very large numbers, often more than a thousand

---

*" THE BIG PUSH. A mushroom as big as a saucer raised a concrete slab weighing more than 1 cwt. as it grew in a garden at Bury St. Edmunds, Suffolk."—*Daily Express*, 6 May, 1950.

on and around a single stump. It appears in late summer and autumn, springing up overnight three or four days after rain, and lasts about twenty-four hours. The cap is whitish or pale buff, becoming greyish, at first scurfy, deeply striate and wrinkled, splitting into a number of ribbons each supporting half a gill and often a very short gill in addition; the gills are whitish, then blackish; the stem, is fragile, and slightly scurfy. The stems are in direct continuity with a network of fine reddish brown strings and hyphae: the hyphae in the wood itself are colourless and thin-walled. The hyphae of the *Ozonium* are thick-walled, and are fused laterally to form thin strings which are tough and resistant to mechanical tearing. It is by means of these strings that the fungus is able to extend to the bare soil around stumps and be provided with nutriment. Occasionally fruit-bodies occur on garden walls and on street pavements, the *Ozonium* having spread from a stump in the garden; it may grow on the surface of the ground or an inch or so below it.

[1] Tougher threads are formed by *Marasmius androsaceus*, which has a whitish or brownish cap which may finally become black, tough with a wiry brownish black stalk and white to pinkish gills which are thin and somewhat spaced: it occurs from summer to autumn, being common on leaves, sometimes being borne on a mass of horse-hair-like mycelium. These strands (*Rhizomorpha setiformis*) are a cause of disease in heather. They wind around the stems and enter them, usually through the dead ends of small branches, then attacking all parts and causing their death. They can be found at any time of the year and it is often possible to unwind a foot or more from an infected plant. Attack occurs principally where the heather is very wet underneath as when there is a good deal of *Sphagnum*. The strands, at first very fine and whitish, are composed of a number of hyphae, the walls of the outer ones being blackened and sclerosed. There are occasionally slight developments of similar threads in the related *Marasmius rotula* and allied species. When dry they are brittle because of the thickened hard walls. The strands resemble the more tough ones of the horse-hair blight, *Marasmius crinis-equi* (*M. epicrinis*), which is common in the tropics, attached to living stems and leaves at intervals and sending out long free threads to adjacent branches: they were " used for sewing on buttons " by American troops.

Similar strands are formed by the tropical *Polyporus Rhizomorpha*. The natives in Gambon and French Guinea use them for weaving cord.

Paul L. de Laszlo

Plate 17. SULPHUR-TUFT, *Hypholoma fasciculare*; on tree-stumps, and garden fences

Plate 18a (above left). Cortinarius violaceus; as the spores ripen they colour the gills rusty brown. (*Paul L. de Laszlo*); *b (above right) Stropharia semiglobata*; a very common coprophilous species. (*Paul L. de Laszlo*); *c (below left) Coprinus micaceus*; the young cap is covered with delicate glistening scales formed of gloular cells. (*Paul L. de Laszlo*); *d (below right) Lactarius pubescens*; usually under birches (*Paul L. de Laszlo*)

Much more substantial strands are very frequent in the Gasteromy-cetes (Pl. 38a, p. 247) but they also occur in other groups. They are particularly well developed in *Collybia platyphylla*. This species has a thin brown or grey cap, covered with brown radiating fibrils, often cracking or tearing; the gills are white, spaced and very broad; the stem is whitish, fibrillosely striate, and springs from a white cord-like mycelial strand about $\frac{1}{12}$ in. thick. These strands, formerly known as *Rhizomorpha xylostroma*, extend for a yard or more around the base of the stem, being attached to twigs, dead roots and leaves buried in the soil; they have been recorded in association with bramble roots and as attacking vine. The cords are composed of a number of hyphae each of which grows at its tip and has its own individuality, but the whole forms a compound structure which acts as a unit, showing differentiation into a protective outer rind and a central portion serving for storage and conduction. The hyphae as a whole run more or less parallel to the long axis. The rind is formed of thin hyphae, some parallel, others arranged vertically to the axis, and, growing out from the surface, develop in the surrounding soil entangling all kinds of organic and inorganic fragments. The centre of the cord is composed of much wider undulating hyphae with very thick walls which fuse laterally, and rarer irregular hyphae with dense brownish granular contents.

The mycelial cords of *Phallus impudicus* are very similar in appear-ance, but are even more extensively developed. Here what may be called the cortex is in two well-defined layers. The external one is formed of wide elongated cells with thin walls, arranged perpendicularly to the long axis and closely packed together; under this is a layer of narrow intertwined hyphae running in a parallel direction, and amongst them a few wider hyphae with refringent contents. The pith is composed almost entirely of wide hyphae which have very thick confluent walls and grow in all directions. Thus there is slightly more differentiation than in *Collybia platyphylla*, but a striking resemblance considering the wide separation of the genera in classifica-tion. In addition to serving as storage organs the cords of *Phallus* play a considerable part in vegetative reproduction. The deeper lying thicker portions act somewhat like the stolons of flowering plants. Thinner branches pass into humus and leaf-mould and these produce the fruit-bodies.

The most highly differentiated strands are those of *Armillaria mellea* (see Chap. 14) and *Merulius lacrymans* (see Chap. 20).

What appear to be special structures serving as resting stages occur in all groups of fungi, when the hyphae become compacted into a solid mass, a *sclerotium*. Sclerotia are frequently more or less rounded and their size seems dependent on the kind of fungus producing them. Usually they are wholly composed of fungal hyphae, and indeed the term is properly restricted to such formations. Occasionally, however, soil, stones, leaves and other materials are included. Such composite bodies may be regarded either as fungus structures with inclusions, or as masses of material held together by mycelium.

Some toadstools when dug up carefully always bring away with them irregular masses of soil held together by mycelial threads: this is so in several species of *Lepiota*, as, for example, *L. cristata*. Several Gasteromycetes also show the same phenomenon; in *Scleroderma* the mycelial cords form a mat-like mass with enclosed soil.

A further stage is found in *Polyporus frondosus*. The fruit-body of this fungus forms large rounded masses,* at the base of frondose trees, particularly oaks, in summer and autumn. It has a thick smooth white stem which repeatedly divides, the ends bearing semi-circular yellowish grey or brownish grey caps with dark radiating fibres on a wrinkled surface, often with a pale edge. The tubes are decurrent and the white pores usually become toothed with age. The white flesh has a mealy smell. The fungus is edible and, though not very common, was formerly sold in Norwich market under the name " morel." It is a parasite, the mycelium perennating in the tree roots and the base of the trunk for several years, producing a white heart-rot. The mycelium spreads into the soil where it forms masses binding the soil together.

Something more definite is seen at times in *Ganoderma lucidum*, a species which grows near the trunks of deciduous trees, especially oaks, in summer and autumn. This beautiful and distinctive fungus has a roundish or kidney-shaped cap, placed laterally at the end of a stem, whose length may be anything from 6 in. to practically nothing, the whole covered with a shining, blood-red, varnished crust, though sometimes lighter and sometimes almost black. The lower surface of the cap has fairly long white tubes which finally become cinnamon: the pores are minute and round. The base of the stem is often continuous with a fairly large irregular body deeply buried in the soil, sometimes vertical, sometimes horizontal. This has a definite rind,

*Clusius relates that a specimen gathered near Leva, Hungary, was so large that it filled a two-horsed cart (ut bigam facile impleret).

brown or brownish red, often incrusted with fragments of stone and roots. The interior is a mass of hyphae and soil: the hyphae show practically no differentiation but are often aggregated towards the exterior. The mycelium which produces these bodies is presumably connected with the roots of the tree, for it is apparently parasitic and causes a white rot, at least in the oak.

The most famous of these masses of mycelium and earth is the fungus-stone, *Polyporus Tuberaster*, Pietra fungaja, a concretion of earth or tufa held together by fungus mycelium. It is irregularly spherical and very hard and elastic. When it is watered it produces an edible fruit-body and does this repeatedly. Such an unusual phenomenon, with its added economic convenience, was formerly the source of both wonder and of various explanations.*

True sclerotia vary in size from small specks like those (*Sclerotium durum*) common on capsules of the Bluebell (*Endymion*), and which are formed by the common grey mould, *Botrytis cinerea*, to solid masses the size of a man's head, such as that known in Australia as Blackfellow's Bread (*Mylitta australiensis=Polyporus Mylittae*). Many large sclerotia occur, principally in the tropics, and, for the most part, belong to the genera *Polyporus* and *Lentinus*.

The largest sclerotium occurring in this country is that of *Polyporus umbellatus*. This fungus is very like *P. frondosus*, with from fifty to a hundred ultimate branches each ending in a circular cap a little funnel-shaped at the middle where it is attached to the stem, grey-bistre or chamois-brown, with a meally surface and often cracked radially. It is edible, but has a disagreeable smell when old. The sclerotium, *Sclerotium giganteum*, is blackish and cylindrical, about 1 in. in diameter, much branched and gnarled, forming entangled masses sometimes a square yard in extent a foot or more below ground level. Some of the branches are connected with tree roots and appear to arise from them. The mycelium presumably attacks the root and gradually fills the interior with a compact mass until only the periderm is left as a covering. When the fungus grows into the surrounding soil it forms more and more numerous branches. These remain slender while at a depth, but as they reach the more fertile soil above they develop more actively. If the surface of the sclerotium is damaged it regenerates. Occasionally the rhizomorphs of *Armillaria mellea* attack the sclerotium which reacts by forming a protective layer of thick walled cells.

*The Canadian Tuckahoo is apparently the same species.

Polyporus umbellatus grows chiefly in relation to oaks, which accounts for its French name Tripe de Chêne. The sclerotium has a well-marked blackish rind formed by the hardening of the superficial hyphae, which are gradually converted into an amorphous homogeneous impervious layer. The interior is white: the outer part consists of narrow hyphae following which is a zone of wider hyphae and then the pith proper composed of very wide refringent hyphae with very thick walls and no lumen.

Several agarics form sclerotia, though these are usually small. *Naucoria arvalis*, however, a fungus with a yellowish brown cap, fleshy in the centre, greasy when moist, ferruginous gills and a long and slender whitish or yellowish stem which is darker below, and is usually described as having a long cottony root-like base, often arises from an oval, dark brown or blackish sclerotium (*Sclerotium vaporarium*) which reaches up to about 1 in. in length; it occurs in garden beds some inches below the surface, among garden rubbish, rotting straw and other debris, and, very occasionally, in sand-dunes. The presence of the sclerotium is generally regarded as of varietal significance (var. *tuberigena*). The sclerotium varies so greatly in size, however, that its presence or absence may be dependent on soil conditions, but the connection with the fruit-body is somewhat tenuous and is easily severed which probably accounts for it sometimes being overlooked. It corresponds to a perennating mycelium and may be regarded as a special form of it developing or not according to certain edaphic factors. If a sclerotium is formed it may, or may not, give rise to a fruit-body, again conditioned by circumstances. When speaking of a fungus having a sclerotium we are sometimes apt to forget that it is not the fruit-body which produces the sclerotium but the reverse.

When animal dung is kept damp *Coprinus stercorarius* is almost certain to appear. It develops from a spherical black sclerotium (*Sclerotium stercorarium*) about ¼ in. in diameter. Found in caves, rich garden-beds, hot houses and other places where there is abundant nitrogenous material isolated sclerotia are apt to confuse the curious, but if kept moist they readily produce the fruit-body. This has a cap which is at first ovate and then flattens, membranaceous and covered with a white meal; the stem is shining white. The rind of the sclerotium is formed of a layer of large isodiametric cells with thick dark walls within which are similar but smaller cells: the white interior is homogeneous, composed of intertwined, very wide, thin-walled hyphae.

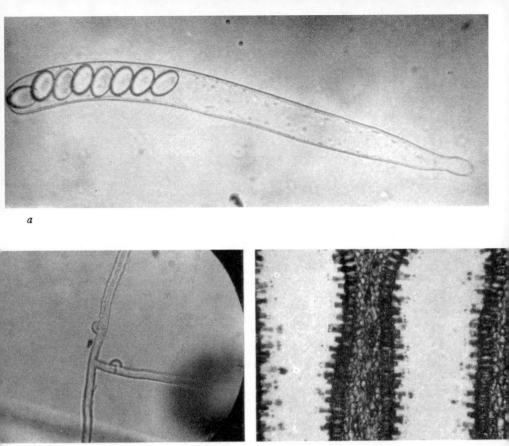

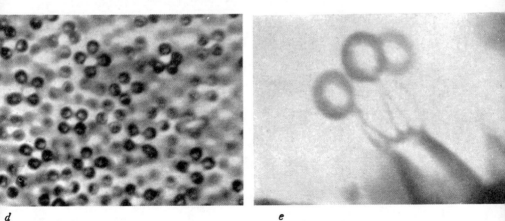

Plate Va. An ascus showing eight spores (*C.T. Ingold*). *b*, Clamp-connections in the mycelium of *Boletus* (*E. H. Ellis*). *c*, Section of gills of *Coprinus atramentarius* showing basidia bearing spores (*Flatters and Garnett*). *d*, Gill of *Coprinus atramentarius* in surface view, showing the basidiospores in fours on the ends of the basidia, the spores out of focus are those of the shorter basidia —this species has dimorphic basidia (*Brit. Mus.* [*Nat. Hist.*]). *e*, Basidium of *Russula ochroleuca* showing three spores (of four) in focus (*C. T. Ingold*)

Plate VIa (left). Cover of chap-book showing fairy folk dancing, the sexes alternate with their backs to the centre where Robin Goodfellow also foots it.

b (above). Seger's illustration of his "Fungus Anthropomorphos" (cf. Plate 24).

ROBIN

GOOD-FELLOW,

HIS MAD PRANKES AND MERRY IESTS.

Full of honeſt Mirth, and is a fit Medicine for Melancholy.

Printed at *London* by *Thomas Cotes*, and are to be ſold by

Sclerotia are also formed by three small species of *Collybia*, *C. tuberosa*, *C. cirrata* and *C. racemosa*; all grow on decaying agarics, or among leaves and humus where these have been. The last is rare, the other two common.

Collybia tuberosa occurs in groups especially on *Russula adusta* and *R. nigricans*. The cap is opaque white, thin, with an ochraceous disc, somewhat silky at first; the gills are white, crowded and narrow: the stem is whitish or rufescent, meally and varying from $\frac{1}{2}$ to 2 in. in length, downy at the base and arising directly from the narrow end of a sclerotium (*Sclerotium cornutum*: *Acrospermum*) which in shape and colour is like an enlarged apple seed but is sometimes $\frac{1}{2}$ in. or more long.

C. cirrata is similar though it is often much smaller. The cap may be depressed in the middle where it is sometimes rufescent and often papillate; the stem is more slender and flexuose and ends in a fibrillose twisted rooting portion which is attached to a small, oval or irregular, yellow sclerotium (*Sclerotium fungorum*, *S. truncorum*). It grows on the ground though often on decayed agarics such as *Armillaria mellea* and *Hypholoma fasciculare*, especially on the gills. There is some question whether a sclerotium is always present in this species. It is often difficult to find when the fruit-body is fully developed, as it readily breaks away from the slender end of the stem which extends for $\frac{1}{2}$ in. or more, and it is often reduced to the hard rind. The general opinion, however, is that there is a variety with and one without a sclerotium and that these remain constant in culture. It is more probable, however, that there has been confusion between two closely allied species.

C. racemosa is very small and wholly grey; the stem is slender, beset with numerous short side branches each of which ends in a hyaline, glutinous, rounded knob composed of ovoid or oblong conidia, and looking like a sterile cap. This unique species grows from a rounded black sclerotium (*Sclerotium lacunosum*) usually about $\frac{1}{10}$ in. in diameter though it has been recorded as large " as a pea or vetch seed." More than one fruit-body may arise from a sclerotium; the side branches begin to form as soon as the stem emerges.

The sclerotia of all three species are formed in late autumn and germinate in the following year. In addition to the difference in colour, shape and size the internal structure also serves to distinguish them. That of *C. tuberosa* has an outer rind of narrow, closely packed hyphae with thickened walls followed by a layer of similar hyphae but with non-modified walls, and a medulla composed of a compact mass of wide, thin walled hyphae; that of *C. cirrata* has a very thin rind of large cells and a medulla of large isodiametric cells with typical hyphae; that of *C. racemosa* is composed wholly of flexuous, non-septate, branching hyphae with a very thin rind formed by the sclerisation of the outermost.

At intervals during the last century and a half occasional mycologists have paid special attention to sclerotia and similar structures but on the whole they have been neglected. Their presence in some species was only gradually realised to be of systematic importance, for they were not recognised as an essential stage in the life-history. Possibly the most neglected of all were the small isolated sclerotia which were found and described by the old mycologists; sclerotia were " mycelia sterilia " and consequently unworthy of the notice of serious students.

The microscopical structure of a sclerotium is often, possibly always, sufficient to distinguish it. This was well shown by R. E. Remsberg in her studies of *Typhula* in 1940. This genus is characterised by its slender fruit-body, usually with a club-shaped head and thread-like stem arising from a sclerotium, and mostly very small: the habitat is generally dead leaves, sticks and vegetable debris. The genus *Pistillaria* is similar but without a sclerotium.

Typhula erythropus has a white clavate head and a filiform brownish horny stem, hairy at the base; the sclerotium (*S. crustulineforme*) is elliptical and flattened, chestnut-brown to blackish. *T. phacorrhiza* is the largest species, white then reddish yellow, paler and minutely velvety at the base, the head passing gradually into the stem; the sclerotium (*S. scutellatum*) is about ¼ in. across, tawny or blackish brown, flattened, sometimes heart-shaped and attached to the substratum by a minute stalk—looking like a Discomycete. The commonest species, *T. quisquilliaris*, has its sclerotium buried in the dried fronds of bracken; the fruit-bodies are white, usually crowded or in lines, the slender stem covered with hairs especially at the base when young, and in damp conditions (*T. puberula*).

The Discomycetous genus *Sclerotinia* is also characterised by a sclerotium. Many of the species are plant pathogens; *S. sclerotiorum* attacks vegetables, *S. Candolleanum* damages oak leaves, *S. tuberosa* affects both wild and cultivated *Anemone*, *S. fructigena* and *S. laxa* (*cinerea*) attack fruit trees. Some species mummify the fruits of Ericaceae, *S. urnula* on *Vaccinium Vitis-idaea* and *S. baccarum* on *V. Myrtillus*.

Several species occur in the culms of rushes and sedges. The best known is *S. Curreyana* which fruits in spring on species of *Juncus*, especially *J. effusus* and *J. conglomeratus*. The bright brown cups are clustered and become flattened with age. They arise from black or dark brown sclerotia which have pink flesh (*Sclerotium scirpicola*). Infected rushes can be recognised in autumn as they are lighter in colour than the other faded haulms and are bent over. Running them through the fingers reveals the presence of one or more sclerotia, ½ in. or so in length, which fill the central cavity; in the spring the culms split as the fruit-bodies develop.

Sclerotinia is of great morphological and biological interest. Many species are known principally in the conidial stage as the familiar brown rot (*Monilia*) of apples and other fruits. There is a difference in the type of conidium in groups of species which has led to the erection of new genera—*Botryotinia*, *Monilinia*, *Myriosclerotinia* and others. Two continental species of the Ericaceous parasites show the kind of heteroecism found in *Claviceps* (Chap. 13).

Many toadstools have stalks which pass down into the soil for several inches. Such a prolongation is usually called a " root " or " rooting base," which, though descriptive of the appearance, are not morphologically exact, and the term *pseudorhiza* has been proposed for them. The best-known examples are found in *Collybia radicata*, *C. longipes*, *C. rancida*, *C. fusipes*, *Tricholoma macrorhizum*, *Pholiota radicosa*, *Coprinus macrorhizus*, but they occur in several other species. They are analogous to sclerotia and mycelial cords as they form a connection between the buried substratum and the fruit-body, but they differ in being a specialised part of the stem, and not of the mycelium proper.

Collybia radicata (Pl. 9a, p. 102) is common in woods, usually associated with beech. It varies a good deal in size, the cap, greyish brown to smoky brown, occasionally white, glutinous, flattened but swollen in the centre, radiately wrinkled; the gills are shining white and widely spaced; the stem is pale brown or white, rigid and with a cartilaginous cuticle, gradually broadening down to ground level and then tapering below to the tree root to which it is attached: the length of the pseudorhiza depends upon the depth below ground of the substratum. The infected root shows a compact mass of mycelium and disorganised wood, its limits being shown by a black plate, seen in section as a black line, similar to what occurs in *Armillaria mellea*. The primordium of the fruit-body forms at the surface of the root and soon differentiates into cap and stem initials, the latter then into stem shaft and pseudorhiza rudiment. The pseudorhiza elongates by intercalary growth and, thickening as it does so, gradually pushes the stem shaft upwards until it reaches the surface; its growth then stops and the stem proper elongates. *Collybia longipes* resembles *C. radicata* but the cap is dry, brownish fawn and covered with short reddish hairs, and the stem dark brown and velvety.

The manner of growth of these fungi shows clearly that it is not a matter of the stem growing downwards in the soil, but the reverse. Confirmation of this is seen by what sometimes occurs in undoubted lignicolous species. Thus *Collybia velutipes*, which is common on old stumps, logs and trees which have been cut back, may occasionally be found apparently growing on the ground. If dug up it will be found attached to underground wood. Thus in some specimens from Dulwich (1944) the largest had a stem of 1½ in. long with a bulbous base and an underground elongation (pseudorhiza) 3 in. long. It is perhaps of significance that this fungus can develop normally in darkness, as for example, on logs in cellars.

Coprinus macrorhizus is very frequent on manure-heaps and masses of decaying vegetable matter. Its cap is rounded at the top, brownish, at first covered with a floccose meal, membranaceous and furrowed from the apex to the margin. The gills are white then black with a white edge. The stem is white and prolonged below as a pseudorhiza, the length of this depending upon the depth at which the fungus originates; if the primordium forms deep down in the mass the pseudorhiza is long, if near or at the surface it is short or absent. The mycelium permeates the substratum and the fruit-body primordia begin as minute balls on the more solid portions. Secondary fruit-bodies may arise if the primary fruit-body withers before expansion, and are normally produced from old and large pseudorhizas.

Mycena pura has a pseudorhiza of a similar type. It is usually solitary but I found a cluster of ten specimens in Epping Forest in 1934, which had apparently arisen from the end of a large underground pseudorhiza in a manner resembling what is not infrequent in *Coprinus macrorhizus*.

Collybia fusipes has a different type of underground structure, which Buller has called a perennial pseudorhiza. This species is common on the ground near trees, especially beeches and oaks. The cap is often deformed and irregular, sometimes splitting, reddish brown or liver-colour, paler with age and often speckled with black. The gills are whitish finally touched with reddish brown. The stem is cartilaginous, spindle-shaped, often purplish black at the base. It grows in clusters joined at the base of the stems, and may arise directly from a tree root or from a sclerotioid, black, irregular, perennial structure which may be a foot long.

The fungus attacks a root causing a white rot. As in *Collybia radicata* the limit of the rot is formed by pigmented hyphae which constitute a black rind, showing as a plate longitudinally—as a black line in section. In the first year the fungus grows out from the root and forms a simple pseudorhiza. This persists after the dying down of the fruit-body. The following year a cluster of fruit-bodies grow from the end of the old pseudorhiza, each with its own pseudorhiza. Dying down and renewed growth occur year after year, the compound mass of pseudorhizas increasing in size and becoming more and more branched, its shape somewhat dependent upon the amount of lateral fusion. The rind of this compound pseudorhiza is continuous with that in the root and the whole has been considered to be an extension of the pseudo-sclerotium.

Time and again in the study of fungi similar structures are found in widely separated groups. This may not be thought strange having regard to the basic element always being the hypha, for in the multiplicity of modifications unrelated fungi might readily solve some nutritional problem by adopting the same methods. Their encounter, however, always occasions surprise. Thus the only fungus known in addition to *Collybia fusipes* in which there is a compound pseudorhiza is a Discomycete, *Anthopeziza mirabilis* (*Sarcoscypha protracta*). This is rare in this country having apparently been gathered only near Ballater. It grows singly or in tufts. The cups have a bright red disc and a lobed margin and externally are covered with soft white hairs. The stem is slender, white and tomentose, and arises from a black pseudorhiza which is attached to a tree root, usually poplar. The mycelium grows in the wood of the root and eventually gives rise to a single fruit-body which grows upwards through the leaf-mould as a slender stalk surmounted by an unopened cup. The lower part persists and acts as a pseudorhiza giving rise the following spring to a cluster of fruit-bodies.

CHAPTER 13

ERGOT AND CORDYCEPS

ERGOT

PROBABLY ergot, produced by *Claviceps purpurea*, is the best known of all sclerotia. As it is most common on rye it is often called ergot of rye. The sclerotia, when ripe, project from the head of the rye as hard purplish black, or black, slightly curved structures (Pl. VIII*b*, p. 143). Ergot is the French name for the spur on the foot of some birds to which the sclerotia bear some resemblance; hence also the English " spurred " rye. These sclerotia fall to the ground in autumn, or they may be harvested with the grain. They germinate in spring, putting forth numerous small purplish pink drum-stick-like structures which grow erect but turn towards light (Pl. VIII*a*, p. 143). These are the fruit-bodies (*stromata*) of *Claviceps purpurea*. The surface of the flattened spherical head is covered with small projections in the centre of which are minute pores (*ostioles*). A longitudinal section through the head shows these pores as the openings to flask-shaped chambers in which there are numerous asci each containing eight long, very slender, thread-like spores.* *Claviceps* is therefore an Ascomycete. Ascomycetes with their asci enclosed in flask-shaped structures (*perithecia*) are grouped as Pyrenomycetes. The ascospores are usually shot out from the asci, even as far as two inches, and are then caught in currents of air and wafted about. Occasionally, however, the spores may emerge very slowly and form a mucilaginous mass at the mouth of the perithecium; these are distributed by insects. The stalks of the fruit-bodies turning under the influence of light, present different sets of perithecia in succession, from which the spores are discharged. This dispersal takes place at the time the flowers of rye are opening, with the feathery stigmas projecting from the glumes ready to receive the pollen from the flowers, and consequently also in a condition to catch

*A sclerotium with fifteen stromata has been calculated to produce over a million ascospores.

the thread-like spores. The spores, when attached, germinate within twenty-four hours. They may alight on the stigma, whence they send out long germ-tubes which grow down the outside of the style and encircle the ovary, which they usually penetrate at the base; usually, however, they catch on the joint of stigma and ovary. Having entered the ovary the hyphae grow rapidly, and in six to eight days produce large numbers of ovate conidia or asexual spores (the *Sphacelia* stage) and secrete an abundance of a sticky, yellow, sugary solution, " honeydew ", which oozes out between the glumes and may drip from the flowers. The period during which infection can occur is only about eight days for an individual floret, but there is successive maturing in an inflorescence and considerable variation in the crop as a whole: further, the undeveloped apical flowers of the spike are imperfectly enclosed by glumes and thus are liable to infection before opening.

Conidia will not germinate in honeydew, but when this is diluted with rain water they do so after ten to twelve hours. The conidia are distributed by flies which are attracted by the honeydew and suck up conidia with it; *Sciara thomae*, *Melanostoma mellina* and *Rhagonycha fulva*, are amongst the commonest of the many insects concerned.

The hyphae gradually destroy the young ovary of the rye, forming a compact, dirty white folded mass of mycelium with irregular cavities. At the lower end numerous new branches are formed, the hyphae become septate, and their walls thicken. As a result of growth and mutual pressure, a hard pseudoparenchyma is produced, which is the beginning of the sclerotium. The process continues upwards and the formation of conidia and honeydew stops. Meanwhile a very thin crust is formed of closely packed parallel hyphae with violet or almost black walls. The top of the sclerotium may remain capped by remnants of the conidial stage, the spores of which remain viable for a year or more. We have here, as is frequent in fungi, two well-marked stages in the life-history; a conidial or asexual stage which is adapted for dispersing the fungus during favourable conditions, and a perfect or sexual stage. In effect the conidial stage is purely vegetative in that the conidia are essentially parts of hyphae, specialised for reproducing the fungus. Perfect stages are often regarded as a device for overwintering, but that can only hold when fertilisation occurs in autumn and the resulting spore-formation in spring: in *Claviceps purpurea* it takes place just previous to the formation of the asci.

The perfect stage is the result of sexuality, and has, primarily, no direct relation to seasons beyond that the period of its occurrence is fixed so that the species can survive. It is clear that overwintering is not accomplished by the sexual stage but by the sclerotium, a purely vegetative structure which falls to the ground as the rye ripens, or is harvested with it. The sclerotium thus acts like the rye grain—it lies on or in the soil during winter; moreover, it can also serve to distribute the fungus.

Claviceps purpurea is not restricted to rye. It is rare on wheat in this country, except occasionally on " Rivet " and its hybrids. It is frequent on a number of grasses, including perennial and Italian rye grasses, and when these are fed to lambing ewes it sometimes causes abortion. In the Fens, where oats are sometimes grown after rye, self-sown rye plants are often found to be ergotised though the previous rye was healthy: care has to be taken that ergot is not fed to horses with the oats.

The size of the sclerotium depends largely upon that of the normal grain of the host plant. Partly for this reason, a small ergot, which is very common on Purple Moor-Grass (*Molinia caerulea*) and also on common reed (*Phragmitis communis*) and Mat-Grass (*Nardus stricta*), is often regarded as a growth form of *Claviceps purpurea*, though it has been described as a distinct species, *Claviceps microcephala*. Another species, *Claviceps nigricans* on *Scirpus* and *Heleocharis*, has been found here in only the ergot stage.

A common phenomenon amongst parasitic fungi is that there are strains within a species, which have different relations to the host plants: (there are also strains in saprophytic species, but here the differences are revealed by the relation to the culture medium). These strains differing in parasitism are common in rust fungi and in mildews. A species common to a number of host plants may show a strain restricted to a few hosts or even to one; it is not able to infect other hosts, nor is the reverse possible. Such strains cannot be recognised from their morphological characters; they are indistinguishable under a microscope. They have been described by many terms, the best known being " physiological races " or " biological races." It has been found that such biological races occur in *Claviceps purpurea*. R. Stäger was able to infect sixteen different wild and cultivated grasses with conidia from rye. This (forma *Secalis*) infects barley and wheat, *Anisantha* (*Bromus*) *sterilis* but not *Zerna* (*Bromus*) *erecta*, *Poa pratensis* but not *P. annua*. Another race on *Brachypodium sylvaticum* infects *Milium effusum* and some other grasses, but not barley. A third, on *Lolium perenne* infects *Zerna* (*Bromus*) *erecta* in addition to other species

Plate VII. Aerial view of Stonehenge showing in the foreground the darker grass of fairy rings. (The circle below centre on right is a barrow.)

Plate VIIIa. Germinating sclerotia of ergot, *Claviceps purpurea*, showing the drum-stick-sh fruit-bodies (*J. A. Crabbe*). *b*, Artificial infection with liquid containing spores of the fungu means of boards with longitudinally grooved needles (*A. Stoll*). *c*, Artificially infected b (*A. Stoll*). *d*, Artificial infection by spraying (*A. Stoll*)

of *Lolium* but not rye. Another form is restricted to *Glyceria fluitans*. There are probably other biological races, but as there are apparently a number of hosts in common, it is difficult to define them. Immunity is not always complete, for in some grasses honeydew may be formed but no sclerotia.

An interesting biological adaptation occurs in the form on *Brachypodium sylvaticum*. This grass is not in flower at the time when the ascospores from the germinated sclerotia are ripe and being dispersed. *Milium effusum* which grows in company with *Brachypodium* and flowers in May, is infected and produces the *Sphacelia* stage in abundance, and later, as the *Brachypodium* comes into flower, it is infected by these *Sphacelia* conidia which are apparently restricted to it. Thus, apparently, this form needs two host plants to complete its growth. The necessity of two host plants for the completion of a fungal life-history is frequent in rust fungi, where many species require alternate hosts. Such " heteroecism," as it is called, is best known in *Puccinia graminis*, rust of wheat, where the uredospores and teleutospores attack wheat and the aecidia (cluster cups) occur on barberry; there is a clearly marked relation to the life-history of the fungus, for the change of host always occurs at the same stage. Nothing so clear is seen in *Claviceps*, for the change of host is related to a biological necessity.

Though ergot of rye is mainly distributed by man's agency—it has been carried to New Zealand—the ergots of wild grasses are not so liable to this. There are occasionally interesting ways by which ergot benefits from a provision normally serving for the distribution of seed. Thus the sclerotium in *Brachypodium sylvaticum* remains firmly attached to the flower, which with its long hooked awn on the lower palea, catches in the coats of animals. In *Calamagrostis Epigejos*,* the ergot, like the light seed, adheres to the paleae which have a parachute mechanism serving to carry them along by the wind. The sclerotia on several aquatic or marsh grasses—*Glyceria*, *Phragmites*, *Phalaris*, *Molinia*—float on water for some time, being especially light owing to contained air.

The story of ergot has many chapters and impinges on mythology, history, biochemistry, and medicine. The first account of ergot of rye is appended to that of rye in the 1582 edition of A. Lonicer's *Kreuterbuch*, where it states that often from the ears of rye or corn, long, black, hard,

*The hybrid *Calamagrostis arenaria* X *Epigejos* does not produce seeds, but will do so when attacked by *Claviceps*.

narrow corn pegs, internally white, protrude like long nails between the grains (*Clavi Siliginis*). They are said to be used by women as a proved means of inducing labour pains.

In 1588, J. Thalius regarded the infected plants as a special form of rye in which the grain had undergone excessive growth, due to an abundance of sap resulting from heavy rain followed by hot weather. Adopting this view, Caspar Bauhin (1591) called the " plant " *Secale luxurians*, and his brother, J. Bauhin, gave a woodcut of it so named in *Theatrum Botanicum* in 1658. Others considered it to be a distemper of ordinary rye brought about by abnormal conditions, such as excess of humidity in air or soil, absence of fertilisation, bites of insects and such like, explanations in common use until a century or so ago, to account for all plant diseases: indeed, until Berkeley's work on the potato disease in 1846, it was generally thought that any fungus present was the result and not the cause of a disease. But it was not at first realised that the sclerotium was a fungus.

None of the old English Herbals mention ergot. Ray, in the 1677 edition of *Catalogus Plantarum Angliae*, gives the first reference, but, obviously, knew of it only from foreign books. The first French reference was in the previous year, when D. Dodart said it was called " ergot " or " bled corn," and had been recognised as causing gangrene.

The true nature of ergot was suspected by E. F. Geoffroy, who, in 1711, thought it rather a fungus than a rye grain, but it was not until 1764 that Münchhausen definitely asserted this, an assertion which proved less troublesome than those which led Linnaeus astray (see p. 20). The belief was gradually adopted and A. P. de Candolle in 1815, called it *Sclerotium Clavus*. Germinated ergot was known by then, but the fructifications were considered to have no genetic connection with the sclerotium, being thought to be merely saprophytic on them.

The honeydew secreted by the infected ovary was first mentioned by K. Schwenckfeld in 1603, as a cause of ergotism—" Manna quadam aerea maligna "—but it was long before it was recognised as being connected with ergot. Léveillé, in 1827, described the conidial stage growing in the infected ovaries and in the honeydew, and named it *Sphacelia segetum*; he believed it to be the cause of ergot, which he thought was a monstrosity of the rye itself. By this time there were supposed to be three different fungi: *Sclerotium clavatum*, *Sphacelia segetum* and *Claviceps purpurea*. In 1853, Tulasne proved conclusively that these were all stages of the same fungus. The investigation was one of the series in which he established the phenomenon of pleomorphy in fungi. That fungi can assume such curiously different forms was so unexpected and so startling, that, as the evidence accumulated, fact was not sufficient for some, and fancy reigned in its stead. What Tulasne was able to prove for comparatively large fungi, where it was possible to be certain of genetic connections, was assumed to occur in microscopic forms where reliance had to be placed on the imperfect methods of cultivation then available. Strange stories, or rather stories that now seem strange, had been told of developing yeast, and of moulds, before Tulasne's investigations, but from 1857 to 1869, there was an avalanche of phantasy which threatened to undermine the very foundations of mycology.

From earliest times ergot has caused serious disease both in man and in cattle, a disease which is now known as ergotism. Ergotism shows two distinct types of poisoning, gangrenous and convulsive: the former was frequent in certain parts of France, the latter occurred in Central Europe. It is now known that the two types are manifestations of the same disease, the convulsive form being the result of ergot poisoning, together with a deficiency of vitamin A, probably owing to a lack of dairy produce.

In gangrenous ergotism the preliminary symptoms are followed, after a few weeks, by the limb affected becoming swollen and inflamed, violent burning pains alternating with very cold. Gradually the affected part becomes numbed, then shrunken and mummified. The extent of the gangrene varies from the mere shedding of nails and the loss of fingers or toes, to that of whole limbs. Sometimes the course of the disease is very rapid, the premonitory signs of gangrene appearing after twenty-four hours.

Convulsive ergotism shows pronounced nervous symptoms, with twitchings and tonic spasms of the limbs, and strong permanent contractions, particularly of hands and feet. In severe cases the whole body is subject to sudden, violent, general convulsions. One of the early symptoms, which often continues, is the numbing of the hands and feet, and a tingling sensation " as if ants were running about under the skin " (formication), though one description speaks of mice!

As would be assumed, such a characteristic disease as gangrenous ergotism was early remarked. The first record dates from 857, when at Kanten, near the Lower Rhine, a great plague of swollen blisters consumed the people by a loathsome rot, so that their limbs were loosened and fell off before death. A plague of " fire " occurred at and about Paris in 945, and in the following century there were several epidemics in which the number of victims was incredibly great: because of the " deadly burning," most chronicles of the eleventh and twelfth centuries refer to it as holy fire (ignis sacer); it was also known as ignis Beatae Virginis.

In 1073, the Order of St. Anthony was founded near Vienne (Dauphiné), the hospital being built near a church containing the relics of the saint. During the twelfth century the holy fire began to be associated with St. Anthony, and those suffering from the disease started to visit the saint's relics. Several houses of the Order were built in different parts of France, and had their walls painted a symbolic red, " le feu de St. Antoine," as Rabelais describes it. At one time, there were 390 houses of the Order in different countries. In many early printed books there is frequent mention of St. Anthony's fire, a designation not used in the chronicles.

Most cases of holy fire occurred in France; it is remarkable that it is hardly mentioned in Germany. Little rye was grown in Italy, and the chronicles of that country do not mention the disease. The same is true of this country, " the long fields . . . of rye " being a necessity of rhyme and metre, and not a fact of agriculture.

The history of convulsive ergotism in Germany, starts with an epidemic in the Duchy of Lüneburg in 1581. Outbreaks then continued at intervals in the seventeenth, eighteenth and nineteenth centuries. The last epidemic of any considerable extent was in 1879, with further outbreaks in 1880 and 1881. A great diminution of the disease after 1772, was due to the more general cleaning of the grain, the improvement of agriculture through drainage, and the great increase in potato growing following the famine of 1770-1. There have been numerous epidemics in Russia, chiefly of the convulsive type, and these have continued to the present day; from September 1926 to August 1927, 11,319 cases became known to the authorities, and, undoubtedly, many were not officially notified. The first recorded outbreak was due to the bad harvest of 1722. This had its influence on politics,* for it prevented Peter the Great from undertaking a campaign against Turkey, as all the cavalry which he had led to Astrakhan was helpless: twenty thousand people died at Nigry.

*Phytopthora infestans, the fungus causing the Potato Blight had even greater political effect a century ago. The Duke of Wellington said regarding Sir Robert Peel and the repeal of the Corn Laws: " Rotten potatoes have done it all; they have put Peel in his damned fright." Disraeli's view as given in Endymion, was that " the mysterious malady of a single tuber changed the political history of the world " —it certainly was responsible for the fall of Peel's cabinet.

Plate 19a. OYSTER-MUSHROOM, *Pleurotus ostreatus*; the cap passes from brownish black when very young to bluish grey and finally yellowish *(Paul L. de Laszlo)*

b (above) *Stropharia merdaria*; coprophilous. *(Paul L. de Laszlo)*;
c (below) DRYAD'S SADDLE, *Polyporus squamosus*; on trunks and stumps of trees, especially elms, from early summer *(Eric Hosking)*

Eric Hosking

Plate 20. CHANTERELLE, *Cantharellus cibarius*; one of the best-known edible fungi

This country has been singularly free from ergotism. Only one record of typical gangrenous type is known, which occurred in the family of an agricultural labourer at Wattisham near Bury St. Edmunds, in 1762. The mother and five children all lost one or both feet or legs: the father suffered from numbness of the hands and the loss of finger nails. As there was no rye in the neighbourhood, ergotised wheat must have been eaten. The incident is commemorated by a tablet in the church tower. Two or three mild cases have also been recorded. The only epidemic occurred at Manchester in 1927 among Jewish immigrants from Central Europe, who lived on bread made from a mixture of wheat and rye. All 200 patients complained of formication, and the general symptoms were of mild ergotism of the convulsive type.

Cattle suffer from ergotism arising from the infection of fodder grasses. The symptoms may be of the nervous type, varying in degree up to complete paralysis, or gangrenous, resulting in lameness, and the sloughing of a part or whole of the hoof.

Hand in hand with the recognition that ergot caused such dire disease, was the knowledge, mentioned by Lonicer in 1582, in the first account we have of the fungus, that it has obstetrical uses. There is evidence that in the eighteenth century, midwives in France, Germany and Italy, administered it: indeed, its use was forbidden in certain parts of Germany. Although it was apparently also used by some physicians, its proper entrance into medicine dates from 1808, when J. Stearns gave " An account of the *Pulvis parturiens*, a remedy for quickening child-birth," in the form of a letter to a New York periodical. So great was the interest eventually aroused in the matter, that the drug was admitted to the United States Pharmacopoeia in the first edition, 1820; and to the Pharmacopoeia of the London College of Physicians in 1836, by which time it had become thoroughly established in Europe.

As would be expected, a drug of such value and a poison of such potency has interested chemists. For well over a century investigation has been carried on to ascertain the chemical substances responsible for the observed facts, and to isolate those of use in medicine; more recently, there have been efforts to synthesise these with a view to commercial production. The chemistry is very complex. The first alkaloid to be obtained pure was ergotinine by C. Tanret in 1875; the second, ergotoxine, was obtained by G. Barger and F. H. Carr in 1906. In 1918-19, two new isomeric alkaloids, ergotamine and

M.T. L

ergotaminine were isolated by A. Stoll. A fourth alkaloid was discovered independently in 1935, at London, Baltimore, Chicago and Basle; this is usually called ergometrine (ergonovine, ergobasine, ergostetrine, ergotocine). Ergosine was isolated in 1936, egrocristine in 1937. In 1943 it was shown that ergotoxine can be separated into ergocristine and two new alkaloids, ergokryptine and ergocornine.

According to Stoll, the present position is that ergot contains six pairs of natural alkaloids, the pairs being isomers and interconvertible.

ERGOTAMINE GROUP	Ergotamine, Ergotaminine. $C_{33}H_{35}O_5N_5$
	Ergosine, Ergosinine $C_{30}H_{37}O_5N_5$
ERGOTOXINE GROUP	Ergocristine, Ergocristinine (Ergotinine) $C_{33}H_{39}O_5N_5$
	Ergokryptine, Ergokryptinine $C_{32}H_{41}O_3N_5$
	Ergocornine, Ergocorninine (ψ ergotinine) $C_{31}H_{39}O_5N_5$
ERGOBASINE GROUP	Ergometrine, Ergometrinine $C_{19}H_{23}O_2N_3$

The first named of each pair is laevorotatory and physiologically active: the second is dextrorotatory and has little physiological activity. The nature of the alkaloids present varies with the geographical source of the ergot. These alkaloids show two different modes of action, the one on the smooth muscles (uterus, blood vessels, stomach, intestines) by the ergotamine and ergobasine groups, the other an inhibitory effect on the sympathetic nervous system by the ergotoxine groups. Ergomonamine ($C_{19}H_{19}O_4N$), an alkaloid differing from all the others in not being an indole derivative, has also been isolated.

Other substances of great biochemical importance have been discovered in the investigations on the chemistry of ergot: histamine, of great importance in allergic reactions, and ergosterol, widely distributed among fungi, and yielding Vitamin D on irradiation.

The chief commercial sources of ergot have been a large region in eastern Europe, chiefly Russia and Poland, and a small one in the north-west of the Iberian Peninsula. Spanish-Portuguese ergot contains more alkaloid, and, as since 1926, the American Pharmacopoeia has prescribed an alkaloid content of 0.05% for liquid ergot, the cost has increased, so much so that it has been adulterated with " sclerotia " made from dough: variations in price depend upon the season. The high price prevailing, and the possibility of lessened supplies following upon improvement in agriculture, have led to efforts being made to obtain sclerotia in pure culture in the laboratory. *Claviceps* is fairly easy to grow saprophytically, but no real success has been achieved, though it is claimed that ergotamine is produced by the mycelium. During the past twenty-five years increasing success has attended schemes to cultivate ergot in the field. The modern method is to obtain conidia by growing the fungus on an agar medium. These are got in suspension by shaking with water, and the spore-suspension is then sprayed on to rye plants in flower; large scale spraying is done by a horse-drawn machine (Pl. VIII*d*, p. 143).

CORDYCEPS

The genus *Cordyceps* resembles *Claviceps* in many ways, but the spores become septate in the asci, and most species are parasitic on insects. *Cordyceps militaris* is fairly common in autumn in hedge banks, damp lawns and woodlands,* appearing as bright crimson or orange-red waxy clubs narrower at both ends, the upper fertile portion showing slight punctations marking the openings to the perithecia. Below ground the fruit-body can readily be traced to a larva or pupa of Lepidoptera. The insect, when cut open, is found to be a solid mass of mycelium, the whole of the inside having been replaced by fungus; the only part of the insect remaining is the integument, which surrounds what is essentially a fungal sclerotium.

The spores are forcibly ejected from the asci: the effect of wind and moisture on this " puffing " was studied so early as 1775 by Müller. They are very long and filiform and break up at maturity into the numerous short segments formed by the 160 or more cross septa. Germination takes place on the skin of a caterpillar if only slightly moist. The germ-tubes penetrate at once, and at any part of the chitinous skin. Here they enlarge into somewhat stouter hyphae, which branch and enter into the deeper layers of the skin, finally reaching the inner surface and passing between the muscles and fatty tubes. Then conidia are formed which enter the blood and are spread throughout the body, filling it by degrees with a dense mass: the insect loses its turgidity and dies. The sprouting conidia develop rapidly, and in one or two days the interior consists almost entirely of a dense weft of fungal hyphae. The sclerotium-like mass can give rise immediately to fruit-bodies from any part of the surface. These vary

*It usually occurs singly or in small numbers. During the British Mycological Society's autumn foray in 1923, however, hundreds were seen on a lawn at Armathwaite near Keswick, looking like a regiment of toy soldiers.

considerably in size, shape and number, according to the nature and habit of the host.

There is a conidial stage (*Cephalosporium*) usually occurring as a delicate down at the base of the fruit-body, or on the surface of the insect: the short erect hyphae have whorls of branches and branchlets, all ending in groups of spores.

A much more prominent fungus, *Isaria farinosa*, is usually considered to be another conidial stage. It is white, plume-like, somewhat tufted, with a distinct smooth stem which is sometimes yellowish, and a more or less branched upper portion which is powdery with the spores. It grows from larvae and pupae, which are affected similarly to those on which the *Cordyceps* grows. Attempts made to connect the two forms by growing them in pure culture have failed.

Though the fruit-bodies of *Cordyceps militaris* are fairly readily detached from the host, it is surprising that so common a European species was not the first *Cordyceps* to be described as entomogenous. This was a species from China: " Hia tsao tom tchom," i.e. plant during summer and worm in winter, three hundred specimens being received by R. A. F. de Réaumur from a Jesuit priest in 1726, with the information that they were to be obtained hardly anywhere except in the palace at Pekin, as they grew only in Tibet* and Szechwan. The specimens were broken, and it was assumed that this accounted for the absence of leaves, flowers and stem. The stalks of the fruit-bodies were taken for roots to which the caterpillars had attached themselves. The fungus is *Cordyceps sinensis*, a celebrated drug in the Chinese Pharmacopoeia.

The ball, however, really started rolling in 1754, when J. Torrubia, a Franciscan friar, described and figured a West Indian species. A translation of the main part of his account was later given in J. Edwards *Gleanings of Natural History* (1763) and so became widely known.

" Being at a Gentleman's country-seat, two leagues from the city of the Havanna in New Spain, on the 10th of February 1749, I found some dead Wasps in the fields, (however they were intire, the bodies, wings and all, and indeed were perfect skeletons). From the belly of every Wasp a plant germinated, which grows about five spans high: the natives call this plant Gia; and as it is full of sharp prickles, their vulgar notion is, that the said prickles owe their growth to the bellies of the Wasps."*

*Capt. F. Kingdon Ward tells me that coolies collect this species in the south and east of Tibet and that his own men were always on the look-out for it; Mr. F. Ludlow that it is sold in the markets at Lhasa.

Plate 21. MAGPIE, *Coprinus picaceus*; in beech-woods. The patches on the expanded cap (*right*) are the remains of the universal veil seen intact in the young state (*left*)

Plate 22a. SHAGGY INK-CAP, *Coprinus comatus*; often in enormous numbers on made-up ground. The zone of ripening

b. SMOOTH INK-CAP, *Coprinus atramentarius*; often attached to buried wood. Edible *(Paul L. de Laszlo)*

The controversies which raged about this so-called "vegetable fly" ranged over a wide field, and have their place in the history of the development of our knowledge of the real nature of fungi, and in the discussions then rampant on spontaneous generation. The vegetable fly reached Europe and became an article of commerce, everyone interested in natural history striving to obtain specimens for his cabinet. John Hill appears to have been the first to suggest "the manner of this phaenomenon's being produced." He called the fungus *Clavaria Sobolifera*. "It grows on putrid animal bodies, as our fungus ex pedo equino [*Onygena equina*] from the dead horses hoof. The Cicada is common in Martinique, and in it's nymphae state it buries itself under dead leaves to wait it's change; and when the season is unfavourable, many perish. The seeds of the Clavaria find a proper bed on this dead insect, and grow."

Six years later, Fougeroux de Bondaroy showed that *Cordyceps sinensis* was a similar fungus attached to caterpillars. He records that the Chinese practise deceit by putting seeds in the stem or elsewhere.

It was not until 1770 that it was realised that *Cordyceps militaris* is entomogenous. It had been described and figured by Vaillant in 1723, and ten years later J. L. Buxbaum had figured it attached to a pupa, without realising the significance of this. Müller, when commenting on an account of the vegetable fly, pointed out that a similar species occurred in Europe; the fungus is parasitic on a chrysalis, and the two can no more be regarded as a vegetable fly, than can man or cattle be regarded as vegetable animals because moss sometimes grows on their skulls. It is probable, however, that T. Holm (Holmskjold) was the first to recognise the relation between the host and the parasite as he studied the problem from 1762. He found the fungus not only on the larvae of *Bombyx rubi* before they change into pupae, which is the most common host, but on the pupae themselves of many caterpillars of various genera. He never found the fungus growing except directly from insects.

"The origin of fungi, their growth and the whole of their structure, display so great a skill, that we recognise in them the power of the supreme

*Throughout cisandine Peru the climbing palm *Carludovica divergens* is thought by the natives to be generated from the insula ant (*Dinoponera grandis*). The ant is often attacked by *Cordyceps*. "Before dying the insula attaches itself to the bark of some trees, and the fruiting body that arises from it has somewhat the resemblance of a plant in germination. The natives, finding these ants with fruiting bodies of *Cordyceps* projecting from their heads, assured me that this was the *tamski* [*Carludovica*] springing from the insula." J. Huber, *Plantas vasculares, etc.*, 1906.

Artificer, who produced them, and so providently and carefully preserves them, that he has built the propagation of certain species on the ruin of some insects, who repay, as it seems, with their life for the eating of fungus flesh, which they too greedily devour, a fact which is proved to us most clearly by the histories of *Clavaria militaris* [*Cordyceps*] and *Ramaria farinosa* [*Isaria*]."

The preliminary account was published in 1781, the full text, with beautiful plates, appeared in 1790-99. It was shown in 1788 that the fungus was not a *Clavaria* but a Pyrenomycete.

Several Australasian species reach a foot or more high, and are popularly known as " vegetable caterpillars."

The largest entomogenous species of *Cordyceps* occurring in this country is *Cordyceps entomorrhiza*, which may reach a height of 7 in. It was originally found on a beetle larva in autumn at Bulstrode, Bucks, and described and figured by James Dickson, a Covent Garden salesman, as *Sphaeria entomorrhiza* in *Plantarum Cryptogamicarum Britanniae* in 1785; it has apparently not been again found in this country. The stalk is slender, flexuose, sometimes forked; it is at first brown below and grey above, becoming black. The head is roundish, violet-grey becoming black and rough owing to the projecting ostioles. Three other entomogenous species occur here—*Cordyceps gracilis*, not infrequent in spring on buried larvae of Lepidoptera, particularly in gardens; it is about 1½ in. high with a stout yellow stalk which expands suddenly into an ovoid chestnut-brown head: *Cordyceps sphecocephala* on Hymenoptera, up to 2¼ in. high with a long flexuose and twisted pale brown longitudinally striate stem and a small cylindrical or ovoid yellow head: *Cordyceps Forquignonii* on flies, up to 1 in. or so high, with a long, slender, irregularly curved, pale ochraceous stalk and a small ovoid, orange-coloured head.

There are two other British species of *Cordyceps* which are parasitic, not on insects but on *Elaphomyces granulatus* and *E. variegatus*, underground fungi similar to truffles (see Chapter 22). *Cordyceps ophioglossoides* is the more common. It is at first yellow or greenish yellow, becoming black, about 4 in. in height with a clavate usually laterally compressed head 1 to 2 in. long, which becomes rough with the projecting mouths of the perithecia, and passes gradually into a smooth somewhat slender stalk, which ends below in bright golden yellow strands and threads of mycelium which are attached in one or more places to the *Elaphomyces*. The threads of mycelium can sometimes be seen amongst mosses, such as *Mnium hornum*, and apparently grow down to the rhizoids which reach to about the level where *Elaphomyces* occurs. *Cordyceps capitata* is also widespread, but not so common. It resembles *C. ophioglossoides*, but has a well-defined ovoid or sub-globose yellow-brown or red-brown head sharply delimited from the yellow stalk which is attached directly to the *Elaphomyces* without intervening mycelial cords; it becomes blackish with age.

The mummifying of an insect host by a fungus occurs commonly also in the house-fly. In the late summer and autumn flies often become sluggish and crawl on to window panes. They are soon covered with a whitish growth and a halo of white powder forms round them. This powder consists of the spores of *Empusa muscae*, which are shot off from hyphae (sporophores) which project from its body. By this time the fly is converted into a sclerotioid mass of hyphae, only the chitinous covering remaining. The disease is sometimes epidemic; it has been popularly called " fly cholera." The fungus is one of the Mucorinii (Phycomycetes).

CHAPTER 14

LUMINOSITY

ARMILLARIA MELLEA, the Honey-Tuft fungus (Pl. 11*a*, p. 110), is one of the commonest fungi on and about tree stumps, forming clusters which may be a yard or more across. It has a world-wide distribution and is common both in temperate and in tropical regions. It is one of the most variable species and there are several definite growth-forms which have received varietal names, as well as two or three apparently distinct varieties.* The cap is typically a dark honey-yellow, but is sometimes lighter, or may be tawny or sooty brown with a greenish tinge, flecked with brown or blackish scales which are more distinct at the centre; at first convex it spreads out and has a thin striate margin. The decurrent gills are whitish often becoming spotted pinkish and finally discoloured. The stem is long and fibrous, hollow, yellowish or brownish, darker at the somewhat swollen base and often becoming greenish black: there is a large white ring, often bordered with yellow, usually persistent and becoming discoloured.

This common saprophyte also acts as a serious parasite of trees; " more trees die, in Europe at any rate, from attack by this fungus than through any other parasitic agent." It is apparently most virulent on poor or badly drained soil where presumably the trees are somewhat weakened. The problem is complicated, however, by the fact that there are undoubtedly physiological races of the fungus which differ in their virility. Shrubs and herbaceous plants are also attacked— privet, *Daphne Mezereum*, tomato, rose, gooseberry, blackcurrant, raspberry, strawberry, hops, parsnip, carrot, rhubarb, potato, and *Iris* are amongst those listed.

So far as is known, infection of living trees never occurs directly from

---

*One of these, var. *tabescens*, which is distinct in having no ring, is usually considered to be a separate species, and placed in the genus *Clitocybe* as *C. tabescens*. It remains constant in culture.

154

spores, these apparently being able to infect only dead stumps. On germination a white mycelium is formed which later turns brown and produces numerous branches giving rise to chains of thick-walled bladder-shaped cells; by the intertwining of this mycelial mass a sclerotium-like structure results. On this an apical point develops and a flexuous root-like structure, a rhizomorph, soon takes shape. Three fairly distinct layers can be distinguished in the growing-point region. On the outside are loosely interwoven filaments, closely applied to the surface and slimy, sending out proliferations which presumably serve for the absorption of water. Following this is the cortex of narrow, closely packed longitudinal hyphae, with numerous cross septa. The central portion (medulla) has much wider thin-walled cells running longitudinally and arranged loosely. The cortical hyphae increase by growth and branching, whereas those of the pith do not, and consequently lag behind; large air spaces develop, usually resulting in a central cavity. At a short distance from the apex changes occur in the three zones. The final result is a black strand extending a little below the surface of the soil and obtaining its food supply from the originally infected stump. Branches arise by new growing points forming in the inner cortex—the first sign of their appearance being a tuft of floccose hyphae.

Infection of living trees and shrubs is by means of these rhizomorphs, which gain entrance at or near the collar or through the larger roots. Apparently penetration of sound bark occurs, though obviously cracks and wounds are more vulnerable. The advancing tip sends out slender hyphae which pass to the cambium, branching and spreading rapidly and infecting the adjoining tissues. A thin white papery sheet of mycelium soon displaces the killed cambial cells and spreads upwards and downwards. Such mycelial membranes in timber were formerly named *Xylostroma*, and, as is frequent, the old generic name is now used as a descriptive term for this distinctive stage in development. This mycelial sheet, which is closely adpressed to the wood, is temporary and much of it disappears in later stages. Meanwhile hyphae extend chiefly along the medullary rays and from thence to the tracheids. When the limit of their extension is reached the hyphae become much more septate and bear short branches which, together with some of the segments of the primary hypha, swell up into bladder-like shapes and gradually thicken and darken their walls. Eventually the tracheid is completely blocked by them. These bladder-hyphae are formed in patches: they spread outwards until they meet with adjoining patches and so form a continuous sheet. Some of the pigment escapes from the bladder-cells and stains the tracheid wall. In transverse section the sheet shows as a black line. Parts of the white xylostroma, which are in contact with the black " line," thicken and develop bladder hyphae and so form a continuation of it. The area surrounded by the black " line " has been compared to a sclerotium.* From the blackened xylostroma branches arise which take the form of flat strands somewhat larger than those in the soil. They have a similar structure. By their apical growth they spread up the tree through the cambial cells already killed. They obtain their food supply by putting forth hyaline hyphae during their progress.

The mycelium which has preceded the advancing rhizomorphs in the cambium makes occasional excursions along the medullary rays and into the tracheids, and other black plates are formed which never intersect; the mycelia approach but there is apparently an aversion between them. This accounts for the parallel black lines so frequently seen in sections of wood. Sooner or later branches of the flattened rhizomorphs grow through cracks in the bark and enter the soil. Travelling to other trees they spread the infection.

Armillaria mellea causes a white rot, fibrous and stringy, and finally flaky. The rot is mainly confined to the sap wood in coniferous trees, but in broad-leaved trees it often affects the whole of the heart wood at the base of the tree.

The rhizomorphs from their manner of growth take on many different appearances. When it became realised, following the work of Hartig in 1874, that they are all manifestations of the same fungus, it became necessary to speak of the flattened network under the bark as *Rhizomorpha subcorticalis* and the rounded underground form as *R. subterranea*. Before this, all the growth forms were regarded as separate entities, and received names. The forms under bark or on wood, often in mines, included *Rhizomorpha corrugata*, *R. corticata*, *R. fragilis*, *R. Harrimani*, *R. intestina*, *R. scandens* (*Clavaria phosphorea*); those more or less free in the ground, *Rhizomorpha dichotoma*, *R. patens*, *R. spinosa*, *R. aidaela* [*Lichen* (*Usnea*) *aidaelus*], [*Fibrillaria subterranea*].

Rhizomorphs frequently invade water-pipes, often growing in running water, though sometimes the structures described as such are roots of trees, often elm and willow.† An example was recorded from

*Decayed stumps often show the black plate exposed, as if they had been charred.
† Thus *Rhizomorpha medullaris* described by J. E. Smith in 1818 from the reservoir of the Derby Infirmary was not a fungus but the roots of willow.

Aberdeen in 1925 of a pipe thirteen feet below ground, six inches in diameter, which was blocked for a distance of seven feet: the origin of the rhizomorph could not be traced, though some disorganised wood was found in the vicinity. Similar rhizomorphs have been named *Rhizomorpha aquaeductorum, R. chordalis, R. fusca, R. Tillettii.*

The fruit-body arises directly from the rhizomorph, occasionally some distance from a tree, but normally if not on a tree or stump, in very close proximity. The connection was occasionally noticed but was regarded as parasitism, for the black strands are so unlike in appearance anything known elsewhere among fungi. Much discussion took place about their nature. Some botanists even thought that they were roots of trees, perhaps now adapted to growing as isolated organisms. Rhizomorphs can reach considerable distances; in gypsum workings in Sussex a mass was found which must have travelled over twenty yards. Even when one knows the facts it is sometimes difficult to trace such growths to their source.

The rhizomorph and mycelium of *Armillaria mellea* are responsible for most, if not all, luminous wood in this country. The emission of light by organisms has been known since glow-worms and fire-flies were first observed. The Greeks knew of the light given off by dead fish and flesh, though it was not until less than a century ago that luminous bacteria were determined as the cause. The peoples of the Mediterranean shores had many fabulous stories through the ages about the " phosphorescence " or " burning of the sea," for which various scientific explanations were later given: it is now known to be caused by several organisms both microscopic and macroscopic. The phenomenon of bioluminescence is widespread in the animal kingdom, examples occurring in at least thirty-nine orders.

That decaying wood is often luminous has been known at least since classical times, for it is mentioned by Aristotle and by Pliny. Indeed, there are indications in sayings, customs and writings that earliest man was acquainted with it. The bush which burned with fire but was not consumed and so attracted the attention of Moses, has been held to be an example of the phenomenon, but Moses was leading his flock and presumably would not do this on a night so dark that luminosity would be noticed. In the Sanskrit *Vetala Panchavinsati*, a favourite collection of Indian fairy tales, it is related how a Siris tree (*Albizzia habbek*) in a cemetery, had branches bearing light from end to end without either the tree, the name-labels of the dead suspended from it, or the fearless climbing monkeys suffering injury.

Trees were much revered in early days, and the possession of a root emitting light was thought to increase the creative ability of its owner even to his being able to produce gold by magic. This may have given rise to the idea of a magic wand, the power being transferred from root to branches, sticks and twigs; of shimmering gold in the *Odyssey*, Aaron's rod, the water diviner's twig, and the conjuror's wand! It seems probable that Beowulf's " fyr on flode " was due to luminous roots or to fungal rhizomorphs.

> " Nearly, as men count the mileage, the waters lie whose shore
> The gnarled wood overhelmeth with frozen boughs and hoar,
> Where each night a fearsome wonder showeth into the gazer's eyes,
> Yea, fire on the flood, nor of mortals liveth so wise
> That he kenneth the deep's abysses."*

In addition to wood Pliny also refers to a luminous fungus

" which grows upon the top of the tree, and gives out a brilliant light at night; this, indeed, is the sign by which its presence is known, and by the aid of this light it may be gathered during the night."

The luminous fungus of the Mediterranean countries is *Pleurotus olearius* which does not occur in this country, but is probably the same as *Clitocybe illudens*, the North American Jack o' Lantern. From the fact that Pliny describes it as white, calls it " agaric " and says that it is " very useful as an antidote " he is evidently confusing it with *Polyporus officinalis*, which grows on the bole of larch, not on oak; *Pleurotus olearius* is bright orange-yellow and grows in tufts at the base of the trunk, and on the roots of trees, principally olive, but also oak and other broad-leaved trees.

Olaus Magnus in 1652 relates how when it is expedient or there is urgent need, the people of the far north use an " ingenious method " for lighting their way through forests in the dark, and when continuous night prevails before and after the winter solstice: they place pieces of rotten oak bark at certain intervals on the proposed route in order that by their glow they may complete their journey. Not only the bark but also the rotten trunk affords this aid " and a fungus itself called Agaricus growing on the upper part of the acorn-bearing tree "; the last obviously copied from Pliny makes for dubiety rather than the added verisimilitude doubtless intended by the Bishop. In addition to this primitive street lamp arrangement, there is ordinary " domestic

* Translation by A. Strong.

Plate 23. CEP, *Boletus edulis*; the renowned cèpe of French cookery

Plate 24. ORANGE-CAP BOLETUS, *Boletus versipellis*; one of a small group of species with rough stems. Edible

use, that is to say, in order that by its light (rather than that of a burning torch or lamp) they may with more safety enter places full of combustible material, such as winter barns, full of harvest crops or hay."

The Elizabethans knew of luminous wood. Ben Jonson exaggerates the strength of the illumination, and mistakes its source in " While she sits reading by the glow-worm's light, Or rotten wood, o'er which the worm hath crept "; Walter Raleigh attempts no explanation: " Say to the Court it glowes and shines like rotten wood."

We owe the first scientific investigation of " shining wood " to Robert Boyle, who, in 1667, showed that air was necessary for the display of light, and tabulated a list of resemblances and differences between such wood and burning coal; he also studied the luminescence of decaying fish. Following him many famous naturalists interested themselves in the glow. The problem was whether the light came from the wood itself or from something growing on it. Early last century it began to be assumed that fungi were mainly responsible because of the smell of the wood. In 1822 B. von Dershau noticed some luminous timber in mines and believed it to be due to the strands of *Rhizomorpha* which were infecting the wood, the tips of the strands being brightest; the light, in some places, was sufficient to obviate the use of lamps. Sowerby, however, in 1797, describing his *Clavaria phosphorea*, which he recognised as the same as *Rhizomorpha fragilis*, says:

" Found in a wine cellar in Little St. Helens, London, creeping among saw-dust and bottles in the autumn of 1796, communicated by Mr. B. M. Forster. It is remarkable for being luminous in the dark, when fresh, at the ends of the shoots. Mr. Forster has doubted whether this phosphoric appearance may not be owing to some vinous moisture imbibed, rather than a natural property of the fungus."

J. F. Heller is often given the credit for first definitely recognising the mycelium and mycelial strands as the source of light in 1843; he later called them *Rhizomorpha noctiluca*.

Luminous wood is well known to woodmen, foresters, timbermen and others who have occasion to pass through woods or timber yards in darkness. The decayed wood itself permeated with the mycelium of *Armillaria mellea* glows strongly so long as growth continues, that is while it remains damp. During the two great wars bits of infected wood left on the road in hauling timber, and noticed to glow in darkness, were sent to the British Museum on several occasions in the belief that they had probably been doped and used for signalling to the enemy. Similar touch wood was used by troops in the trenches of the western front, stuck in the straps of their steel helmets or on the foresights of their rifles to obviate collisions in the darkness. In a London anti-aircraft station the floor appeared to be covered with glow worms, but when daylight came these were found to be " fragments of decayed wood." " The next night, we put the chump from which these fragments had come on a post in the compound. Shortly afterwards the sentry on duty blew his whistle and reported a strange light." I was informed during the recent war that wood in a timber yard near London glowed so brightly on moonless nights that men on fire-watch covered it with tarpaulin for fear it would attract enemy aircraft. The airborne troops digging trenches at Arnhem were surprised to see luminous bodies in the dark. When traced they proved to be tree roots. Sgt. O. M. Frazer sent me a specimen, which was infected with the mycelium of *Armillaria mellea.**

Linnaeus presided over the thesis of C. F. Adler in 1752 on *Noctiluca marina*, in which it is stated that wood infected with *Byssus violaceus* is luminous. Linnaeus consequently altered the name to *Byssus phosphorea* in *Species Plantarum*. Sowerby figures the fungus as *Auricularia phosphorea* though with no reference to its reputed qualities: it is *Corticium caeruleum*, a common species on dead wood, branches and twigs, forming beautiful azure-blue patches usually with a white fimbriate border. Though there is no further evidence for luminosity in this fungus, Linnaeus's statement has been repeated for two centuries. It is probable that the specimen was growing on rotten wood infected with *Armillaria mellea*.

There are several other British species which have been reported as luminous. *Fomes annosus* is often quoted following a record by Worthington G. Smith. The fungus was growing in a mine and both fruit-body and mycelium were said to have been luminous, though they were not so when received. It is probable that the wood was infected by *Armillaria* but exceedingly doubtful if the *Fomes* was in any way connected with the phosphorescence with which Welsh miners were " well acquainted."

*17 Oct. 1944 " during the recent operation at Arnhem in Holland. On taking up defensive positions in a wood by Oosterbeck it was necessary to dig slit trenches to a depth of some five feet. When night fell I was attracted by what at first I thought were several glow-worms on the side of the trench, but further investigation proved that they were luminous roots. I took a length of this root and on slitting it open discovered that the whole fibre throughout its length was brightly luminous. I enclose a small piece of this root which I brought back with me but was disappointed to find, on my return, that all signs of phosphorescence had then disappeared."

Another common fungus which has often been reported as luminous is *Polyporus sulphureus*, which occurs as sulphur-yellow brackets, often overlapping, on the trunks of both deciduous and coniferous trees. J. J. Paulet in 1793 apparently started the delusion by saying of a specimen found in an old hollow oak " il ressemblait à des flammes de feu dans l'obscurité." He was, however, probably merely describing the colour, for he had previously said that the fruit-bodies were remarkable " par leur couleur de feu ou aurore." A short time ago a specimen was sent to me for identification with the information that it shone in the dark. No light was emitted when tested and the sender was asked to make careful observations. He then reported that the fungus was not luminous and added that it was not dark when he had first noticed it. It may be that we have here an instance of what is sometimes called the " Elizabeth Linnaeus phenomenon," as it was first noticed by Linnaeus's daughter in the flowers of the garden Nasturtium (*Tropaeolum majus*): the corollas appeared to flicker or spark intermittently during twilight in June or July. There are many reports of orange and yellow flowers " throwing out flames " in warm and sultry weather. The explanation usually given is that these flashes are electrical discharges, but it has also been thought that the phenomenon is subjective due to after-images in partially dark-adapted eyes.

F. Ludwig recorded luminescence in the germinating sclerotia of *Collybia tuberosa* (1882) and *C. cirrata* (1885), but his observations have not been confirmed.

Two other common species, *Xylaria Hypoxylon* and *X. polymorpha*, according to some investigators, have luminous mycelia. Both grow on tree stumps: *Xylaria Hypoxylon* is the Candle-Snuff Fungus which has a black, corky, flattened, simple or branched fruit-body, with white tips when young due to the production of conidia, but entirely black when old and showing a punctate surface where the perithecia form; *X. polymorpha* has black swollen club-like fruit-bodies with a punctate surface. The evidence for and against luminosity seems equally strong. In nature, as *Xylaria* has a similar habitat to *Armillaria mellea*, there is a danger of confusing the two mycelia but the mycelium has been studied in culture; it is possible that the composition of the culture medium may play a part. Another possibility is that different physiological strains of these fungi exist, one luminous and one non-luminous. This is known in another common species, *Panus stipticus*, which occurs on old stumps, usually as small, thin, overlapping ear-shaped fruit-bodies with a scurfy cap, cinnamon coloured when moist and paler when dry, thin gills of the same colour and a paler lateral stalk which is broader and compressed above. In America this species has long been known to be luminous, principally in the gills but also in the cap and mycelium. It is morphologically indistinguishable from the British form of the species which, so far as is known, is always non-luminous. Thus two distinct physiological forms exist. The mycelia from them have been mated and it was found that luminosity acts as a dominant Mendelian character and is governed by a single pair of factors.

In examining fungi for luminescence it is essential that there should be complete darkness and that sufficient time should be allowed for the eye to become adjusted—a period of ten to fifteen minutes is necessary. It is in the tropics and the Antipodes that luminous fungi are most common. Many species have been described, particularly of *Pleurotus*, and there are glowing accounts of the amount of light which is emitted, " a blaze of light " in which one can see to read. In New Caledonia maidens use them as ornaments for their hair. Miss L. E. Cheesman told me that when in the New Hebrides she was bushed one night, and, passing near a village, said she must have a light. Boys collected a luminous fungus with a glutinous cap which they stuck all over themselves. She could then see a column of boys trailing through the forest. Troops serving in New Guinea during the last war were well acquainted with what appeared to be green eyes staring in the darkness, and the American war correspondent, George Wellerk, gives an amusing account of them: " Darling, I am writing to you to-night by the light of five mushrooms."

The colour of the light varies somewhat. It may be white as in *Pleurotus japonicus*, white with a faint bluish green tinge in *Armillaria mellea*, greenish white in *Panus stipticus*, or greenish as in *Pleurotus Gardneri*. In *Armillaria* the spectrum stretches from about the middle of the yellow region through the green and well into the blue. Emission of light stops in nitrogen, hydrogen, ether and chloroform. As Boyle first showed, oxygen is necessary for the display; moisture and a certain temperature are also needed. Buller found that *Panus stipticus* emitted light so long as it was discharging spores, but ceased when dried; if then moistened, even after six months, it again became luminous. The minimum temperature at which light is given off is 2° to 5° C., the maximum 35° to 37° and the optimum 10° to 25° C. It is obvious that the production of light is a result of physiological activity for which oxygen, water, and some photogenic substance are the requisites; juice extracted from a luminous fungus is inactive. The photogen is assumed to be the same as that known in luminous animals, consisting of luciferin which is thermostable and luciferase which is thermolabile. Theoretically, luciferin is oxidised by luciferase in one part of a cell producing oxyluciferin which in another part is reduced again to luciferin.

It has been suggested that luminous fruit-bodies attract insects which, becoming dusted with the spores, aid in their dispersal. It is difficult to claim any such biological advantage for the luminosity of *Armillaria mellea*, which is restricted to the mycelium of young rhizomorphs.

In 1846 C. V. Naudin, while walking through a forest at night, noticed luminosity among some fallen leaves. He thought the light was caused by glow-worms, but on tracing it found that it arose from decaying oak leaves. Two years later, Tulasne in his investigations on phosphorescence in fungi also observed the luminosity of decaying leaves; the light appeared in spots, especially in paler parts. Since then the phenomenon has been frequently noticed both in leaves of deciduous trees and in coniferous needles: it is more frequent and stronger after rain. It was at first thought that the luminosity was due to the dead tissues themselves, and it was regarded as distinct from that displayed by living organisms. H. Molisch, in 1904, demolished this view and attributed the light to fungal mycelia occurring in the tissues of the leaves. He observed wefts of mycelia but was unable to get them into culture.

The probable source of the light has been found by F. Bothe who, in 1930, recorded that the mycelium of *Mycena tintinnabulum* is luminous. In culture from spores it glows for fifteen to twenty days while the mycelium remains white; as the culture gradually becomes reddish brown light ceases. A culture of *Mycena parabolica* was also luminous. He investigated other species of *Mycena* (1931); most are small with a delicate conical or bell-shaped cap which is never incurved at the margin, where it is often more or less striate; the spores are white and the stem cartilaginous. Some grow on stumps, some on leaves and some on the ground. Six additional species, *Mycena galopus*, *M. sanguinolenta*, *M. epipterygia*, *M. dilatata*, *M. stylobates* and *M. zephirus* produced luminosity in culture, both on artificial media and on leaves and pine-needles. It appears certain that some, if not all, of the luminosity of leaves is due to species of this genus.

The luminosity in culture is not so regular or so constant as that of *Armillaria mellea*. Usually it is seen only just after inoculation, though it may begin to show much later as in *Mycena epipterygia* and *M. stylobates*, where there is an incubation period of 130 days. The light may be intermittently weak or strong with intervals of darkness. Usually no light is seen while the mycelium is loosely felted but only when it becames patchy, interwoven, or in strands.

Though the phenomenon is chiefly associated with the mycelia, Bothe noted patches of luminosity on the gills of *Mycena galopus*, *M. sanguinolenta*, *M. epipterygia*, *M. zephirus* and *M. pura* and on the stem also of the last.

He also mentions that he had found the mycelium of *Mycena polygramma* luminous.

Bothe used mass cultures in his first experiments. Later (1935) he examined monospore (haploid) cultures of two different collections of *Mycena galopus* and *M. polygramma* to see whether they also were luminous. In both species some single spore haploid mycelia were luminous, others not. Moreover, luminosity when present varied in intensity and in duration.

When mycelia of different strains were mated the results showed that the phenomena are very complex. Some diploid mycelia arising from the fusion of haploid luminous mycelia are non-luminous, but as no fruit-bodies were formed in culture it was not possible to determine whether this is a constant character. It may be due to an inhibiting gene, dominant or recessive, which prevents or weakens luminosity. Bothe's conclusions are that the results of his experiments can be explained only by assuming that six factors are concerned, though his suggestions about their nature require confirmation before they can be accepted.

Though so many species of *Mycena* displayed luminosity several others proved negative. Bothe lists *M. galericulata*, *M. vulgaris*, *M. metata*, *M. crocata*, *M. haematopus* and *M. ianthina*: all except the last are well known British species.

Recently (1950) a variety of our common *Mycena rorida* has been described, var. *lamprospora*, of which the damp spores are luminous, as seen around the base of the stem on sticks and leaves. It was recorded from Rabaul and Malaya. Here may be mentioned that Fabre found that two Phalloids, *Clathrus ruber* and *Phallus impudicus* (Chap. 15) emitted radiations which would pass through a cardboard box, for example, and affect photographic plates whereas, the luminescent *Clitocybe olearia* had not that property.

CHAPTER 15

PUFF-BALLS AND EARTH-STARS

PUFF-BALLS

PUFF-BALLS ARE AMONGST THE COMMONEST FUNGI in meadows and pastures, ranging from about half an inch to a foot or more across. Not only are some of the twenty or so British species very common, but they are known by several popular names of which puff-ball is the most frequent; others are fuzz-ball, bulver, bullfist, satan's or devil's snuff-box. The largest species is *Lycoperdon giganteum* (*L. Bovista*) (Pl. 32*a*, p. 191), the Giant Puff-Ball, occurring in pastures and orchards and occasionally on road-sides. Although it is common it often excites wonder, and frequently rivalry is shown about whether the specimen found is the largest ever; doubtless if the fruit-body remained as stable at death as do heads and horns, we should have corresponding competing records. *The Field* gave the following particulars of a specimen gathered in 1919; weight 10 lb. 2 oz., height 11¼ in., circumference 49 in. This is not exceptional, however; W. G. Smith records one 64 in. in circumference. It would be interesting to see such a one as that reported from New York State in 1877, which, at a distance, was mistaken for a sheep; it measured 5 ft. 4 in. in its greatest diameter, 4 ft. 6 in. in its least, and 9½ in. in height, and was therefore bigger than the specimens described by H. G. Wells in *The Food of the Gods*, for the local vicar attempted to measure one of those by embracing it. A specimen of average size was found under an oak tree in Kent during the late war, and was approached with caution as it was thought to be an explosive. Later, labelled " Hitler's Secret Weapon," its exhibition helped the local war-savings group.

In 1928 workmen found several specimens under the floor of a drawing-room at Kew, and for a time mistook them for human skulls. The police eventually called in the help of the authorities at the Royal Botanic Gardens and the mystery was solved.

Lycoperdon giganteum is readily distinguished by its size and its white skin, which is at first downy and then smooth like white kid; " having no hole or breach in them, whereby a man may see into them." The skin of puff-balls is known as the *peridium* (Greek, *peridion*, a little pouch); there is an outer layer (*exoperidium*) and an inner one (*endoperidium*). The fruit-body is roundish or flattened and its base is usually grooved; it is attached to the soil by a cord-like mycelial strand. The flesh is white and of a cheesy consistency. As development proceeds, a spore-producing region (*gleba*) is differentiated which becomes yellow and finally olivaceous. At maturity this is composed of olivaceous brown spores, and brown sterile threads (*capillitium*) which are attached to the endoperidium. The gleba fills the whole of the interior except for a thin sterile base, which, however, is occasionally wanting. The outer layer of the wall cracks in the upper portion and falls away leaving the brittle inner layer exposed, and this, in its turn, collapses and releases the mature spores which are dry and powdery.

The manner in which the spores are expelled when the fruit-body is touched or rain-drops fall upon it, led to the old Latin name *Crepitus lupi*, and the French " vesse-de-loup," from which Tournefort coined the name *Lycoperdon*. Fabre, commenting on this, says:

" The history of plants abounds in terms which it is not always desirable to translate. Bequeathed to us by earlier ages less reticent than ours, botany has often retained the brutal frankness of words that set propriety at defiance."

This savours of the *Botany for Ladies* period. There are certainly a few mycological names, which, if explained, might cause a blush or a grin, but those who understand them are little affected, and those who don't, not at all.

But what of the English names? Gerard says, " Puffes Fistes* are commonly called in Latin *Lupi crepitus*, or Woolfes Fistes . . . in English Puffes Fistes, & Fussebals in the north "; Parkinson says, " Fusse balls or rather Foist or Fist balls "; I. Withers, in *Emblems* (1635), writes of " That uncleanly mushrom ball which in some countries we a Puffyst call." The word puff apparently means no more than fungus; foist, fyst or fist, are the same as crepitus— breaking wind. Puckfist and Bullfist are other old names. The German Bofist was turned into *Bovista*, which is a generic name in

*The index gives " Puffe Fistes."

Paul L. de Laszlo

Plate 25. Boletus Satanas; poisonous when eaten raw. The photograph is of an old, somewhat faded specimen; the stem is usually more obese

Plate 26a (above). *Panaeolus campanulatus* ; on highly nitrogenous soil. Poisonous. The stem is reddish and mealy when young. (*S. C. Porter*); *b (below left)* *Polystictus versicolor*; an extremely common saprophyte. The colour of the upper surface varies, being lighter in the shade. (*Paul L. de Laszlo*); *c (below right)* *Polyporus radiatus*; usually on alder. The pore-surface glistens (*Eric Hosking*)

the Lycoperdaceae, the puff-ball family. The setting of propriety at defiance is widespread, and hardly merits castigation.

Gerard, who says little about fungi, dwells especially on this fungus and repeats most of his statements. The fruit-body " being trodden upon do breathe foorth a most thinne and fine powder, like unto smoke, very noisome and hurtfull unto the eies, causing a kinde of blindness, which is called Poor-blinde, or Sand-blinde "; " divers have beene pore blinde ever after, when some small quantitie thereof hath beene blowen into their eies."

A mature specimen is so attractive to the young that it has even been suggested that fuss ball is a local variant of football. It is refreshing to find that the learned and versatile Clusius when he wrote the first known monograph on fungi, *Fungorum historia** in 1601, should have remembered at the age of seventy-six that as a boy he and his schoolfellows were accustomed to kick the mature puff-ball to scatter the dust.

The spores are globose and warted, measuring 3-5 μ in diameter. The vast numbers of spores produced by fungi have been already mentioned. Buller calculated that a dried fruit-body of *Lycoperdon giganteum*, 16 × 12 × 10 in., produced 7,000,000,000,000 spores.† It weighed 232 grs. An overwintered Canadian specimen was found in 1939 measuring 14 in. high, 14 in. wide, 16⅝ in. long and 50 in. in circumference. After being air-dried it weighed approximately 715 grs. and was, therefore, estimated to contain over 20,000,000,000,000 spores. This species heads the list for single fruit-bodies and is probably the most prolific organism living on our planet. Even in days of war debts and their ramifications, these seem amazing terrestrial numbers, and consequently an organism so ambitious in its projected progeny might readily be labelled as potentially successful. What if the success materialised? What if the spores all fulfilled their function and produced fruit-bodies? Seven billion of these of average size placed end to end would put a girdle round about the earth more than five times; if their spores were equally successful the resulting fruit-bodies would stretch twice to the sun and back, and form a mass eight hundred times the weight of the globe. We are on safe ground in asserting

*Appended to *Rariorum plantarum historia*.

† The spores of *Lycoperdon giganteum* may, or may not, be stalked (*pedicellate*); those of some other species of the genus are almost invariably so. H. Baker in *The microscope made easy*, 1742, noticed them. " The Globules . . . had each a little Stalk or Tail." The appearance of a warted pedicellate spore misled him. " They are, evidently, so many minute *Puff-Balls*, furnished with Stalks or Tails to penetrate easily into the ground."

that this does not happen. The spores mature and are capable of forming mycelia and, eventually, fruit-bodies if conditions favour their production. We know that over the years the Giant Puff-Ball varies little in frequency; in some seasons it appears to be comparatively abundant, in others relatively rare. There is never a suggestion of the colonisation of any appreciable area. A sterilised substratum such as we have in pure cultures (cf. Pl. 45, p. 274) or one which is especially favourable to the colonist and free of competitive organisms are prerequisites for inordinate increase. Every biologist, no matter how he may be influenced by special contrivances for dispersal, food-reserves and all the peculiar endowments for exploiting particular habitats, is brought up against the fact that the number of individuals of a given species remains more or less constant under normal conditions. Though there is undoubtedly an imposing increase here and there, in special habitats or new areas of dispersal (introduced species), a balance is finally reached, with the net result that there is no real increase in the number of individuals. This problem was discussed by Linnaeus when postulating as the hypothetical paradise an island at the equator, crowned with a very high mountain, where a pair of every living thing created in the beginning could find a suitable habitat, and be conveniently placed there for Adam to name. After giving examples of plants producing numerous seeds he points out that if only two seeds were to germinate successfully each year they would give a population of 1,048,576 plants in twenty years, and that various methods of vegetative reproduction have also to be taken into account. He found no difficulty in understanding how plants can spread, for there are devices for this that are apparent to anyone with a garden or who has glanced at bombed sites. There are also contrivances for protection against animals, sometimes diabolically obvious, sometimes masked. The difficulty was, and is, to explain satisfactorily the balance which is ultimately attained. Linnaeus later spoke of " Bellum omnium in omnes," Hobbes's " Bellum omnium contra omnes " of sociology, Darwin's " struggle for existence."

To return to *Lycoperdon giganteum*. It is certain that on the average only one fruit-body is formed from the enormous mass of spores, on the assumption that the fungus is an annual. This, however, is not so, for it often grows in rings; some enormous specimens were found forming a very large interrupted ring during a foray of the British Mycological Society at South Walsham, Norfolk, in 1922. Theoretically one spore was capable of giving rise to the ring, and probably for a century numerous fruit-bodies had been formed, each with its billions of spores without hope of posterity. What is it that decides which of these spores, if any, shall bear fruit? Such myriads of spores must find themselves in conditions of infinite range. We may assume that the one spore that is successful, the one which comes through the mesh, whatever constitutes the sieve, has something in particular not possessed by the others. It is extremely difficult even to imagine what that something is in relation to the complex welter which constitutes environment. How can we assume that any variation of the kind usually considered has survival value? A fungus spore grows and produces mycelium if it chances to reach a suitable environment; this persists and produces a fruit-body if it is able to withstand the competition it encounters there. It survives because it is able to do so, not because it is best fitted to do so. If spore-production be the criterion of success, *Lycoperdon giganteum* is certainly successful. It appears to be impossible to find any satisfactory explanation for the enormous wastage. Obviously with such a colossal number of spores dispersed far and wide we may assume that some fall on good ground, but we cannot reasonably postulate that the super-abundance is designed to ensure this; it is a possible but not a purposeful result.

Lycoperdon giganteum was known to the ancients; it is probably the " pezis " of Theophrastus. Gerard says of it, " In English Fusse bals, Pucke Fusse, and Bulfists, with which in some places of England they use to kill or smolder their Bees, when they would drive the Hives, and bereave the poore Bees of their meate, houses, and lives; these are also used in some places where neighbours dwell farre a sunder, to carrie and reserve fire from place to place." Puff-balls are still used to smoke out bees. *Lycoperdon giganteum* is the *Bovista officinalis* of older works and " sumnopere laudata " according to Vittadini, the mature fungus being much used by barber-surgeons* together with other species, to staunch bleeding. Later, surgeons used it as a haemostatic and considered it an invaluable remedy for preventing the healing by first intention. In farm-house kitchens a string of dried puff-balls may occasionally still be seen awaiting emergencies. The Romanys have a couplet, " Quanda mandi chivs moilee ke vindi morripude "—when a man cuts his finger he uses a puff-ball. Within recent years it has been proposed to use puff-balls as a styptic in veterinary work. Gerard

---

*J. D. Hooker relates that the Lepchas use a piece of smouldering puff-ball as a moxa. Hippocrates has several references [to cauterisation by fungi—probably the flesh of *Fomes* or *Polyporus*, as with Laplanders.

says, " the powder of them doth dry without biting; it is fitly applied to merigals, kibed heeles and such like."

Another large puff-ball, *Lycoperdon caelatum*, the Mosaic Puff-Ball, is common on downs and calcareous pastures. It is large, usually somewhat top-shaped, tapering below into a short, stout, stem-like base. It is white at first, becoming yellow, brownish or greyish. The outer layer is woolly, particularly in the upper portion, and as growth proceeds, it becomes torn into flat pyramidal warts, or star-shaped areas. At maturity the outer layer at the summit breaks off and exposes the inner wall which later flakes away and liberates the spores. Only about half the fruit-body is devoted to spore-production, the lower portion remaining sterile, and cut off by a distinct membranous diaphragm. As a consequence, when all the spores have been liberated the sterile base remains whole, becoming smooth and brown. It is remarkably persistent and being impervious to rain may remain in place for months, or become free and be blown about, in either event often puzzling the country rambler; indeed not only them, for a genus, *Hippoperdon*, was erected on such sterile bases.

Puff-balls differ not only in size and the structure of the outer layer of the wall (ornamentation) but also in the colour, size and sculpturing of their spores, the structure of the capillitium and its method of attachment, the presence or absence of a sterile base and the manner in which the peridium breaks and liberates the spores.

In British books three genera are usually distinguished, *Lycoperdon*, *Bovista* and *Bovistella*, though a fourth, *Calvatia*, is often given. In *Lycoperdon* the capillitium threads are attached, either to the wall or to a central column of sterile tissue (*columella*); in *Bovista* and *Bovistella* they are free. The generic distinction upon which *Calvatia* is founded is the falling away of the upper portion of the peridium to release the spores, as in *Lycoperdon giganteum* and *L. caelatum*. Thus we have the two names *Lycoperdon caelatum* and *Calvatia caelata*, for the same fungus; such synonyms are a little confusing at first but the difficulty is soon resolved by a knowledge of the significance of the generic characters adopted in the books consulted. Synonyms, however, have run away with the Giant Puff-Ball in a manner which is not only puzzling but annoying.

Lycoperdon saccatum is another common puff-ball of large size. The subglobose upper portion is plicate below and passes into a thick, often scrobiculate, stem-like sterile base which may be more than half the total height. It is whitish or greyish when young, and covered with small spinulose warts and granules, usually decreasing in size from above downwards and soon disappearing from the upper portion. The inner very thin endoperidium gradually becomes tinged with brown and falls away in patches.

All other species of *Lycoperdon* dehisce by an apical mouth. The commonest British species is *L. perlatum* (Pl. 31*a*, p. 190). It varies a good deal in size and shape, and, snow-white when young, becomes yellowish and then brownish. The fertile upper portion is subglobose, generally plicate below, and has a small protruding apical tip; the sterile portion may be well developed and stem-like, about half the width of the head, or very reduced so that the fruit-body is top-shaped, often attached in pairs to a white mycelial cord.* The head is covered at first with long fragile spines surrounded at their base with small warts; the warts occur also on the stem, decreasing in size downwards. The spines easily fall off and in this condition the fungus was called *Lycoperdon gemmatum*. As maturity is reached the ornamentation falls away, often leaving a network-marking. The spores are liberated through a small mouth formed at the tip.

Lycoperdon hiemale (*L. depressum*) (Pl. 31*b*, p. 190) is likewise common; it is top-shaped and contracted at the base and plicate, often appearing flaccid because of the sides being compressed; at first yellowish white, it becomes dull yellow then brownish. It is covered with intermixed large and small spines and powdery granules, all of which soon disappear. The sterile base often extends to about half the total height, and is separated from the gleba by a diaphragm. There is a well-defined apical mouth which later extends down to the persistent sterile base. It can often be found in the winter months.

Lycoperdon echinatum is not so common. It is essentially a woodland species occurring principally under beech. It is brown when mature and has well-developed persistent spines, which are purplish brown, with much smaller surrounding warts; when the spines disappear, which is usually not until the fungus is old and weathered, they leave a well-marked pattern.

Lycoperdon pyriforme (Pl. 33*a*, p. 230) is readily recognised, for it is our only species which occurs on wood, tree-stumps being its favourite habitat. Moreover, it usually grows in dense clusters springing from

*This mycelial cord enables the fungus to spread in a remarkable manner. It grew in a garden in Birmingham, " coming up between the sets in the street, under the tarmac on the foot-path, between the bricks in the front wall and all round a lime tree in front of the house."

white mycelial cords. The fruit-bodies are pear-shaped or subglobose; white at first and covered with minute spines and granules which disappear and leave the smooth white, grey or brown, thin and flaccid endoperidium. There is a slight umbo in which the small irregular mouth is formed. Fruit-bodies occur through the winter. Occasionally growth appears to be terrestrial, but if the mycelial strands be followed they will be found to be attached to buried wood.

Lycoperdon pusillum is our smallest species. It occurs in sandy soil in heathland and on hedge banks. It is first white and covered with mealy squamules, then yellow, smooth and shining; the upper portion is globular, and narrows below to a tapering root-like portion. There is no sterile base.

Two of our commonest puff-balls are classed in *Bovista*. In this genus there is no sterile base and the threads of the capillitium are free, consisting of a thick stem and long, forked, pointed branches. Both species occur in pastures and heaths in summer and autumn, and being globose, smooth and white, look something like ping-pong balls, and, at a distance, have an irritating resemblance to golf balls. They have a papery exoperidium which soon flakes off from above and leaves a tough shining endoperidium, which liberates the spores through an irregular torn mouth. *Bovista nigrescens* is larger and becomes brown and then almost black; the mature gleba is purple. In *B. plumbea* the wall becomes lead-colour and the gleba purplish brown. It may be to these species that Dryden refers:

> *My Phillis me with pelted puff-ball plies,*
> *Then tripping to the woods the wanton flies.*

Parkinson mentions the age-long pastime:

> " While they are young and white, as Clusius saith, he and others of his schoole fellowes, being children, would in sport throw one at another."

The sport mentioned by Clusius, however, appears to have been restricted to scattering the spores of the Giant Puff-Ball.

All puff-balls arise from white mycelial cords, sometimes fairly stout and very apparent in certain species. The Giant Puff-Ball is well-known to be edible but must be eaten while the flesh is white. It is highly esteemed in Denmark and indeed during the reign of King Christian VIII its regular cultivation was contemplated, but not achieved. Some other species are equally good and none are poisonous.

EARTH-STARS

The Earth-Stars (*Geaster*) are closely related to puff-balls, and, when young, much resemble them in appearance. They always arouse interest when encountered in field or wood because of their strange shapes. As in puff-balls the wall consists of two strata, an outer (*exoperidium*) and an inner (*endoperidium*). The exoperidium is much more substantial than in *Lycoperdon* and is in three layers, mycelial to the outside, fibrillose in the middle, and fleshy within. At first the exoperidium closely invests the endoperidium, but at maturity it separates and splits from the apex downwards to slightly below the centre, forming four to fourteen rays which simply expand (*Geaster triplex*, Pl. 33*b*, p. 230), or may become inturned (*Geaster fornicatus*, Pl. 34, p. 231). The general appearance is that of a small puff-ball, with or without a stalk, borne on the exoperidium.

In the majority of earth-stars the endoperidium opens by a single mouth, and there is only one stem; the capillitium threads are branched and there is a central columella. There are two British species which differ from the rest, and these have been placed in separate genera. The first is *Myriostoma coliforme*, which has several mouths and several stalks. It is very rare, its discovery being due to S. Doody who found "this elegant *Fungus* . . . this *September* 1695, in the Lane that leads from *Crayford* to *Bexley*-Common. in Kent."* It was next found in Norfolk in 1782; it reappeared in the same district in 1880, and has since been gathered two or three times in the same hedge bank. It has also been recorded from Suffolk, and once from Worcester. The young fungus is globose, ochraceous, and covered with loose, angular, dark brown scales; it remains for three or four months, apparently unchanged, with its top at or just above the surface of the soil. The outer layer, in opening, splits almost to the middle into four to seven segments. The inner peridium is lead-coloured or brownish with a silvery sheen, minutely warted, roundish, and borne on numerous slender stalks which are sometimes branched; it opens by several ciliated mouths. There are several columellas.

The second, *Astraeus hygrometricus*, differs from *Geaster* in having no columella and in the threads of the capillitium being much branched; there are other slight differences but hardly of generic significance. The exoperidium is tough and leathery, and on drying becomes

---

*In the Appendix to the second edition of Ray's *Synopsis* (1696). There is confusion in the third edition (1724) owing to synonymy.

deeply cracked and almost horn-like in consistency; it splits nearly
to the base with seven to twenty acute lobes which are strongly hygroscopic, becoming rigidly inflexed when dry and uncurling when moist
—"champignons baromètres". The endoperidium is sessile, grey or
brown, and the mouth torn. It often becomes free from its attachment
and is blown about.

Geaster mammosus is similarly very hygroscopic and about the same
size, but the seven to ten lobes are more acute and much thinner and
the inner peridium has a well-defined, even, conical mouth surrounded
by a pale, silky, depressed zone.

G. triplex (Pl. 33*b*, p. 230) is a large species, frequent in the beech-
woods of the south of England, where, late in the year, numerous dry
specimens may be found blown into ditches. Before it splits it is pointed
at the top and not rounded as is usual in other British species. The
outer layer divides into six to eight segments with long pointed tips
which expand or become revolute under the flat, or, less often, arched
base. The fleshy layer is thick and pinkish brown, cracking and partly
flaking away, often with a small basal portion persisting as a collar
round the base of the endoperidium. This is sessile and has a fibrillose
mouth which becomes lacerated, and is surrounded by a more or less
definitely outlined broadly conical area.

In *G. rufescens* the fleshy layer of the exoperidium is thick and
reddish flesh-colour; it cracks transversely and when weathered often
breaks away in flakes or dries up almost completely. It splits into six
to nine segments. The endoperidium is usually sessile but may be
shortly stalked. The mouth is slightly projecting and often torn. It
occurs in oak-woods, buried in debris until it expands.

G. fimbriatus is probably our most frequent species, usually occurring
in colonies; I have a note of over two hundred specimens in a beech-
wood near Canterbury in 1936, " looking like miniature cottage loaves."
The outer membrane splits to near the middle into a variable number
of segments, usually six to nine, which on expansion are strongly
revolute, and bent underneath, the undivided portion forming a cup
round the base of the sessile endoperidium. The pale buff fleshy layer
is fairly thick. The mouth is conical, ill-defined and fibrillose.

*G. Bryantii** is characterised by having a deep circular groove at

---

*Charles Bryant, after whom this species was named, privately published *The
Historical Account of two Lycoperdons* in 1782. So struck was he by the (hygroscopic)
movements of the segments of some species and of the hairs surrounding the mouth,
which continue until all the spores are shed, that he interpreted them as being

Plate 27a. Polyporus giganteus; in dense tufts, often in great quantities at the base of deciduous trees *(Paul L. de Laszlo)*

b. Sparassis crispa; looking like a large bath-sponge at the base of pines. Edible *(Paul L. de Laszlo)*

Plate 28a (above left). *Clavaria fusiformis*; often in fairly dense tufts among grass. (*Paul L. de Laszlo*); *b (above right) Clavaria rugosa*; among grass and on bare soil. (*Eric Hosking*); *c (lower left) Clavaria corniculata*; varying in size, taller and laxer in long damp grass and shade, more compact in the open. (*Paul L. de Laszlo*); *d (lower right) Clavaria stricta*; on or near rotten wood, attached by white mycelial strings (*Paul L. de Laszlo*)

the base of the endoperidium where the slender stalk is attached. The exoperidium splits into eight or twelve segments which become recurved; the fleshy layer is white then ochraceous. The mouth is long and conical.

In *G. fornicatus* (Pl. 34, p. 231) the exoperidium splits into two layers, the inner of which divides to beyond the middle into four, or rarely, five lobes which bend strongly backwards and downwards so that they stand erect, the tips remaining attached to an equal number of shorter lobes on the margin of the outer layer which remains as a membranous cup in the ground; the fleshy layer is dark brown. The endoperidium has a ring-like swelling (*apophysis*) where it is attached to the short stalk, and is sometimes enlarged below. The mouth is ciliate, conical, then tubular. It is our largest species and grows in grass usually on the borders of woods. When two or three specimens are growing together they give the impression of manikins, so much so that when first described in 1688 G. Seger gave it the name *Fungus Anthropomorphos* and in his figure provided the endoperidium of one specimen with a human profile! (Pl. VI*b*, p. 135.)

G. coronatus was long overlooked in this country and long confused abroad with *G. fornicatus*, which it much resembles but is only about half the size and more slender. The mouth is projecting. It occurs amongst pine-needles.

In discoursing on the strange habits of fungi Badham (1847) states that *Geastrum*,† aspiring occasionally to leave this earth, had been found suspended, like Mahomet's coffin, between it and the stars, on the very highest pinnacle of St. Paul's, and in a footnote says, " Withering found one of these plants on the top of St. Paul's Cathedral; the first he had seen! "

Scleroderma is often confused with *Lycoperdon*, and sometimes with truffles; Earth-ball is a book-name for it. There are two common species which are collectively known as *Scleroderma vulgare*, but, more correctly as *S. aurantium* (Pl. 32*b*, p. 191) and *S. verrucosum* (Pl. 39*a*, p. 254); the solid somewhat marbled flesh and the firm wall (*peridium*) at once distinguish *Scleroderma* from *Lycoperdon*. The spores are liberated by the breaking or weathering of the peridium.

Scleroderma aurantium is whitish or pale brown often tinged yellow,

voluntary and of animal nature. The prehensile properties of the " claws " continue even after death for a specimen of *Geaster rufescens* had held an unfortunate *G. fornicatus* in its merciless grip for several years in a drawer of his cabinet.

† This " hybrid " emendation of Micheli's name *Geaster* is due to Persoon. As he used it in his *Synopsis* (1801) there has been a tendency recently to adopt it.

with large scaly warts, globose, or flattened at the top, sometimes plicate at the base; the peridium is thick, whitish in section often becoming pink. The flesh (gleba) is greyish then purplish black, traversed by whitish veins (*tramal plates*).

S. verrucosum in spite of its name is less warty than *S. aurantium*; the warts are small and brownish and often soon disappear leaving the ochraceous or dingy brown peridium smooth. It is usually a little smaller than *S. aurantium* and more flattened with a thick stem-like lacunose base: it can be distinguished by its thin peridium and its umber gleba.

Both species have mycelial cords and both grow in woods or on heaths, particularly on sandy soil, *S. aurantium* being the more common: both are hosts of *Boletus parasiticus* (Pl. 39a, p. 254).

Because of the marbled flesh of *Scleroderma* when it is immature, slices of it, sometimes darkened, are sold as truffles or used to adulterate them; paté de fois gras, galantine and dinde and poularde truffée are the vehicles of this deceit in cheap continental restaurants. *Scleroderma* is usually considered harmless but it is worthless and its taste certainly bears no resemblance to that of a truffle. Simple microscopic examination reveals the fraud. In Breslau the sale of *Scleroderma* is specifically forbidden by the authorities.

The fruit-body of *Lycoperdon* begins as a small outgrowth on the mycelial strands, formed of loosely interwoven hyphae. Those in the middle become more compacted and then are torn away here and there to form large irregular spaces; these are the primary glebal cavities. Small compacted areas are developed around them, the primary tramal plates. These enlarge and by growth, branching, and anastomosis divide the primary glebal cavities into smaller ones; meanwhile cavity formation takes place further outwards until eventually the whole interior is converted into chambers. These glebal cavities become lined with a hymenium composed of ranks of basidia. When the spores are ripe the tramal plates break down and the spores lie free inside the peridium. At an early stage the peripheral hyphae become very much septated, the cells inflate and then lose their contents and so form the exoperidium. Later the endoperidium arises by the hyphae immediately below this becoming radially arranged; as it matures, thick-walled hyphae gradually replace the original ones forming a compact persistent layer.

When the tramal plates begin to break down, thick-walled hyphae grow into the glebal mass and form the capillitium.

In *Scleroderma* the peridium is a single thick layer of closely-woven hyphae; the warts, scales and other ornamentations of the wall are modifications of the exterior. The tramal plates are often somewhat persistent: there is no capillitium. When the spores are about half-grown the hymenium breaks down into a translucent almost structure-less mass within the glebal cavity and surrounds the spores which are then lying free; they continue their development apparently at the expense of this matrix. The exact details of this peculiarity are not yet ascertained. It has been stated that the spores are first surrounded by a sheath of nursing cells.

In the related genus *Pisolithus* the spores similarly continue to enlarge after detachment from the basidia and are probably nourished in the same way. In development glebal cavities are formed at the apex and then progressively downwards, but the tramal plates instead of breaking down and freeing the spores become gelatinised into a firm elastic and translucent jelly so that the interior of the mature fruit-body is a honeycomb-like structure with the chambers filled with a powdery spore-mass. The individual chamber is usually called a peridiole (*peridiolum*).

Pisolithus tinctorius (*P. arenarius*, *Polysaccum pisocarpium*, *P. crassipes*) is very rare in this country occurring in sandy or gravelly places. The first and for a long time the only record was by Sowerby, as *Lycoperdon capsuliferum*, from the top of Highgate Hill. As it has a world-wide distribution and varies considerably both in its external and internal appearance, different forms have been regarded and named as distinct species.

The fruit-body is ochraceous, then brown to blackish, almost smooth, irregularly rounded or pear-shaped, narrowing below to a solid, firm, stem-like base, which is irregular and of variable length and thickness, sunk in the ground and passing into extensive greenish yellow mycelial cords at the base.* The peridium is very thin and brittle, soon cracking into flakes above and falling away. The glebal chambers are subspherical, irregularly angular and usually compressed, larger above and at the periphery, white or yellow in section, then reddish brown and finally nearly black as the powdery spore-mass ripens. The " party " wall between the peridioles is a densely woven mass of delicate hyphae with the gelatinous layer on both sides; at maturity the jelly becomes dry and brittle.

As the peridium flakes off the peridioles are exposed gradually and,

*It is eaten in parts of Germany as the Bohemian Truffle.

breaking down, liberate the dry spores. The lower ones thus remain intact for some time. The hard sterile and discoloured base may last in place for several months.

The epithet "*tinctorius*", which was part of the original descriptive name given by Micheli, refers to its long continued use for dyeing wool; it is apparently still employed for this purpose in parts of France and the Canaries. The bright olivaceous yellow pigment is contained in the violaceous black jelly between the peridioles and in the peridium. The pigment in the first is masked by a second purple one derived from the ripening spores which, however, when fully mature are dark brown with usually no trace of purple.

Glischroderma cinctum is another very rare Gasteromycete, so far known only from Western Germany and the Wyre Forest where it occurs on charcoal heaps. It looks very much like the common Mycetozoon *Lycogola epidendrum* seated on a circular mass of mycelium, and moreover, like it, has pink spores. The fruit-body is hemispherical, pale grey and somewhat sticky, becoming darker and slightly scurfy; it opens by a well-defined central pore which becomes larger. There is a well-developed hyaline capillitium attached to the inner wall of the peridium.

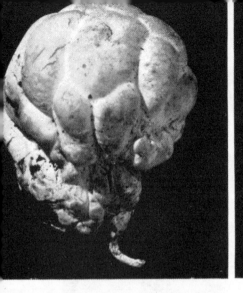
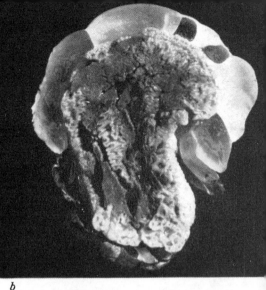

b

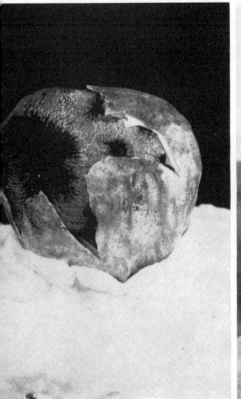

d

Plate IX. Clathrus ruber. a, Unopened "egg." b, Section showing the gelatinous wall and young tramal plates. c, "Egg" just bursting (on damp cotton-wool in the laboratory). d, Fully developed ; (cf. Plate 37b). (*Photographs Brit. Mus.* [*Nat. Hist.*,] *a, b, c and d J. A. Crabbe*)

Plate X. Dictyophora duplicata with well-developed net-work indusium. New Forest. *a*, Showing a fly feeding on the spore-containing mucus. *b*, An hour later, the mucus almost wholly removed by flies. *(Photographs by Harry Meyer)*

CHAPTER 16

STINK-HORNS AND OTHER PHALLOIDS

PHALLOIDS are distinguished amongst Gasteromycetes by the spore-mass being mucilaginous at maturity and borne on a specialised receptacle with a cup-like volva at the base. When Tennyson wrote:

> *As one*
> *That smells a foul-fleshed agaric in the holt,*
> *And deems it carrion of some woodland thing,*
> *Or shrew or weasel, nipt her slender nose*
> *With petulant thumb and finger shrilling ' Hence '.*

he showed himself a good naturalist, though his taxonomy was licensed, or erroneous, for the fungus referred to was doubtless the Stink-Horn, *Phallus impudicus.* Plot says that this species " sends forth that filthy stink, by the help whereof they are commonly found; though often too pass't by, upon that very account, many thinking it to be *Carrion,* lying hid somewhere near, and so heeding it no further," and early in the last century, S. F. Gray said that it was " oftener smelt than seen, the fetor being so like that of carrion causing persons to avoid the spot." But it is not all one-sided; trying to track the Stink-Horn by scent often leads to a dead stoat or a gamekeeper's " larder."

The fungus has an extensive system of white cord-like strands which spread widely through layers of leaves and loose earth about decaying tree-roots and stumps. Here and there small globular bodies are formed which increase in size until they look somewhat like hens' eggs (Pl. 38*a*, p. 247). When these are mature they break open at the top* and the fruit-body emerges leaving the outer skin (*peridium*) as a cup at the base of the stem: the process is similar to what occurs in *Amanita phalloides.* The mature fungus consists of a cap, stalk and volva. The cap is conical and cylindrical, and attached at its summit to the stem which passes through it. At first it is covered by an olive-

---

*Bulliard (1784) says that the egg always bursts with great force and explodes at times with a noise like a pistol shot; and that if enclosed in a glass or earthenware vessel which it completely fills shatters it.

green mucus which drips from it and is the seat of the " filthy stink ";
it is very attractive to flies, which soon remove it (Pl. 37a, p. 246), leaving
the surface a white, honeycomb-like network. The fungus is then
without smell. The stem is white, spongy and hollow, and perforated
at the summit; it tapers upwards and narrows also at the base. The
volva is whitish and persistent. The emergence of the fruit-body is
very rapid, about 3 in. in half an hour; under a bell-jar it is often
complete in an hour and a half. That it is expansion, which is remarkable, and not growth, which would be inconceivable, is clear if an
unexpanded " egg" is cut lengthwise: this shows the cap fully formed,
but the base of the stem extremely short and compact. The skin
consists of an outer and an inner membrane, and a thick middle
gelatinous layer which is formed by the breaking down of hyphae.
This gelatinous substance can be felt under the skin of the egg.

The details of the development from the earliest stages to the fully
mature egg are too complicated to explain in non-technical language.
Gelatinisation begins at the apex and proceeds outwards and down,
and forms the middle layer of the volva: the stem is the first part of
the fruit-body to become differentiated. This is soon followed by the
bell-shaped rudiment of gleba and pileus. What remains of the tissue
represents the veil, and occasionally a trace of this can be seen in
mature specimens. A branched stem is occasionally seen. At Albury,
Surrey, in 1932, I found five complete fruit-bodies with the bases of
their stems enclosed in a single volva.

The spores are borne on basidia within the cavities of the reticulated
pileus. This spore-bearing mass is known as a gleba as in puff-balls.
During elongation a large part of the substance of the gleba becomes
converted into the thick, dark green slime which contains the spores.
A portion of it usually drips off, some is washed off by rain, some is
devoured by flies* and by slugs.

Though dung flies are the main agents for the removal of the dark
green sugary mucus, the process is either begun or ended by the slow-
motion nocturnal activity of slugs, particularly *Limax maximus*, of which a
belated specimen is shown in Pl. 37a, p. 246. Some slugs prefer fungi
to green plants if a choice is offered them: they detect them by smell.
Their tentacles are extremely sensitive to certain gases and make

*N. A. Cobb found that spores of the related *Ithyphallus coralloides* (which he
thought to be the cause of a root rot of sugar cane in Hawaii) were not injured by
passing through the digestive tract of flies. He showed by actual spore-counts that
a single " fly speck " often contained as many as 22,400,000 spores. (*Ithyphallus* is
a synonym for *Phallus*. The species is doubtless *P. aurantiacus*.)

characteristic responses, a fact that was recalled when the need for a gas-detector by the United States forces arose when they went to the western front in the 1914-18 war. It was found that the tentacles of *Limax maximus* are sensitive to 1 in 10,000,000 of mustard gas, whereas man is sensitive only to 1 in 4,000,000. This sensitiveness accounts for a slug being able to locate *Phallus* (or other fungus) six or seven yards away.

The Stink-Horn is often the cause of needless anxiety about sanitation. Some years ago I was able to recognise the " nasty smell " which was ruining the business of an ex-service man's tea-garden near the Norfolk coast, and to demonstrate the origin in an adjoining woodland; previously he had concentrated on the " drainage." An extreme example of a common experience, is that of a family moving into a house built in a spinney at Leicester in 1935. " They could not at first find the source of the smell and had all the drains and sewers overhauled and at one time were forced to leave the house altogether for a month." A more amazing occurrence was at Bedford in 1931. The fruit-body of the fungus " going strong " appeared on the concrete floor of a newly-built house greeting a newly-married couple: the mycelial cords had spread from an old stump in the garden and the threads had passed through a crack in the concrete.

It is not surprising that in earlier times the undeveloped fungus should have been mistaken for eggs and have given rise to wonder as their origin was so mysterious. The only explanation possible was that they were eggs of spirits or of devils.* It would be interesting to learn whether at any time the fruit-body was associated with rites and ceremonies connected with nature worship. A possible hint of this was given me by Miss L. S. Gibbs who mentioned that the natives of New Guinea " seem to pay special attention to *Dictyophora* (*Phallus*) *indusiata* " which when growing in colonies with its lace-like indusium expanded in sunlight " looked like a miniature ballet."

German hunters call the Stink-Horn " Hirschbrunst " because they believe it grows where stags have rutted. The fruit-bodies were formerly used by country people in Central Europe in ointments and powders for gout, rheumatism, and epilepsy, and love potions were brewed from them. The powdered fungus was employed as an aphrodisiac and is still used for cattle in parts of France and Germany. Possibly the belief that it is poisonous has its origin in Clusius's statement that

---

*Dodoens (1563) gives this as " Manium sive Daemonum ova," de l'Obel (1576) as " Manium, cacodaemonumve ova."

flies perish through eating the mucus. The eggs are eaten in some continental districts and may be seen in the local markets. Rabbits eat the porous stems quite readily. When in full array it deters even the most confirmed mycophagist, though the Chinese consider the not dissimilar *Lysurus mokusin* a great delicacy, and a remedy for gangrenous ulcers. It is sold in London, dried, at a high cost.

In a sorcery case in France in 1926, two men and ten women, adherents of the sect Notre-Dame des Pleurs, were charged with falling upon and grievously wounding an Abbé with the hope of eradicating diabolic possession which had enabled him to cast spells on certain members of the sect. They accused him of sending birds to fly from Bombon to Bordeaux over the gardens of the founder of the sect, where their droppings gave rise to fungi of obscene shapes which emitted such appalling odours that those who breathed them were smitten with horrible diseases.

In a letter to *The Times* in 1865 it was seriously suggested that the Stink-Horn was probably the cause of cholera and similar epidemics.

The strands of *Phallus impudicus* have been recorded as penetrating the roots of roses, converting the tissues into a white friable mass.

There is another British species of *Phallus*; it occurs in sandy places, particularly on sand-dunes. The first account of it in this country was given by John Curtis in *British Entomology* (1833), where the plate for *Borborus hamatus*, a fly, also figures a *Phallus*, which was said to have " a scent somewhat like violets at a distance, when growing, but was very offensive when dried." It was found in some abundance on the sand-hills near Lowestoft during October, and flies of all kinds, as well as bees and beetles, were attracted by the gluten which dropped from the cap. The drawing shows an old specimen. It has a pink volva, but the cap is free of mucus and shows serrate edges to the reticulations. Curtis regarded it as differing " materially " from *Phallus impudicus*, and Berkeley named it *Phallus iosmus* drawing up his diagnosis from Curtis's description and plate: " I am unable to find any account of it, though possible some of the Herbalists may have noticed it "—as indeed they had.

A violet-scented *Phallus* would certainly be exceptional. Doubtless Curtis got his impression from specimens past their prime; even *Phallus impudicus* sometimes has a sweetish smell when all traces of gluten have disappeared. No one else has recorded fully-developed *Phallus iosmus* with the character denoted by its specific epithet, violet-scented. Most people would agree with Badham who, after finding

Plate 29. Clavaria vermicularis; amongst grass in meadows, very fragile. Edible

Plate 30. *Clavaria pistillaris*; in deciduous woods, especially beech

some specimens wrote to Berkeley " If you had smelt it you would have christened it differently." He described the egg as having the shape of a snail-shell; it developed three hours after gathering, in five hours the head was fully out and in fifteen the specimen had acquired its full size. At first there was not much odour, but the green slime which covered the head was the principal source of an " intolerable foetor as of human excrement." The pileus was of a beautiful carnation hue. It is usual to treat this fungus as a variety of *Phallus impudicus* and, as such, it receives only casual mention.

Professor F. W. Oliver mentioned to me that *Phallus iosmus* grew amongst Marram Grass at Blakeney Point, Norfolk, and later sent me several eggs. These developed under a bell-jar. From the pink colour and more ovate shape of the egg, and the disc to the cap being larger and flatter than in *Phallus impudicus*, I concluded that it was the same as *Phallus imperialis*, first described and figured in 1873 from light warm sandy soil in Hungary, where it is sometimes parasitic on vines, its hyphae weaving a close network about the rootlets and penetrating into the tissues: it has also been recorded as affecting the roots of *Gleditschia, Robinia* and Couch Grass. The full-developed fungus had a disagreeable odour, but with a suggestion of sweetness which was more noticeable at a distance. Carleton Rea, when he saw the species in France, had been puzzled by the scent being described, as he thought, as " odeur d'église," wondering whether it referred to " the damp earthy smell we meet with in some of our churches on Sunday, or was it that of spent incense? "; it proved to be " odeur de réglisse," which well describes the underlying sweetness. Some authors have held that *Phallus iosmus* and *P. imperialis* are different species, or that they are distinct varieties of *Phallus impudicus*. It has been suggested that *Phallus imperialis* is confined to inland situations in south-east, central and south Europe, whereas *Phallus iosmus** is restricted to sand-dunes in the North Sea and Baltic regions. Whether the sand-dune fungus is a distinct species, a variety of *Phallus impudicus*, or a form influenced by the special habitat, are all matters in dispute. In my opinion *Phallus iosmus* is recognisable in all its stages and is sufficiently distinct to be regarded as a species. It is variable but indistinguishable from *Phallus imperialis*. So far all British records are from sand-dunes.

It is remarkable that this species should have been the first Phalloid to be described. Hadrianus Junius (Aadrian de Jonghe) found it on sand-dunes in Holland, and in 1564 published an account of it both

*Specimens from Latvia have been named *Phallus dunorum*

in prose and verse with illustrations on two plates; this is the source of the name *Phallus*. The description and figures obviously refer to *Phallus iosmus*, but a remarkable confusion arose. The pamphlet is rare, and though it was frequently mentioned by writers of the seventeenth and eighteenth centuries, few appear to have seen it. His figures strangely enough were almost completely disregarded, and some perpetrated by de l'Obel in *Plantarum seu stirpium historia* (1576) gained currency. Though the description is based on that of Junius and a portion of his poem is cited, the figures bear no relation to the original nor to any known *Phallus*, as they show a double volva with the outer layer reflexed. These figures were copied in several books, including Johnson's Gerard (where they are printed upside down) and Parkinson. The result was, as no one could find anything like the figures, the fungus became a mystery under such names as *Phallus marinus* (Dodoens) *Phallus hollandicus* (Parkinson) and appears in Persoon's *Synopsis* and Fries's *Systema* as *Phallus Hadriani*, a name proposed by E. P. Ventenat; Fries doubted whether it was not a monstrosity. It looks at first sight that the name Persoon used should be adopted, but both he and Ventenat had not Junius's fungus in mind but the strange figure that had misrepresented it for over two centuries.

Plot (1679) referred to the common Stink-Horn as *Fungus phalloides* or *Phallus hollandicus*, thus showing that he considered the two as synonymous. Sir Thomas Browne also uses the name *Phallus hollandicus* for the common Stink-Horn.

Another *Phallus* appears in English and French books as *Phallus impudicus* var. *togatus*. It was recorded as such from France in 1895; British specimens have been found in Yorkshire in 1915 and the New Forest in 1934 (Pl. X, p. 179). It occurred several times in Germany in the thirties and has since been found in Denmark and Sweden. The fungus differs from the ordinary Stink-Horn in having a persistent net-like collarette hanging from within the cap.

In the early developmental stages of *Phallus impudicus* there is often a small, irregular, evanescent membrane below the cap. This is the remnant of the veil, the tissue of the peridium left over when the different parts of the fruit-body are laid down, whereas an indusium is a distinct layer formed between the stalk and the pileus. The collarette of *P. impudicus* var. *togatus* is an indusium; such a prominent, regular, reticulate indusium characterises the genus *Dictyophora*. The fungus is obviously *Dictyophora duplicata*, a species common in North

America. The question arises here as with *Lysurus* (p. 188) and
Queletia (p. 249) whether the species is native to Europe or introduced.
The suggestion has been made that it has been brought over with
American trees, particularly Douglas Fir, as it seemed to be associated
chiefly with this tree in Germany, and as it fruits only in hot seasons.
Both assumptions are questionable. Trees were introduced from North
America probably almost from its discovery; certainly the eastern
part was a happy hunting ground a couple of centuries ago, as the
names of John Bartram, Peter Collinson, and others, show. Moreover,
the Douglas Fir, which was introduced from western North America
in 1827, is not native where *Dictyophora duplicata* is abundant. Further,
as the climate of eastern North America is not particularly hot and
dry it does not seem necessary to postulate special conditions in
England, France, Germany and Austria to account for its occurrence.

Phallus impudicus is one of the best known fungi and it seems certain
that a similar fungus with a collarette would have been mentioned if
it had been seen by anyone with even slight knowledge of mycology.
There is no known record, however, until this century. We must
assume, therefore, either that it has always been exceedingly rare and
therefore overlooked, or that it has only recently arrived in Europe by
one of the many ways open to it. If a recent arrival, it is more logical
to assume that there was a single introduction and then a spreading
to those localities where it was able to get a footing in suitable habitats,
rather than that every occurrence denotes a new introduction with
American trees and exceptional climatic conditions. The mistake
should not be made, however, of regarding the first recorded finding
of this or any other fungus as necessarily indicating the original
introduction.

Mutinus (Cyanophallus) caninus, the Dog Stink-Horn, is another
common British Phalloid. It grows amongst dead leaves and on old
stumps. The " egg " is white or yellowish, smaller and narrower than
that of *Phallus*, being up to ¾ in. long, and, like it, arises from white
mycelial cords. When expansion begins the egg-wall is split above
into two or three lobes. The mature fungus consists of a hollow white
stalk with a porous pitted wall, sometimes flushed with pink, or
occasionally orange, slightly tapering below, and a red cap, adnate
to the upper portion of the stem, like a fingerstall. The cap is covered
at first with a green mucus containing the spores, but the smell is slight.

There is also a tropical species of *Mutinus*, *M. bambusinus*, which
is listed in our floras. It differs from *M. caninus* in the bright red or

pinkish cap tapering into an acute purplish red point and extending downwards to half the total height.

The British record is from a nursery at Sunningdale, Berks, where a bed of *Arundinaria japonica* (*Bambusa Matake*) was transplanted in 1888 and the ground replanted with plum trees. The following July a number of egg-like bodies were seen in the bed which all developed, and were identified by M. C. Cooke as *Mutinus bambusinus*. " Although the circumstance is somewhat unusual and inexplicable, it is nevertheless true that a genuine tropical species of *Phallus* has lately made its appearance in the open ground, amongst young plum trees." It again appeared in 1929 when four specimens were seen, in 1930 ten, and in 1931 six. I was informed by the late Mr. H. White some years ago when I asked him to send me specimens if they again appeared that his firm had never had dealings with Java or any other country from which the fungus might have been imported; he also wrote that slugs are very fond of the eggs as they first show through the soil. The identification has been queried; E. Fischer and T. Petch who both examined the dried specimens decided that in all probability they were merely *Mutinus caninus*, certainly not *M. bambusinus*. It is difficult to believe that Cooke, who doubtless knew *M. caninus* well, and indeed described and figured it for comparison, should not have recognised it. He writes that on receiving a fresh specimen he was " struck at once with the very strong and foetid odour which escaped from the box in which it was enclosed, whereas our common *Mutinus caninus* is almost inodorous. The rosy stem and more elongated pileus were also striking." The odour may be discounted to some extent for it would be accentuated by the specimen being enclosed. Although the stem of *M. caninus* is usually white it is not infrequently tinged pink and occasionally orange.

The coloured plate illustrating the record does not help in identifying the Sunningdale fungus. Of the seven figures of *M. bambusinus*, one shows the spores. Only two are stated to be " from British specimens " and they do not represent the same species; one might well be a form, or variety, of *M. caninus*, the other (by G. E. Massee) looks so much like artistic anticipation of the further development of the emerging receptacle shown in two of the figures copied from Javan drawings that it cannot be regarded as factual. We are thus left with the one figure and that possibly tinged with conviction.

In 1949 I received from South Devon a particularly robust form of *M. caninus* with a bright orange stem and when the box was opened the smell encountered seemed more fetid than is usual with the common form. It grew among the cast-off spathes of bamboo. It agreed in essential microscopic characters with *M. caninus*; it was certainly not *M. bambusinus* though possibly meriting some distinctive appellation. It is possible that it was this or some similar form that Cooke described and figured so poorly. Unfortunately eggs sent later became mouldy and failed to develop.

Clathrus ruber (*C. cancellatus*) (Pls. 37*b*, 246, IX, p. 178) is one of our most attractive fungi in appearance. In its earliest stages it is very much like the Stink-Horn but later the wall of the egg shows network markings which are formed during development. The wall is of three layers, the inner and outer ones thin, the middle thick and gelatinous. The receptacle as it expands bursts the external wrapper and shows itself as a handsome vermilion or coral-pink hollow spherical lattice-work. The arms have fine horizontal ribs on the exterior but the inside is more regular and is covered with olive-brown mucus with such a fetid smell that more than one artist has related that it was impossible to paint it without discomfort. When the colour photograph (Pl. 37*b*, p. 246) was taken it would have been pleasing to have shown one or two flies at work, but they settled in such swarms that they had to be driven off.

The expansion from the egg as in all Phalloids is accomplished rapidly, and the fact that it is expansion and not development in the sense of the forming and maturing of new structures is probably more readily seen here than in other genera. It is fascinating to watch the outer white skin crack and the coral-pink lattice-work emerge leaving the skin as a cup at the base (Pl. IX, p. 178).

Clathrus ruber is usually regarded as a species of southern Europe. It is, however, frequent in the Isle of Wight in garden borders and on heaps of leaves, common when rains follows a warm dry spell in the Scilly Isles, in undisturbed soil under the hedges used as windbrakes round the small bulb fields, and has been recorded several times in various places on the South Coast—Sussex, Hampshire, Dorset and Devon. Although it is this comparative frequency which is stressed in trying to trace the connection with continental distribution it is often overlooked that the fungus was recorded from a wood near King's Lynn in 1859. Moreover in recent years it has been found in east and north-west Kent (Pl. 37*b*, p. 246), Essex, Berkshire, Hertfordshire, and several times in Surrey (Pl. IX, p. 178). The finding of a number of specimens in a flower-bed near Kimelford, Argyllshire, in 1917, seems to make it probable that the fungus occurs naturally in Great Britain rather than that it is a continental species introduced with soil or leaf-mould.

In Gascony the peasants regard *Clathrus* as a cause of cancer, and bury it deeply under mosses and dead leaves for fear lest it should be touched. In other districts of France it is thought to produce skin eruptions if handled, or, again, convulsions by its deleterious and abominable exhalations. *Clathrus ruber* is the only European representative of the genus, though it occurs also in Asia, Africa, West Indies, and Japan; eight or nine other species are known.

Another Phalloid of interest has been recorded four times for this country under two different names. It was first found at Kidderminster, in 1902, in a pasture field adjacent to a flour mill near where refuse and dirt had been deposited from sacks which had contained wheat, probably from Australia. It was called *Lysurus australiensis*; the arms were yellowish brown. A second collection was made at Manchester and was named *Lysurus borealis*; the arms were red. The third record was from stable-refuse at Chiswick in 1917 and 1918 (Pl. XI*b*, p. 194); it was then named *Lysurus borealis*; the arms were a beautiful pale red. A fourth record (as *L. australiensis*) was from wood-shavings, mixed with stable-manure, at Leeds in 1944.

The egg is globular, and grows from white cord-like mycelial strands. The outer membrane tears irregularly when the receptacle emerges. This consists of a whitish, cellular, cylindrical stem, narrowing below, hollow, surmounted by five to seven orange-red to reddish brown triangular arms which are erect, but slightly incurved at the apex, with a longitudinal groove down the middle and transversely ribbed. The brownish mucilaginous spore-mass is borne on the inside of the arms and is slightly fetid.

The first European record of this species was from Germany in 1902. It was found in an asparagus bed which had previously been a city dump, deeply dug and dunged with manure from a Dragoon regiment. It was determined as being the same species which had been described as *Anthurus borealis* from temperate North America in 1894, though of a paler colour and, therefore was given varietal rank (var. *Klitzingii*). The species has also been found in France, on waste jute used instead of tan for the culture of ferns. It has also been recorded twice from Holland and also from Sweden, Norway and Portugal.

Though on its first discovery in Germany it was regarded as native, for it " could not have been brought to Mecklenburg from elsewhere," the general opinion is that the fungus has been introduced from overseas, and support for this view is gained from the habitat—wheat-refuse, manure from stables where horses were fed on imported corn, shavings from imported wood, garden soil and so on. If the fungus is an introduction in Europe where is it native?

The first British record identifies the fungus with the Australian species *Lysurus australiensis* (1889): the first European record with the North American *Anthurus borealis* (1894) and transfers it to *Lysurus*. The dates are of no consequence except for nomenclature: the two names are now regarded as referring to the same species and the older specific epithet has precedence. The fungus is common in Australia and New Zealand but has been found only about half a dozen times in north and central United States, and, indeed, has been supposed to have been almost certainly introduced there from the tropics or south temperate regions. It now seems very probable that it is the same species as *Lysurus Gardneri* (1846), a common species in Ceylon, India and Java and, if so, this is the correct name.* Thus we have a range : Asia, Australia, N. America and Europe. It appears more logical to assume that the fungus in Europe growing in highly manured and loose ground is in its natural habitat, and that as it is known to occur in northern temperate, southern temperate and tropical regions it is no more an introduction than are the more common fungi with a similar distribution. On this view it would be regarded as a rare species in Europe, strictly localised in its appearances but usually occurring in some quantity. Though the first European record was in 1902, that in North America was only eight years previous and the Australian thirteen.

The distinction between *Anthurus* and *Lysurus*, as the descriptions were originally drawn up from dried specimens, was not clear: examination of fresh fungi has shown that the arms of *Anthurus* are at first joined at their apices and that the spore-mass is carried on the outer walls of the chambers of the arms, whereas in *Lysurus* the tips are usually free, though connivent, and the spore-mass is borne on a series of plates of pseudoparenchyma closely compacted together. The fungus under discussion is therefore a *Lysurus*.

A species of *Anthurus*, *A. Archeri* (*A. aseroeformis*), was found near Penzance in 1945, about rotten stumps of *Escallonia*. In this there are

*Petch, who studied *Lysurus Gardneri* in Ceylon, held that it was distinct from *L. australiensis* and that it showed certain characters which warranted its separation from *Lysurus* as a new genus, *Mycopharus*. G. H. Cunningham, studying *L. australiensis* in Australia, found the same characters!

five to eight orange-red arms, united at the tips when first emerged and breaking away later. The olivaceous mucilaginous spore-mass is borne on the transversely wrinkled inner surface of the arm which is longitudinally sulcate on the outside. The stem is short, narrowed and white below, slightly expanded and red above, dividing directly into the arms. The egg is dirty white and scurfy.

In 1953 further specimens were found on a grass bank in an orchard near Fairways, Sussex. The arms were bright red, usually four but one or more divided at the tip, the stem pale pink, the volva white.

The variations in the number of arms (the first British specimen had seven) and the mode of attachment of the ends has led to many names for the fungus.

Anthurus Archeri again raises problems of distribution. Phalloids are poorly represented in Europe and consequently there is always a tendency to regard rare forms as having been introduced. *A. Archeri* is frequent in Australia, Tasmania and New Zealand; it is also known from the Malay Archipelago and probably South Africa. The first European records were from the Vosges where it appeared in several localities from 1920 onwards, particularly in the region of Raon-l'Etape. With one exception all the stations in the first ten years were where formerly American camps had been and it was believed to have been an adventitious introduction with Army stores, though it was realised that the fungus was unknown in America. It has persisted in the area, and meanwhile has been found in Sweden (1936), Western Germany (1938), Norway and Switzerland (1942), England (1945), and Austria (1948). From the known facts it would seem that *A. Archeri* was introduced into the Vosges and spread down the Rhine valley to several localities and continued in some unknown manner to extend its range. There is, therefore, the problem both of the original introduction and the spread. The fungus was first recorded from Tasmania in 1860.

There seems no doubt about *Aseroe rubra* which occurred in a stove at Kew on soil from New Zealand sometime previous to 1836. It is a native of Australasia, where it is common. When fully developed it has a hollow stem, surrounded at the white narrowed base by the cup-like remains of the peridium, pinkish above and expanding into a broad, horizontal, bright red, orbicular disc, to which five to nine horizontal bifid rays are attached horizontally, the whole somewhat resembling a sea anemone.

Plate 31a. COMMON PUFF-BALL, *Lycoperdon perlatum*; the spines soon fall off, leaving the surrounding rings of warts, and net-like markings. Edible (*S. C. Porter*)

b. *Lycoperdon hiemale*; the small spines and granules soon disappear, leaving the surface smooth. Edible (*Paul L. de Laszlo*)

Plate 32a (above). GIANT PUFF-BALL, *Lycoperdon giganteum;* the largest puff-ball, often growing in rings. Edible. (*Stuart Smith*); *b* (*below*) *Scleroderma aurantium;* the skin is thick and scaly (*Paul L. de Laszlo*)

CHAPTER 17

GRASSLANDS, MARSHES AND
SAND-DUNES

THE STUDY of the ecology of fungi is difficult. Though we have an accumulation of assorted facts we have, so far, little real understanding of their significance. It would probably be more profitable to study the biology of single species (autecology) than attempt premature generalisations. But whatever method be adopted there are always two difficulties, the ephemeral nature and occurrence of the fruit-bodies, and the uncertainty of their season, even of their appearance. The various factors which influence growth and development play an essential part in determining the distribution of fungi, for they are all constituents of that complex we call environment. But all the factors have not been studied in the laboratory and indeed could not be. There is abundant scope for field observations which might help in unravelling some of the problems. For any given species to succeed in a certain area there must be conditions which permit of growth throughout the whole of its life-cycle, and these are not necessarily the same for each stage of development. Moreover each of these conditions, or factors, must be present in sufficient degree at the necessary stage or there will be no appropriate growth; each can act as a limiting factor and there is also some dependence of one on another. Thus a very heavy rainfall may so saturate the soil that the air spaces are filled and the fungal mycelia cannot breathe. In dry seasons heavy mists often have a surprisingly beneficial effect on the occurrence of fruit-bodies, especially of the smaller ones.

Spores are produced in such myriads and are so widely dispersed by air currents that it may be assumed that for most species it is not lack of opportunity which limits dispersal.

In addition to climatic factors (light, heat, moisture) and edaphic factors (chemical and physical nature of the soil) there are the

191

biological. The last are of supreme importance, for they include competition for space, and all that goes with it, by organisms of all kinds, including other species of fungi and other individuals of the same species. A spore on arrival at a given spot has not only to find general surroundings suitable for its development but there must not be antagonistic organisms already in possession.

As fungi are dependent for their carbohydrates principally on vegetation, it follows that their occurrence is more directly associated with this than with the soil itself. Moreover the type of vegetation, in addition to the kind of humus it forms, greatly influences the myco-logical flora. Thus, though altitude of itself has no marked effect on the distribution of fungi*, the species differ in relation to the zoning of the vegetation. In mountainous regions on the Continent a character-istic fungal flora occurs in the spring on the edges of melting snow-patches, developing in the moisture there and disappearing with it, the spores being able to ripen in the particular conditions: in addition, other species not restricted to the habitat are found there. Probably many of these special fungi will be found to occur also in this country.

GRASSLANDS

It is immediately apparent when field-work is started that the species of fungi occurring in grasslands differ from those of woodlands. There is an almost complete absence of *Amanita*, *Lactarius*, *Russula*, *Cortinarius* and *Boletus*, except where there is a fringe of trees, whereas *Hygrophorus*, *Clitocybe*, *Panaeolus* and *Lepiota* are frequent. The differ-ences are due to the type of humus consequent upon the general vegetation, and to the amount of exposure, grasslands, being more subject to insolation, winds and variations in temperature, have a relatively less humid atmosphere than have woodlands.

Our information is not yet sufficiently detailed to attempt to group fungi in the divisions, acidic, basic and neutral grasslands of the plant ecologist. Some species seem to be closely associated with flowering plants, as *Tricholoma melaleucum* with *Carex flacca* and *Cortinarius anomalus* with *Helianthemum Chamaecistus*, both on chalk, but on the whole the differences seem rather of relative abundance of species than of kind.

*Greville describing *Amanita* (*Amanitopsis*) *nivalis* in 1823 says that it "is the most alpine species of fungus I am acquainted with. It grows on the bleak summits of the loftiest Grampians, and really enlivens the few turfy spots which occur in those desert regions." It is not an exclusively alpine species for it occurs at all levels.

Fungi are usually absent from pastures which undergo winter flooding, for waterlogging of the soil prevents the aeration essential for existence. This also accounts for clay soils being relatively unfruitful. Luxuriant grassland is unproductive of larger fungi; indeed their prevalence seems to be in inverse proportion to the size and density of the herbage.

Generally speaking grassland species are small compared with woodland species. It is worth noting that there is sometimes a relation between the length of the stem and the height of the grass. At first sight it looks as if the fungus were attempting to free its cap so that spore dispersal should not be unduly hampered, though probably the explanation lies in the relative humidity: some species, however, have longer stems when growing on bare soil than in short grass. Sandy grasslands, especially when fairly rich in humus, produce the best collecting grounds.

Two points which bear on the distribution of grassland species are the occurrence of perennial mycelia and the effects of dung. When the mycelium persists in the soil it often has a suppressing effect on the surrounding plants, which clears space for the production of fruit-bodies; moreover, the mycelium can exist for many years in a purely vegetative condition.

In considering grassland fungi it is only practicable here to treat pastures, meadows, parks and lawns as a whole indicating the species which favour especially drier or wetter areas.

LIST OF SPECIES

FIELDS

In addition to the Common Mushroom, *Psalliota campestris*, the Horse-Mushroom, *P. arvensis*, and the Yellow-Staining Mushroom, *P. xanthoderma*, there are *P. villatica*; *P. Bernardii*, confined to pastures washed by sea-spray; *P. comtula*.
Stropharia coronilla; S. melanosperma; S. aeruginosa, also in clearings in woods; *S. albocyanea*, in damp places; *S. inuncta*.
Pholiota praecox and *P. dura*, early spring in pastures, on road-sides, and under trees.
Naucoria Vervacti, fields and gardens; *N. semiorbicularis*.
It is not uncommon for species which are frequent in pastures and heathlands to be found in grassy places in woods. *Lepiota procera*, the Parasol-Mushroom (Pl., II, p. 35) and several related species are of this kind—*L. rachodes, L. gracilenta* (Pl. 5, p. 66), smaller, more slender and paler than *L. procera* with a less scaly stem and a membranous ring; *L. mastoidea; L. excoriata; L. permixta*, uncommon, usually in hill pastures; *L. acutesquamosa*, sometimes on bare soil in gardens; *L. naucina*, in pastures and gardens, occasionally in salt-marsh pastures; *L. holosericea; L. echinata (haematosperma)*, chiefly in gardens and hedgerows, the mycelium at the base of stem

compacting the soil into a ball; *L. cristata*, often in the shade of trees; *L. (Armillaria) constricta*, where grass has been scorched with urine.

Several species of *Tricholoma* are frequent: the St. George's Mushroom, *T. gambosum*, one of the earliest spring agarics, in pastures and on downs; *T. irinum*, forming rings in damp grass; *T. personatum*, Blewit (Pl. p. 6, 67), an autumn species which persists until winter; *T. panaeolum; T. sordidum*, in pastures, richly manured garden beds, and on compost heaps; *T. grammopodium, T. melaleucum* and *T. brevipes*, the commonest of a group of closely allied species; *T. carneum* in short grass; *T. atrocinereum; T. cuneifolium; T. bufonium*, frequent in chalk pastures and on downs, also in pine-woods.

Entoloma clypeatum, vernal; *E. prunuloides*, autumnal; *E. porphyrophaeum*, in meadows, the similar *E. jubatum*, in mossy grassland and *E. helodes*, in heathy pastures and bogs; *E. costatum*, usually in clusters in damp places; *E. sericeum; E. griseocyaneum; E. ameides*, with a characteristic sweetish smell something like that of burnt sugar.

Most species of *Clitocybe* are sylvicolous though there are a few grassland species. *C. rivulosa* and *C. dealbata* sometimes grow together with the Field-Mushroom and the Fairy-Ring Champignon; *C. ericetorum; C. gigantea* sometimes over a foot across the cap; *C. geotropa* and the rarer *C. maxima*, probably only a variety of it; *C. cyathiformis*, usually lasting throughout the autumn.

Clitopilus prunulus, a well-known edible species, varying in appearance with age and weather; *C. popinalis* in pastures, on downs and sand-dunes.

Leptonia is essentially grassland: *L. chalybea* usually in shade; *L. serrulata; L. lampropoda; L. incana; L. (Entoloma) sericella.*

Psilocybe semilanceata, one of the most easily recognised and commonest fungi with its acutely conical yellow cap, often distinctly pointed, which has given it the appropriate name Liberty Cap; *P. foenisecii*, very common in summer especially in lawns; *P. ericaea* and *P. subericaea*, common particularly in grassy heaths.

Mycena is not well represented: *M. avenacea; M. ammoniaca; M. flavo-alba; M. quisquiliaris*, on faded grasses.

Nolanea pascua (N. hirtipes), in pastures and woodlands from spring onwards; *N. staurospora (N. proletaria); N. mammosa; N. papillata.*

Several species of *Galera* occur in grass but the genus is more addicted to damp moss: *G. tenera*, the commonest species, is polymorphic; *G. spartea, G. silignea* and *G. lactea* are less common.

Psathyrella gracilis frequent on roadsides; *P. corrugis; P. subatrata; P. conopilea; P. atomata*, common from spring onwards.

Omphalia fibula, common, and var. *Schwartzii* in damp, often mossy, places; *O. pyxidata; O. muralis*, not infrequent on walls; *O. rosella* on lawns.

Eccilia (Clitopilus) undata; E. vilis; E. griseorubella; E. Mougeotii, occasional in boggy meadows.

Tubaria furfuracea, very common among grass, leaves or on bare ground throughout the year.

Species of *Hygrophorus* are amongst the most brightly coloured and most conspicuous pasture fungi. *H. coccineus* (Pl. 13a, p. 118) with a bright slimy scarlet cap which changes to golden yellow from the centre outwards, yellow gills which are purplish at the base, and a compressed hollow stem concolorous with the cap but yellow at the base; *H. miniatus; H. Reai; H. turundus*, on peaty ground or on *Sphagnum; H. conicus; H. nigrescens; H. puniceus* (Pl. 12, p. 111) the largest and most beautiful

John Armitage

Plate XIa. Dog Stink-Horn, *Mutinus caninus*.

b, Lysurus australiensis; stable refuse, Chiswick, London, 1918.

Somerville Hastings

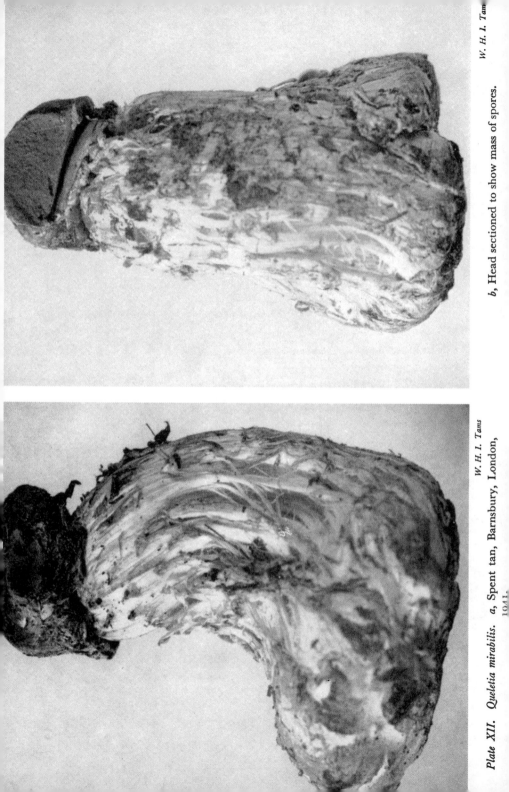

b, Head sectioned to show mass of spores.

W. H. I. Tams

W. H. I. Tams

Plate XII. Queletia mirabilis. a, Spent tan, Barnsbury, London, 1941.

species, with a viscid blood-red campanulate cap, the stem yellow to blood-red but always with a white base; *H. obrusseus; H. chlorophanus; H. ceraceus; H. psitta-cinus; H. calyptraeformis; H. unguinosus; H. nitratus; H. laetus*, more especially in grassy heaths; *H. virgineus; H. niveus; H. russicoriaceus; H. pratensis.*
Several species of *Clavaria*, some true "fairy-clubs," others branched or tufted; *C. vermicularis* (Pl. 29, p. 182) forming dense shining white tufts; it is brittle, cylindrical with a pointed apex and no distinct stem. *C. acuta*, usually in shade; *C. fumosa; C. inaequalis (dissipabilis); C. luteo-alba; C. pulchra (C. persimilis)* prefers shade; *C. fusiformis* (Pls. 28a, p. 175, XIX, p. 258), clear canary-yellow, often densely tufted and occasionally branched or forked; spindle-shaped with sharp tips, becoming hollow, often wavy or twisted and flattened. *C. corniculata* (Pl. 28c, p. 175) forming short dense egg-yellow tufts, with a very short stem, and slender branches which fork two or three times.
Also black club-shaped fruit-bodies of the Ascomycete *Geoglossum*, resembling in shape some species of *Clavaria*. *G. (Trichoglossum) hirsutum* with a wide habitat range from sand-dunes to peat bogs; *G. difforme (G. Cookeianum)* (Pl. 44, p. 271), in short mossy grass: it is caespitose with the head often deformed and irregularly bent, somewhat viscid especially in damp weather, the cylindrical stem half or more of the height. *G. viscosum; G. glutinosum; G. glabrum*, often amongst *Sphagnum; G. ophioglossoides.*
Microglossum olivaceum, in hedge-banks and open grassy places; *M. viride* in hedge-banks or in woods.

<h3 style="text-align:center">DUNG</h3>

Many fungi are more or less confined to highly nitrogenous places and some occur on dung itself.
Dung is obviously not a substratum which permits of a long-living mycelium for it is so soon acted upon and broken down by organisms of different kinds. It follows that coprophilous fungi grow directly from spores. Many facts go to show that these spores for the most part are not blown on to the substratum but are already present in the dung when it is voided and must therefore have passed through the alimentary canal of the animal. Horse-droppings collected in London streets, in places where infection would be most unlikely and before it had much chance, show a rich crop of fungi after a period if kept moist and covered.
Animal dung provides habitats for an exceedingly rich and varied fungus-flora which, flourishing on the nutrients there available, does much to convert the pabulum into a form suitable for green plants.

The first fungi to appear are Mucorineae (Moulds) and may comprise some of the most interesting genera and almost certainly *Pilobolus crystallinus.*
Then follow a number of Discomycetes, Ascobolaceae which, under the microscope, are amongst the most beautiful of all fungi. *Lachnea stercoraria. L. coprinaria* and *Humaria granulata* are also common. *Peziza vesciculosa* (Pl. 41b, p. 262) frequent, in clusters on manure-heaps, the individual deeply cup-shaped fruit-bodies often distorted through mutual pressure, the disc pale brown, the exterior whitish then yellowish.
Pyrenomycetes, principally Sordariaceae, appear after the first crop of Discomycetes
M.T.   O

—*Sordaria*, *Delitschia*, *Sporormia;* *Gymnoascus*, on old dung, is sometimes seen and very occasionally the interesting *Poronia punctata*.

The minute pink clubs of the mould *Stilbum* (*Stilbella*) *erythrocephalum* are rarely absent from rabbit pellets.

Many Basidiomycetes are coprophilous, a large proportion belonging to dark spored genera, but no reasonable hypothesis to account for this has so far been proposed. Species of *Coprinus* are the first to appear, usually after the Ascomycetes are well under way, and are the main crop in laboratory cultures. One of the commonest of all fungi, *C. radiatus*, occurs on dung everywhere, the thin delicate cap shaped like a minute Chinese hat, " very tender, so that a breath destroys it." Other common small species are *C. pseudoradiatus*, *C. ephemerus*, *C. cordisporus*, *C. Hendersonii* and *C. ephemeroides*. *C. niveus*, *C. narcoticus* and *C. sterquilinus* are larger. *C. comatus* (Pl. 22a, p. 151), though not fruiting on dung, requires a supply of nitrogenous material. It frequently grows in enormous hordes where ground has been made up with town refuse, and occasionally on cinder paths and hard tennis courts where its mycelium passes down as much as a yard to old dung, sticks or leaves. *C. atramentarius* (Pl. 22b, p. 151) grows usually near partly buried stumps, near gate-posts and fences, but often on paths, roadways and hard courts, when its mycelium can usually be traced to buried wood—it is not coprophilous.

Bolbitius vitellinus (Pl. 13b, p. 118) varies much in size and appearance. The egg-yellow, viscid cap is thin and membranous, the thin, crowded gills brownish ochre, the very slender, fragile stem, whitish.

Several other agarics grow on dung or in well-manured places. *Stropharia semiglobata* (Pl. 18b, p. 131) is common on dry dung throughout the year. The cap is hemispherical, lemon-yellow and viscid, the gills dark brown to blackish, the long stem yellowish and viscid up to the ring; *S. stercoraria* is probably a growth form. *S. merdaria* (Pl. 19b, p. 146) has a pale tan, viscid cap, darker when moist, smoky brown gills and a short straw-white stem.

Anellaria separata, common most of the year, solitary or in large numbers particularly on heaps of horse manure; *A. fimiputris*.

Several species of *Panaeolus* are common on dung and in highly manured places: *P. campanulatus*, *P. papilionaceus* and *P. sphinctrinus;* *P. retirugis*, *P. fimicola* and *P. subbalteatus* are less frequent.

MARSHES, FENS, BOGS AND HEATHS

Soil moisture has a marked influence on the distribution of fungi and this is seen in grasslands as in other vegetation. Several species have already been mentioned as preferring damper or drier spots and with greater moisture, as with less, these are accompanied by others more exacting in their needs.

Many fungi grow amongst reed swamp and marsh bordering rivers, streams, lakes and ponds, most of them small, living on plant remains and able to thrive in the still, moist atmosphere. As there is a certain amount of host specialisation it is possible to co-ordinate in some degree the ecology of the hygrophilous flowering plants and the fungi. But this is intricate and at present we have too few facts, for such habitats rarely attract mycologists. There are the species of *Sclerotinia* on rushes and sedges of which the fruit-bodies appear in spring but the sclerotia are to be found throughout the year. *Omphalia Belliae* is restricted to *Phragmites*, *O. candida* to Comfrey, while some other species are only slightly less particular. Several small Ascomycetes (Discomycetes and Pyrenomycetes) and Fungi Imperfecti are confined to definite hosts.

Mitrula paludosa, very common in spring on decaying and submerged leaves on the mossy margins of ponds or streams, is a Discomycete, with a bright orange-yellow club-shaped obtuse head and a slender whitish stem. *Ombrophila clavus*, also common in spring on vegetable debris.

Moist ground on the edges of lakes or streams is the habitat of the rare and interesting *Boudiera areolata*.

Branches and sticks in water may show species of *Vibrissea* and *Apostemidium*, with long, thread-like septate spores which, when ejected from the asci, may remain attached by one end to the disc waving about like floss silk.

Humaria Oocardii occasional on water-soaked logs and wet stones.

Overhanging branches, floating twigs, and fruits are often covered with a white mouldy growth, usually of Saprolegniaceae. The white slimy tufts in polluted streams is " sewage fungus," usually *Sphaerotilus natans*. Less conspicuous but fascinating microfungi abound in the decaying vegetation on the banks and the beds of stretches of water, and fresh-water algae are often affected by members of the *Chytridiales*.

Psathyra Typhae on the stems of *Phragmites* and *Scirpus; Coprinus tigrinellus (phaeosporus)* on dead reeds and grasses, *C. Friesii* on rushes and grasses.

There is a transition from marsh to fen in flat districts where there is little or no silting and the rise in the surface of the soil results almost entirely from dead vegetation. This is best known in East Anglia where the soil water comes from calcareous rocks and gives the peat an alkaline reaction. The flora of fens is very varied owing to the unevenness of the soil, the different modes of growth of the plants and the disturbances caused by cutting. As many of the plants are the same as those of reed swamp and marsh so are the fungi found amongst them, but the greater variety of the flora is more than matched by them. The abundant remains of herbaceous plants and dead tussocks of grass and sedge, and the consistently damp still air ensure vast numbers of smaller Basidiomycetes and microfungi, but outside the shade of trees there are few of the larger agarics.

Several species of *Typhula* and *Pistillaria* occur some in quantity; *Omphalia integrella* mainly on the leaf bases of *Cladium; O. gibba* on general plant remains; *Marasmius Menieri* on decayed leaves of *Cladium* and *Typha*.

Bogs in the ecological sense differ essentially from fens in having acid, not alkaline or neutral ground water. Different kinds are recognised but we need consider only the fact that bog moss, *Sphagnum*, is a dominant constituent of the flora. It is somewhat surprising that a number of fungi are apparently restricted to *Sphagnum* and that other acidiophilous moisture-loving species often find their habitat there. Where flowering plants grow up through the moss additional species of fungi are found which obtain nutriment from their remains; but fungi growing on *Sphagnum* itself presumably have no source of mineral salts except the small amount in dust deposited by wind and rain. The strictly sphagnicolous species are character-ised by small caps, and by long and slender stems, buried in the substratum, which may be an adaptation to its soft, spongy consistency and its rapid growth in height. It is possible that there is some definite relation or association between fungus and moss but, so far, this has not been studied. *Sphagnum* absorbs about twenty times its weight in water and is never entirely dry.

Collybia leucomyosotis, very common; *Naucoria myosotis.*

Species of *Psilocybe* are common and characteristic: *P. elongatum* is usually present; *P. uda* not only on *Sphagnum* but also on bare peat (when its stem is much shorter); *P. Polytrichi* mostly amongst *Polytrichum* and other mosses in woods and on heaths.

Several species of *Galera* such as *G. hypnorum, G. mycenopsis, G. sphagnorum* and *G. tibii-cystis* grow on mosses: *G. sphagnorum* and *G. tibiicystis* are sphagnicolous; *G. Sahleri* usually on bare peat.

Tubaria paludosa, sphagnicolous. *Pholiota mycenoides* among *Sphagnum* and in mossy places. *Stropharia sphagnicola (psathyroides)* restricted to *Sphagnum.*

Cortinarius is well represented. *C. cinnamomeus* var. *lutescens* frequent on moors; *C. cinnamomeus* var. *croceus; C. cinnamomeus* var. *paludosus* and *C. uliginosus* are special to *Sphagnum.*

Clitocybe ectypa, rare, in bogs amongst sedges and *Sphagnum,* singly or in small loose tufts.

Omphalia sphagnicola. O. philonotis and *O. oniscus* are common on *Sphagnum;* the last also grows amongst other mosses.

Heath communities are of various types: here they are considered only as areas where heather is dominant. In mycological writings the habitat of many species is given as " woods, heaths, and pastures " though not always in that order. This is misleading. If one visualises a south country heath, for example, one has an overall picture of *Calluna* with, here and there, its usual associated flowering plants—but also of colonisation by trees, chiefly birch and pine; of wetter areas covered with Moor Grass, and boggy places with *Sphagnum* and other mosses; of burned patches; of bare peat or with a partial covering of lichens; of more or less bare sand; of rough grass where there is grazing or where the shade of trees kills out the heather —and so on. Moreover tall heather provides conditions of moisture and shelter somewhat resembling those of woodlands. With such a variety of habitats it is necessary to state more precisely where certain fungi are found.

Several fungi are frequent on bare peat, some even seem to prefer it. The commonest is *Omphalia umbellifera. O. grisella* and *O. griseopallida,* common amongst heather and lichens but not restricted to it; *O. rustica,* partial to sandy places.

Some of the fungi growing in heaths or peaty grassland have already been mentioned. To these may be added several additional species of *Hygrophorus. H. subradiatus, H. lacmus, H. metapodius* and *H. ovinus.*

Several species of *Marasmius, Collybia, Clitocybe, Mycena, Eccilia, Psilocybe* and *Lycoperdon* are frequent, most of them being found also in woods or in pastures. *Laccaria laccata* and *Clitocybe aurantiaca* are often abundant, the latter usually in a pale form.

Entoloma Bloxamii, fairly frequent; *E. madidum* grows on heaths but has a wide range of habitats; *E. ardosiacum* in bogs.

Clavaria argillacea. very common and characteristic

SAND-DUNES

At first sight sand-dunes would not appear to be a likely habitat for the larger fungi; certainly none would be expected, nor is to be found, on the foreshore with its constant washing by the sea. An occasional small agaric may be seen on cast-up bits of twig or wood; and Pyrenomycetes and other microfungi on seaweeds and on constructional timber provide a field for investigation which has hardly been entered.

So soon as the sand has some degree of stability fungi begin to appear. Traversing the dunes there is increase in their numbers and in their kinds as the vegetation becomes more abundant until we reach dune pastures or conifer plantation. Most species are obviously associated with the vegetation but many appear to grow on pure sand. On the whole these are drab coloured and so are difficult to distinguish from the substratum with its animal droppings, though it would be a flight of fancy to think of this as an example of protective coloration.

British coasts apparently do not have specialised species, such as the *Coprinus*-like *Montagnites Candollei* and the somewhat similar Gasteromycete, *Gyrophragmium Delilei* of the Mediterranean shores. Moreover, most of the species occur in sandy places elsewhere than on dunes. *Geopyxis (Sarcosphaera) ammophila*, a Discomycete, occurs in some abundance particularly on parts of the east coast of Scotland, on dry sand close to the upper tide limit, usually near *Elymus*. It pushes its way through the sand as a fleshy, brittle sphere, very pale brown, and so covered with sand as to be easily overlooked; it gradually opens apically exposing the brown disc. Buried in the sand at the base of the cup is what is usually described as a stalk, which may reach as much as 4 in. in length; it is composed of sand compacted round the threads of the basal mycelium. These threads are probably connected with buried bits of *Elymus*.

Psilocybe ammophila has a similar adaptation. It grows on the exposed slopes of high dunes usually amongst tufts of Marram Grass but sometimes on bare ground; the lower half of the stem is sunk in the ground and appears club-shaped because of its thick covering of mycelium mixed with sand grains and which passes downwards permeating and compacting a column of sand which simulates a tapering root-like base. The ends of the mycelium are attached to decayed *Ammophila* leaves.

Phallus iosmus occurs in summer about the base of Marram Grass, with a second crop in autumn.

Microglossum (Corynetes) arenarium is a rarer species of the same sort of habitat.

Inocybe halophila, I. serotina, I. maritima and *I. dulcamara* occur in the same situations as *Psilocybe ammophila*, the first named approaching most closely to the sea, but there are several other species common in the dunes generally. Indeed *Inocybe* is the best represented genus in the formation. Some species like *I. caesariata* and *I. carpta* are definitely arenicolous often growing on bare sand whereas others which accompany them such as *I. fastigiata, I. brunnea* and *I. eutheles* have a wide range of habitats. Almost all of them grow abundantly and for an extended season under *Salix repens*, in the older dunes, usually with a much developed mycelium amongst the tangled roots; generally speaking they are more robust in the shade than in the open. Where conifers are planted additional species occur.

The dune " slacks " or flat valleys between the dunes, with their more mixed vegetation and damper sheltered conditions, have a more varied fungus flora as the formation goes through its developmental stages until the innermost dune passes into sward. In the open association behind the outer dunes many agarics grow, with brown-spored forms predominating. Species of *Inocybe*, *Pholiota praecox* in early spring, *Clitocybe brumalis* in late autumn, *Entoloma sericeum*, *Hebeloma mesophaeum*, *H. testaceum*, *Naucoria semiorbicularis*, *Bolbitius vitellinus*, *Galera rubiginosa*, and *Marasmius oreades* are to be found. Many other species are able occasionally to gain a footing and even to grow on bare sand if they can make do without humus and with the nutriment provided by green and blue-green algae where these are present. Discomycetes occur in the slacks often in surprising numbers: *Leptopodia* (*Cyathopodia*) *Corium*, *Galactinia brunneoatra*, *Pseudoplectania nigrella*, *Ciliaria trechispora* growing amongst moss; *Sepultaria arenicola* and *S. sepulta* developing underground until maturity usually with a basal mass of mycelium binding together a large ball of sand, with the threads sometimes attached to the roots of *Ammophila*.

Morchella esculenta is occasional also; *M. elata* which, like the more frequent *Gyromitra esculenta*, is typically an inhabitant of coniferous woods—it occurs sometimes in pure sand, sometimes amongst *Salix*. *Verpa digitaliformis*, usually a hedge-bank species, has been recorded.

The inner series of dune slacks finally end in a more or less closed association of *Salix repens*, or, when swampy, of mosses and aquatic plants. Fungi become more abundant and in addition to those already mentioned include mainly species found elsewhere in sandy or marshy places. The inner dunes are frequently planted with trees, usually conifers, and their usually associated fungi are " introduced with them "—but how is in question. Probably in such a habitat mycorrhizal fungi must be present if the trees are to flourish. Gradually the dunes pass into a dune sward or pasture, the links of Scotland and northern England. Here there occur the usual grassland species with an especial abundance of puff-balls. Species of *Geaster* are occasionally found, and also *Tulostoma* which may occur throughout the formation, even on the inner slopes of the outer dunes.

CHAPTER 18

MYCORRHIZA AND OTHER FUNGAL ASSOCIATIONS

A GLANCE through a " Flora " of the higher fungi shows that the habitats of many species are given as under certain trees. The common Fly-Agaric (*Amanita muscaria*) is usual under birches, the scarlet white-spotted caps gleaming in the sun against the silver bark of the tree and autumn tinted leaves, making a picture which so impresses the most casual observer that it is the only fungus he appears to notice. It is not confined to birch, but is also found, more rarely, under conifers. *Lactarius turpis* is equally common under birch, but is frequently overlooked because of its dark olive-green cap and short stem usually a little paler. Another common species is *Cortinarius hemitrichus*, which has been said to follow the birch like a dolphin follows a ship. The well-named golden yellow *Boletus elegans* is closely associated with larch, very rarely indeed to be found away from it; the greyish *Boletus viscidus* is similarly restricted to larch. Several species of *Boletus* occur under pines, *Boletus luteus*, *B. variegatus*, *B. bovinus* and others: also under pines grow *Russula drimeia*, *Lactarius deliciosus* and the five British species of *Gomphidius—glutinosus*, *gracilis*, *maculatus*, *roseus* and *viscidus*. Similarly under beech there are *Russula lepida*, *R. fellea*, *Hygrophorus eburneus* and *Craterellus cornucopioides*. *Naucoria escharoides* occurs under alder, the Discomycete *Selpultaria Sumneri*, appears in spring under cedar.

Though if one were asked where to find *Boletus elegans*, for example, the reply would certainly be " under larch," the assumption that wherever the fungus is found, there is the tree—*ubi Papa ibi Roma*—is not correct.

The older mycologists were well aware of these specialised habitats; thus Berkeley, not realising that *Boletus viscidus* had been described, named it *Boletus laricinus*. When an explanation for the facts was

201

sought, it was reasonable to assume that it lay in the special conditions obtaining under the tree—the particular humus formed there, the amount of shade, moisture, acidity; in fact, all that is expressed by environment—though the tree itself enters more deeply into the environmental complex than was suspected.

The fact that fungal threads are constantly associated with roots of flowering plants has been known for over a century. So early as 1821 G. Graves held that the common view that *Monotropa Hypopithys*, the Bird's Nest, is a root parasite was erroneous—it was " decidedly not attached to the roots of other plants ": moreover, its roots were covered with " a whitish, silky, somewhat fibrous matter, connecting them with the decayed leaves and other vegetable substances among which they grew." This outer covering was recognised as fungal by Fries, in 1832; he named it *Tuburcinia Monotropae*. Further controversy ensued, but it was eventually realised that the roots were normally surrounded by a mantle of fungal hyphae some of which penetrated between the outer cells. F. Kamiensky in 1880-81 gave a very clear account of the structure and found that beech-roots among which *Monotropa* was growing had a similar fungal sheath. There are clear indications of clamp-connections in one of his drawings of *Monotropa*, showing that the fungus is a Basidiomycete.

A large number of miscellaneous observations on the roots of trees had meanwhile been made. As early as 1840, T. Hartig, the son of a famous forester and father of one more famous, distinguished between long roots and short or absorbing roots, in many trees, a distinction which is still recognised, though originally its true significance was not realised. Although there were previous indications of the nature of these absorbing roots, the first significant account was in a report by G. Gibelli on the " ink disease " of the Sweet Chestnut in 1883; he gave an extended and detailed description of the roots of a series of trees which he compared with those of *Castanea*, and stated that many were normally infected by fungal hyphae, including all the Cupuliferae. It was the investigations of A. B. Frank (1885-94), however, which focused attention on the phenomenon. He began his researches following a request from the Prussian Minister for Agriculture, Lands and Forests, to study the possibility of breeding truffles. This entailed a consideration of the conditions of their occurrence and development. Their association, and that of the similar *Elaphomyces*, with the roots of trees had been recorded by earlier observers, and when he realised the fact that the absorbing rootlets of forest trees normally had a fungal sheath, the governmental direction was apparently lost in the contemplation of what rightly appeared to him to be of great fundamental, theoretical and practical importance. He regarded the infected root as a definite morphological unit, giving it the name Mycorrhiza or Fungus-root. In 1887 he distinguished between two main types of mycorrhiza, *ectotrophic*, in which the hyphae occur principally on the outside of the root, and *endotrophic*, where they are within the root-cells. His continued investigations and those of others firmly established the constancy of the relation in a wide range of species and his theories aroused a vast amount of controversy, and inspired research. Through the years the remarkable fact has emerged that no single woody plant is known to lack mycorrhiza in all environments.

Infected roots of forest trees have a characteristic appearance. (Pl. XIII, p. 210.) They are swollen and branched, the type of branching depending upon the kind of tree; dichotomous in pine, monopodial in oak, beech and birch. They are usually yellowish brown or dark brown, but may be white, yellow, pink, bluish, violet or black. Mycorrhizas on the same tree, even in close proximity, are often differently coloured. A transverse section shows an external layer of closely packed and interwoven hyphae looking somewhat like parenchyma: the mantle sheaths the whole of the rootlet including the tip. Some hyphae pass between the external cortical cells of the roots; seen in surface view they simulate a network, and were first described as such by Hartig in 1842, who regarded them as intercellular branched canals surrounding the cells. Consequently, even after the correct interpretation was reached, they continued to be known as " Hartig's net."

Mycorrhizas have no root-hairs; indeed, the piliferous layer is often disorganised and odd cells may be found dispersed in the fungal sheath: moreover, there is no root-cap and the cortical cells are larger and more numerous than in uninfected roots. No cork cambium is formed.

If the hyphae of the mantle are teased out and examined under a microscope, they frequently show clamp-connections, a proof that they are Basidiomycetes (Plate V*b*, p. 134). Several early observers traced the continuity of the hyphae to neighbouring toadstools, success being most frequent where the mycelium was coloured. This connection can be made out with little difficulty where toadstools form a ring round a tree if the fruit-bodies are carefully dug up.

Apart from the fact that fruit-bodies appear usually for a restricted period their absence from the vicinity of a tree does not signify that its roots are not infected. It has long been known that several different species of fungus may form mycorrhizal roots with the same species of tree; indeed, it is chiefly this which is responsible for the differences in the colour, and sometimes in the general appearance of mycorrhizas. Although the reasons for these different associations are not yet understood they obviously are related to the general conditions of growth of both partners. What is frequently overlooked is that many fungi are more affected by soil factors than is a tree and that these, to a large extent, determine which species will be present and therefore available.

During the last thirty-five years the intensive study of tree mycorrhizas carried out by E. Melin and his school, has provided experimental proof for what formerly was deduced from careful observations, and has also provided additional facts of great practical importance to foresters and of theoretical interest to botanists. In 1917 he found that seedlings of pine and spruce which occurred spontaneously in newly drained peat bogs, grew normally only when they acquired mycorrhizal roots: uninfected seedlings showed clear evidence of nitrogen starvation and eventually died. This has been confirmed repeatedly in various parts of the world. Melin's real step forward, however, was in 1921 when he isolated several species of fungi from pine and spruce roots and synthesised mycorrhizas in seedlings grown in sterilised soil or sand to which nutrient solutions had been added. Later he experimented with the mycelia of fungi found growing in association with trees. His first list of successful syntheses was:

Pinus sylvestris:	*Boletus badius, B. granulatus, B. luteus, B. variegatus, Amanita muscaria, Cortinarius mucosus, Lactarius deliciosus, Russula fragilis.*
Pinus montana:	*Boletus granulatus, B. variegatus, Cortinarius mucosus, Lactarius deliciosus, Russula fragilis, Tricholoma virgatum.*
Picea excelsa:	*Boletus luteus, Amanita muscaria, Cortinarius balteatus, Lactarius deliciosus.*
Larix europaea:	*Boletus elegans, B. luteus, B. variegatus, Amanita muscaria, Cortinarius camphoratus, Tricholoma psammopus.*
Larix occidentalis:	*Boletus elegans, B. luteus.*
Betula sp.	*Boletus edulis, B. versipellis, B. scaber, Tricholoma flavum.*

It will be seen from this list that a fungus may be highly specialised as, for example, *Boletus elegans*, which is apparently confined to larch; others, like *Boletus luteus*, are less so in that they may occur with several kinds of conifer, whereas *Amanita muscaria*, though in this country chiefly associated with birch, occurs also with pine. Since that time over fifty Basidiomycetes have been proved to be mycorrhiza formers —chiefly *Boletus* (sixteen species), *Tricholoma* (ten species), *Amanita* and *Lactarius* (each five species), and *Cortinarius* (three species). Amongst Gasteromycetes only *Scleroderma* and *Rhizopogon* have yet been shown to form mycorrhizas. *Pinus sylvestris*, whose roots have been most investigated, has so far been proved to be intimately associated with over thirty species, and probably many others will be added. The explanation of this variety is doubtless due in part to the fact that the different species are related to the conditions of the habitat. Most prefer a soil with an acid reaction, but there are degrees of preference: *Amanita muscaria* grows best in a highly acid soil, *Boletus granulatus* in a slightly acid one. There is evidence that some species favour a neutral or slightly alkaline soil.

Though it is extremely probable that certain Ascomycetes enter into mycorrhizal relations, no successful experimental syntheses have yet been made. It has been suggested, however, that *Cenococcum graniforme*, which occurs abundantly in forest soils as small, black, brittle sclerotia of different sizes, often resembling shot, may be a sterile stage of an Ascomycete. It has a jet-black mycelium and the mycorrhizas it forms with pine, birch, spruce, aspen, lime and other trees, are also black, with abundant radiating hyphae.

There has been much research on the physiology of mycorrhiza, but, in spite of the number of hypotheses, we seem still to lack a comprehensive explanation of its real significance. It is reasonable to suppose that the fungal member of the fungus-root combination originally entered it as a parasite. Symbiosis, even when it is regarded as the living together of two organisms for mutual benefit, does not necessarily imply that they are simply helpful partners, obeying, as it were, the injunction to seek peace and ensue it. More probably it usually represents a balance resulting from attack and defence. Consequently the equilibrium is not necessarily stable but changes according to conditions, even to the extent of one or other partner succumbing.

In considering the relation between mycorrhizal fungi and tree roots we have to bear in mind that the soil is not a sterile medium save for them, but is occupied by an abundance of micro-organisms many of which are normal inhabitants of the soil, passing there the whole of their existence.

The distribution of soil microfungi raises many problems, some of them important in soil fertility, others in plant disease. In the last two decades it has been repeatedly shown that the microflora is greater in the region of actively growing roots than in the soil generally: this is perhaps particularly true of bacteria, but also holds for fungi. This root-zone of increased population is known as a *rhizosphere*. The relative increase in the number of organisms in this zone and on the surface of the root must play a part in general mycorrhizal problems. Many suggestions of its importance and of its origin have been made: food is provided by dead root cells; decomposable products are exuded by the root; growth producing substances are formed; carbon dioxide is released; the acidity (pH) in the neighbourhood of the root is constant. All these may play a greater or lesser part in the phenomenon, but, nevertheless, their relative importance is uncertain.

The excretion of a particular substance by a root may determine which mycorrhizal fungi are able to infect it. This presumably would entail the concept of specific differences in the substances exuded by different kinds of tree, for otherwise it is difficult to understand why all mycorrhizal fungi growing in the sphere of influence of the root are not able to enter into a structural relation with it. Further, we have to envisage an additional " antibiotic " substance, or substances, which prevents the entry of members of the rhizosphere, for the thin outer wall of the rootlet seems almost to invite penetration; such substances may also come into play in restricting the advance of a mycorrhizal fungus within the root.

There is usually similarity between the rhizospheres surrounding tree roots, with variation according to the kind of tree, and doubtless closely connected with the soil. Apparently there is some difference where a tree is growing in unfavourable conditions; the poor state of the tree, however, is presumably due to its situation, and only indirectly to its attendant organisms. It is in such trees, particularly, that a mycorrhizal fungus gets out of hand and enters the cortical cells, filling them sometimes to a considerable depth. This is frequent, for example, in pines growing on heaths. Roots of trees in poor condition are often parasitised by other fungi; many soil fungi appear to act in this way once the defensive barrier has broken down. Sometimes a parasite produces an appearance somewhat resembling a mycorrhiza, consequently called a *pseudomycorrhiza*. It is usually unbranched, darker and more slender than a true mycorrhiza; the mantle is poorly developed or absent, and the cortical cells of the root show no enlargement. Known chiefly in the pine it was first recognised in moorland afforestation after draining. On the view taken here the debility of the tree is not directly due to fungal attack.

The benefits derived from the associations have been a subject of controversy for well over half a century. Mycorrhizas develop more abundantly in soils where there is a deficiency in nutrients; a high percentage as a rule reduces the amount of mycorrhizal infection. The nutritional deficiencies in the soil are those of nitrogen, phosphorus, potassium or calcium, and it has been shown that mycorrhizal roots absorb much more of the first two than do uninfected roots. Mycorrhizas develop best when trees grow in strong light, that is, more than 25 per cent full daylight, and where there is a certain but not too great a deficiency of assimilable nitrogen and phosphorus; associated with this is the fact that they are more characteristically developed when the roots contain an abundance of soluble carbohydrates. Fungi are able to utilise complex nitrogenous compounds of the soil and thus can supply the tree with easily assimilable nitrogen of which there is a deficiency in the soil.

It would thus seem that the tree benefits by obtaining certain elements from the soil more easily and in greater amount than when it is unassisted. There are also suggestions that the fungus may contribute some growth substances of use to the tree.

The fact that mycorrhiza develops where there is an abundance of soluble carbohydrates in the root gives a possible clue to the activities of the fungus, for it has been found that many mycorrhizal fungi require sugars, such as glucose, as a source of carbon. Many also apparently depend very largely upon a supply of growth substances, especially vitamin B_1 (aneurin). This is produced by green plants, and it has been assumed that the fungus obtains its necessary requirements from the tree. This is very doubtful. Mycorrhizal fungi are by no means exceptional in needing aneurin, and there seems to be sufficient for their purpose in the soil and soil litter. It is probable that there is some give and take between root and fungus, and doubtful whether either has any greater advantage.

It is generally believed that the fungus obtains something from the root which is necessary for the production of fruit-bodies, and trenching experiments are held to have proved that mycelium not in mycorrhizal association is doomed to sterility. If this were true it would mean that the fruit-body is formed from hyphae growing directly out of the mycorrhizal mantle of the root, for otherwise it would follow that either the accessory substance is exuded some considerable distance from the root or that it is passed back along the hyphae in the opposite direction of growth, neither of which seems likely.

In my experience, though the fruit-bodies of mycorrhizal fungi are remarkably closely associated with their respective trees, so much so that an isolated species in a mixed wood will have its attendant fungus, very occasionally a fruit-body is found with no known partner, or, indeed, any other tree in sight. Further, in woodlands where the trees have been thinned by felling one frequently sees fungi growing in circles in bare places, sometimes from where it is obvious that trees have been removed. There is a possibility that roots of trees which have been felled may remain alive for some time with the fungus in association with them, but this would not account for the continuance of the circles over several years. If, however, the whole of the trees are felled the fungi disappear after a year or two. This is doubtless due to the changes in the habitat caused chiefly by the removal of the tree canopy.

The fact that mycorrhizal fungi can apparently grow normally in the soil, shows that the production of fruit-bodies is dependent on certain factors, chiefly climatic, and is not due to the intimate association of the mycelium with tree roots. Both tree and fungus favour the same habitat, and thus may be considered as members of the same community. There may be special edaphic conditions in the neighbourhood of the tree which are favourable to the full development of the fungus; certainly in the immediate vicinity of the roots these occur and have their effects, as we see from the rhizosphere.

A possible picture is that the mycelium enters the rootlets in search of food, for many fungi and bacteria are competing for the nutrients in the soil, and soluble carbohydrates are in great demand. The root is able to restrict the fungus, turning the attack to its own advantage in forming a mycorrhiza. When the rootlet dies the mycelium continues its growth in the soil, having benefited from the food it has obtained from the tree.

B. Peyronel (1921) lists a large number of agarics which he believes form mycorrhizas with different trees. He suggests that each species of fungus normally assumes a different aspect and size according to the tree with which it is associated. He instances *Boletus scaber* in association with *Betula alba* as generally larger, with a stouter stem and lighter-coloured cap than the forms associated with *Corylus*, *Quercus* and *Castanea*. He suggests that *Boletus versipellis* is perhaps nothing but a specialised form of *B. scaber* resulting from its connection with *Populus tremula*. This, if true, would give very strong support to the view that the tree has a great influence on sporophore-production.

A similar view is put forward by V. Melzer and J. Zvara (1927) in their study of *Russula xerampelina*. This very variable fungus is held to be characterised by its flesh being instantly coloured green on application of iron sulphate, and tardily brick-red after aniline water. Five main types are distinguished—associated with oak, poplar and birch, beech, elm and conifers—which are so unlike in appearance as to have been given different specific names. The variation is accounted for by the influence of the soil and of the tree in which it grows. " A cet égard *R. xerampelina* peut être le document classique de la révélation de l'origine des espèces attaches par la symbiose à certain arbres et nommées *espèces biologiques*." Here the study was of the variation of a species in different habitats, but something more than crude chemical reactions of the flesh is needed before important conclusions about the variations of a species can be accepted. If such a marked effect on the fruit-body of a mycorrhizal fungus can be proved, it will have a decided influence both on our views on mycorrhiza and on our ideas on the evolution of toadstools.

Though, in trees, the ectotrophic type of mycorrhiza is the best known it is mainly confined to Cupuliferae, Betulaceae, Salicaceae and Abietineae. Most other woody plants have endotrophic mycorrhizas. Here the infection is of a particular kind, which, moreover, is also that most frequent in herbaceous plants, the principal exceptions being Orchidaceae, Ericaceae, Empetraceae, Epacridaceae, Burmanniaceae and Gentianaceae. In this common form, which is found also in liverworts and ferns, the fungus usually shows finely-branched endings (*arbuscules*) with characteristic granular masses (*sporangioles*) when they are being absorbed by the host plant, as well as swollen portions (*vesicles*). As the fungi appear to be Phycomycetes they are mentioned merely to complete the picture. It may be noted, however, that this vesicular-arbuscular type occurs in relation to the oldest known vascular plants, those of the Rhynie Chert—*Rhynia, Hornea*—as well as in carboniferous strata, where it has received various names—*Palaeomyces, Peronosporites, Protomycites, Mycorhizonium*.

Endotrophic mycorrhizas are best known in Orchidaceae and Ericaceae, where the fungal hyphae within the cells are wound round in a characteristic manner. In orchids the fungus is restricted to cells of the cortex, usually having a well-defined distribution. It never penetrates into the central stele of vascular tissue; finally much of it degenerates. The general facts about orchid mycorrhiza were well known when the work of Noel Bernard (1899-1909) revolutionised ideas about its significance. The germination of orchid seeds had presented such difficulties that an occasional seedling was of sufficient interest to be described and illustrated. Bernard suspected that the fungus in the roots was in some way connected with germination. He extracted the fungus, cultivated it on a nutrient medium, and sowed the seeds on it. Abundant germination followed and the seedlings grew to maturity. This method of raising orchid seedlings has since been carried out on a commercial scale in several countries.

Orchid seeds are very minute. The outer integument is in the form of an open network which is adapted to dispersal by wind. The embryo consists of a small number of cells. There is no differentiation into young stem (plumule) and root (radicle), and only occasionally is there a suggestion of a cotyledon: usually there is merely a difference in the size of the cells, those at the suspensor end being the larger. The fungus mycelium enters the suspensor end, winds round in a cell and then passes to the next one. It does not penetrate into the smaller cells at the opposite end, where rapid division takes place and the growing points of stem and root are laid down.

The fungus in our British and in most cultivated orchids is always the same genus, though different species and strains occur. Bernard regarded the fungus as *Rhizoctonia*, one of the Fungi Imperfecti. Because of its similarity to *Rhizoctonia violacea*, which is a sterile stage of *Corticium Solani*, one of the resupinate Basidiomycetes, it was thought by Bernard that the orchid fungus is similarly a sterile Basidiomycete. In 1929, G. Catoni found such a perfect stage in isolations from *Cypripedium*, in which the fertile mycelium showed clamp-connections, and recorded it as *Hypochnus*, H. Burgeff later giving it the name *Corticium Catonii*. A similar species was isolated by F. Sprau in 1937 from *Orchis mascula*; it also showed clamp-connections in culture and was named *Corticium masculi*. An unnamed basidia-forming species of the " Rhizoctonia " type, isolated from an orchid in Wisconsin, was recorded by J. T. Curtis in 1937, but no further details appear to have been published.

The evidence suggests, therefore, that the fungi of this common type of orchid mycorrhiza are Basidiomycetes.*

An interesting variant is presented by the Japanese orchid *Gastrodia*

*Those of heather and other Ericaceae are species of *Phoma* (Fungi Imperfecti).

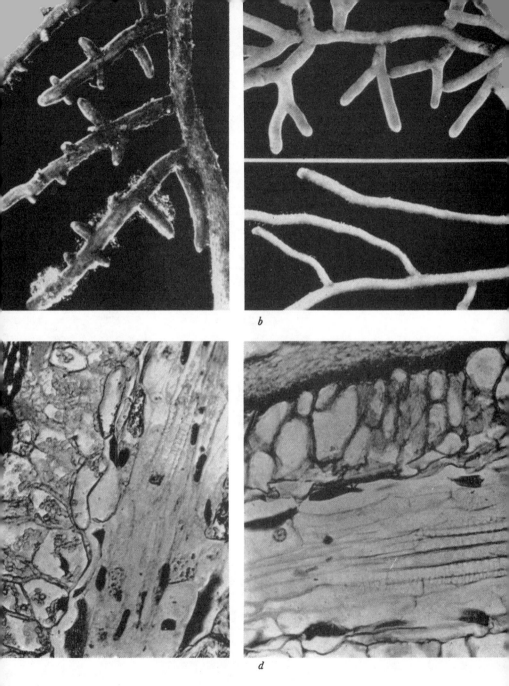

Plate XIIIa. Typical ectotrophic mycorrhiza in spruce. *b,* Typical ectotrophic mycorrhiza in pine (*above*) : root without mycorrhiza (*below*). *c,* Longitudinal section through ectendotrophic mycorrhiza in pine, strong intercellular net-work, and thick fungal hyphae within cells of primary cortex; fungal mantle very thick. *d.* Longitudinal section of spruce; strong hyphal mantle but thin intercellular net-work. (*Photographs by E. Bj*/*orkman*)

Plate XIV. Bird's Nest Fungi
(*Photographs by Somerville Hastings*)

a. Cyathus striatus

b. Nidularia pisiformis

c. Sphaerobolus stellatus

d. Crucibulum vulgare

elata. This is a holosaprophyte and possesses a tuber much like that of a potato. Each year it puts out a " dropper " and these become progressively smaller until the process can go no further. If, however, rhizomorphs of *Armillaria mellea* attack the tuber they fasten on to it like a dodder does to heather, but, whereas if a potato is the intended victim it is soon reduced to a putrescent pulp, the *Gastrodia* sends out a dropper the following year which develops a flowering stem. Sections through the infected tuber show a typical mycorrhiza of roughly three zones, an outer where the fungus mycelium fills the cells, a middle where there is a kind of balance between fungus and flowering plant, and an inner where the orchid cells are absorbing the mycelium. As the orchid is unable to manufacture its own carbohydrates it is clear that these must be obtained from the fungus, one of the most destructive parasites known. We may have here a clue to how the mycorrhizal habit might have arisen. Burgeff, 1932-33, working in Java and the Philippines, extracted the mycelia of several Basidio-mycetes from the roots of holosaprophytic orchids.

Trying to replace the actions of the fungus Bernard experimented with different concentrations of a decoction of salep (powdered dried orchid tubers) with or without the addition of saccharose. He found that the beneficial effect increased with the concentration, and that with *Cattleya* 4 per cent salep gave as good results as did the fungus.

This aspect of the problem has since been taken up by several investigators, the results of L. Knudson (1922-29) having received most attention. He obtained abundant germination in aseptic cultures by the addition of 2 per cent sugar (glucose, fructose or saccharose) or of plant-extracts with traces of sugar. The seedlings removed from the medium after a time were able to continue growth and eventually to flower. These results have been amply confirmed by later workers and the " asymbiotic method " of raising orchid seedlings is used by many commercial firms. Knudson further showed that several fungi other than the " appropriate " *Rhizoctonia* enabled seeds to germinate in culture: he held that this was because of their ability to produce in the medium the necessary concentration of sugar needed by the seed for germination. That a medium can so be converted has been shown also by other investigators: C. Cappelletti (1935) germinated seeds of *Cymbidium* hybrids by growing them with *Hypholoma fasiculare* and other agarics. These results have been held to disprove " the so-called symbiotic theory of germination," but they deal with conditions in culture which differ enormously from those in natural habitats. A sterilised medium with a 2 per cent content of sugar, and seeds having sterilised seed-coats have no existence without man's connivance. The fungi which alter the culture medium do not enter the seed, or, if they do, kill it. Further, although the specificity of the fungus from the roots is not as strict as was at first thought, the fungus is always a *Rhizoctonia* in terrestrial hemisaprophytic orchids, and is always present in some of the roots in natural habitats.

Orchid seeds, having no reserve material, are in need of a source of soluble sugars to begin growth. If this is present in the medium it is made use of, but in natural soils can rarely be available, for even if it occurred there would result so great a competition by thieving saprophytic organisms that the suppliant orchid seed would be left to perish or be overwhelmed by their growth as it is if placed in a culture tube without previous sterilisation of its seed-coat. If the soil or medium is not specially adapted for orchid seed germination the necessary sugars are provided by the fungus; occasionally it may be that some fungus other than *Rhizoctonia* may bring about the necessary changes of the medium in the immediate neighbourhood of the seed, but generally it is a species of *Rhizoctonia*, usually that which is in the cells of the root, which penetrates into the seed and presumably carries nutrient with it. There is some evidence that vitamins are also provided, but there is doubt which. According to Burgeff, Vitamin B is needed by some seeds, whereas Cappelletti believes that Vitamin C was required with the seeds with which he worked.

It is difficult to see what is gained by the fungus from its penetration into the seed. There is no reserve food, except fats, to attract it until the chlorophyll appears and begins to form carbohydrates. As a mycorrhizal fungus in the strict sense, that is, present in the roots, the problem is much the same as in ectotrophic mycorrhiza except that a good deal of the fungus is digested by the orchid. Doubtless the portion that remains alive obtains carbohydrates and possibly vitamins. Any " shelter " it achieves is very problematical, for it apparently can withstand desiccation as well as the root.

In considering mycorrhiza in a general sense it should not be overlooked that the mycelia of some parasites are perennial in the host plant, principally in the rhizome or rootstock. This is not rare in rusts and smuts, the mycelium invading the developing stem and leaves giving rise to what is known as systemic infection.

Mycorrhiza is one of the classical examples of the living together of two dissimilar organisms in intimate association. It is customary to call this kind of union *symbiosis*. Originally, when coined by de Bary in 1879, the term signified no more than this co-existence, and, indeed, so little regard was paid to the relations existing between the two organisms that de Bary in defining parasites said, " Their relationship with their hosts is that of a common life, a *symbiosis*." Obviously, the concept was too wide in its original form and its use has led to some confusion because most writers have restricted its sense. Thus P. Vuillemin defined symbiosis as the phenomenon where two organisms live together and reciprocally develop an equal activity to their mutual advantage; to this in 1889 he opposed *antibiosis* where one organism acts deleteriously on another with no reciprocal reaction.

Many terms have been proposed to define the relation between two organisms living together. The interaction, however, is rarely if ever constant, as there is continued interplay which defies precise definition throughout its course, though it may be clear at certain stages.

Fungi take part in many other close associations in addition to mycorrhizal ones. With green and blue-green algae they form composite structures—namely Lichens—where the union is so close that distinctive appearances result, so characteristic that they were classed separately as Lichens before their nature was realised, and are treated as a distinct group in all systematic works. The fungus is the dominant partner, for it imposes a definite shape on the thallus and provides the fruit-bodies; these are Ascomycetes except in three tropical genera, *Cora*, *Dictyonema* and *Corella*, in which they are Basidiomycetes. The fungal partner has not yet been cultivated beyond the early stages but the algae are often known in a free-living state.

Fungi also enter into symbiotic relations with bacteria. The old English Ginger-Beer plant is a globular gelatinous white mass usually about the size of a pea and is used for fermenting sugary fluids. It is composed of a yeast and a bacterium; the bacterium has a pellucid, swollen, glutinous sheath, and the yeast appears to be mechanically entangled in the matrix of coiled filaments. The yeast ferments the sugar and the imprisoned carbon dioxide causes the mass to rise to the surface, where the gas is liberated, after which it sinks slowly to the bottom. This up-and-down movement accounts for the common name Bees.

Tea-Cider, which has become very popular in parts of the Orient, is made by fermenting sweetened tea by a " mould " of which the chief constituents are again yeast and a bacterium. A heavy gelatinous scum forms on the surface.

Various fermented milks—Kephir, Koumiss, Leben, Mazu—similarly result from yeasts and bacteria acting together.

Fungi are associated with insects in several ways. The most picturesque of these is the fungus-garden found in special chambers of the nests of South American leaf-cutting ants. It was T. Belt who, in 1874, first stated that these ants cultivate toadstools and eat them. The ants, in procession, strip plants of their leaves which they take to the nest. There the workers cut them into pieces sufficiently small to be subjected to a long chewing process and then plant them in the fungus-garden, where they soon become permeated with the mycelium. The fungus apparently is definitely cultivated and forms abundant clusters of small spherical swellings (bromatia) upon which the ants feed and also nourish the larvae. Any extraneous fungus is said to be weeded out. The virgin queen on her nuptial flight carries a pellet of the fungus with which she starts a new garden.

There are probably several different agarics cultivated by the hundred or so kinds of ants but owing to " cropping " by the insects they do not reach the fruiting stage while the nest is still occupied: so far four species have been described from old nests.

Other ants have also been thought to cultivate fungi. Dark coloured moulds occur in the black, earthy, brittle carton used in the construction of the nests of *Lasius fuliginosus* and *L. umbratus*, two common British species, and apparently give stability to the walls by ramifying through them and binding the particles: the mould in the first is *Cladosporium*, in the second *Hormiscium*. The ants are said to weed out other fungi, and as spores are never found they probably have a place in the diet of the insects. The occurrence of a particular fungus in so special a habitat does not necessarily mean that it is actually cultivated, and the cropping of it may merely be to ensure living space.

Certain termites (white ants) are generally believed to cultivate fungi. They live in large nests, termitaria, which may be under or above ground where they are variously shaped and mud-covered. The comb of the nest is formed of wood said to have passed through the intestines of the termites. The internal walls of the comb-cells have a hoary covering which J. G. Koenig in 1779 recognised as fungal and thought it probable that it served as food for the larvae. H. Smeatham, two years later, reported that the nurseries were always found slightly overgrown with mould, and plentifully sprinkled with small white globules about the size of a small pin's head. Feeding experiments and dissections have been thought to establish that these spheres are the termite food: the fungus-gardens are nurseries full of newly-hatched young which graze on the fungus like " miniature sheep."

Recent French work has thrown doubt on this interpretation. It suggests that the comb is formed from woody material which is masticated by the workers but not swallowed. Moreover the larvae cannot eat the fungus because of the structure of their mouth parts: it is not cultivated but is tolerated and controlled—the nest is its natural habitat.

R. Heim has shown that the spherules, previously classed as *Aegerita*, are the primordia of agarics which have long been known to arise directly from the combs, and of which about a dozen species have been described. All show structural characters in common which has led to their being placed in a new genus *Termatomyces*.

Certain beetles are credited with making use of fungi for digesting cellulose. In 1836 J. Schmidberger described how the larvae of some wood-boring insects feed on the white glistening substance lining the burrows, which he thought was extruded sap and, confusing mythology with mycology, called *ambrosia*. Hartig later recognised that it was a fungus to which he gave the name *Monilia candida*; he believed that it was the outcome of the stimulation of wood cells by beetle secretion —it was a period when a belief in heterogenesis flourished.

There are about four hundred true ambrosia beetles. They bore deeply into the sapwood, sometimes of healthy trees, usually in those weakened by some cause. The walls of the tunnel are covered with a white or creamy mould which rapidly darkens; it thoroughly permeates the cell walls which become stained dark brown or black. The spores of the fungus form the chief food of the developing larvae. The beetles get rid of any intrusive fungus: if the beetles are removed alien fungi soon fill the tunnel. Though it is certain that ambrosial fungi are introduced by the beetles there is controversy about how it is done.

Though many different species have been isolated from tunnels in various parts of the world it is often assumed that there is only one ambrosial fungus. It would be astonishing if so many different species of tree in such diverse conditions provided nutriment precisely adapted to the needs of a single fungus and that this should be distributed by hundreds of kinds of insect. That some of the fungi show a considerable amount of similarity is accounted for by the somewhat specialised habitat.

It is an easy step from the staining of wood by fungi serving as food for beetles to discoloration by fungi gaining admittance together with or in the path of insects. Blue-staining fungi are apparently invariably introduced by engraver beetles (*Scolytus*); they are mostly species of *Ceratostomella*, a Pyrenomycete characterised by its long neck. The colour of the wood is usually that of different intensities of blue-black ink. The fungal hyphae are brown, the blue appearance being due to the scattered light rays from the hyphae being seen through the translucent cell-walls of the wood.

The association of engraver beetles with *Ceratostomella* and other fungi is of great economic significance. The Dutch elm disease, so called because it was first recognised in Holland, which has caused so much loss and alarm in this country is due to *Ceratostomella* (*Graphium*) *Ulmi*. The attack first shows as a wilting and drying of the leaves, particularly of the end branches; death may ensue after one or two years. A fairly constant symptom is a brown discoloration in the outer annual ring of the sap wood of an affected branch, often forming a complete circle. If the cut end of the branch is kept moist the characteristic conidial stage (*Graphium*) soon appears.

Engraver beetles are mainly responsible for spreading the disease. The larvae pass the winter under the elm bark and on emerging are contaminated internally and externally with the spores of the fungus chiefly those of the conidial stage which are borne in sticky masses. Infection occurs through feeding wounds made by the beetle on young branches or when the bark is bored to establish brood channels.

There is an interesting association between *Stereum sanguinolentum* and wood wasps. *Stereum* is a Basidiomycete which grows on wood forming flattened patches closely attached to the substratum, or, if on an upright support, with the upper edge reflexed in a shelf or bracket-shape. *S. sanguinolentum* is common on dead branches and stumps of conifers where it forms a pale greyish or fawn skin, which may be free at the thin, white, acute margin and reflexed to form a narrow cap with a whitish grey to greyish surface, satiny with radiating fibrils. When the hymenium is cut or bruised it exudes a reddish liquid.

The fungus is always present in the larval and oviposition tunnels of *Sirex gigas* and *S. cyaneus*. It occurs in the intersegmental sacs at the anterior end of the ovipositor of adult females and the egg becomes infected with fungal oidia at the start of its passage down. When growth begins the mycelium advances sufficiently in front of the boring larvae, between oviposition and hatching, to form food for them or to have acted on the wood and made it available as nutriment. The larva can live and grow on a pure culture of the fungus in the laboratory.

Many fungi are able to follow on after insect attack; indeed some could not gain entrance into a tree without this active or passive aid. Thus *Peniophora gigantea*, a common fungus on coniferous logs where it forms an irregular waxy crust looking like candle grease when moist, often reaching a foot across, usually causes a light brown discoloration of the sap wood. Wood boring beetles (*Monochamus*) which infest recently-felled logs lay their eggs in the inner bark. The newly-hatched larvae feed there and in the outer layers of sap wood where they become contaminated with the fungus. As they approach maturity they bore deeply into the heart wood carrying the fungus with them. It spreads from the larval tunnels and causes a reddish brown decay.

Septobasidium, a large, mostly tropical genus, somewhat similar in appearance to *Stereum*, but with transversely septate basidia, always grows in union with scale insects. The details have been most fully ascertained in the American species *S. Burtii*. The brown superficial patches of the fungus show two layers, the upper one supported by ridges which branch and join to form a labyrinth of channels and tunnels. Healthy insects (*Aspidiotus osborni*) occur, usually singly, in the cavities but there are also a considerable number of parasitised ones more or less embedded in the lower layer of the fungus. The thick dense mat which partly covers the dorsal scale and posterior part is not in close contact but is attached by coiled hyphae which allow the insect freedom of movement to breathe; they pass through natural openings into the body forming densely-coiled haustoria in the circulatory system. Oil globules in the fungal mat show that it is obtaining food from the insect which thus pays its toll for protection against adverse environmental conditions including predators.

To round off the story mention may be made of internal yeasts which, sometimes in association with bacteria, apparently are constant both in identity and arrangement in certain insects—generally speaking those feeding on substances rich in carbohydrates and poor in nitrogen, on plant juices, on vertebrate blood, or on horny substances, hair, feathers and so on.

This constant association of insect and yeast, and the fact that there are elaborate devices for ensuring its continuance, suggest that it is advantageous to both partners.

By sterilising the surface of the eggs of *Sitodrepa panicea*, the flour beetle, on which the yeast is carried over, larvae free from infection can be hatched. The normal beetle grows much better on white flour, which is deficient in the vitamin B group than do those which are yeast-free; but in diets rich in vitamins there is no such difference. Normal larvae grow on an artificial medium where none of the vitamin B complex is present: yeast-free larvae fail to grow if any is lacking —all are needed and the yeast supplies them. The only benefit that seems to be gained by the yeast is the assurance of a favourable habitat.

In some habitats insects and yeasts are generally found in company. Usually the yeasts acting on a medium containing sugar convert it into something which can be used by the insect; from one point of view the insect uses the fungus to predigest its food, from another it consumes the yeast's left overs. The reverse is seen where aphids and other insects living on plant juices void the sugar-rich honey dew, and this becomes infected by yeasts and yeast-like fungi. The latter are often black and disfigure the leaves and the surrounding vegetation and pavements.

Where insects and fungus are in close association we must avoid anthropocentric views, which mask the truth. Further, it does not help if we simply label all associations of fungi and other organisms as symbiosis and assume that everything is for mutual benefit, with, give and take. Relations are more often strained than not and the constituent " partners " behave as if they regarded themselves alone.

CHAPTER 19

WOODLANDS

PRESUMABLY because the common mushroom grows in pastures there is a tendency to regard fields as providing the most suitable habitats for the larger fungi, but a little experience in collecting soon shows that woodlands produce a much better harvest.

There is an obvious relation between the nature of the soil and the kind of woodland inhabiting it, but the details of this are still a matter of much study. There are many fungi which seem to be indifferent to the type of woodland and as most of these are very common they tend to blur the picture though there is often a difference in the percentage of abundance. The fact, however, that some mycorrhizal fungi are restricted to one kind of tree and that some parasites and saprophytes are almost equally limited shows at once that there must be characteristic species of the different communities. Woodland fungi can be grouped according to the nature of the soil on which they are found, but as this is usually covered by humus or leaf-mould in which their mycelia grow, it is more logical, where possible, to relate their distribution to the nature of the humus, which, in its turn, is dependent on the vegetation which forms it. Thus it is better to speak of the fungi of oak-woods, of beech-woods, of pine-woods, rather than of calcicolous and siliceous species.

Edaphic factors in so far as they determine the particular type of woodland may be regarded as doing the same for fungi. What must be borne in mind, however, is that these are an essential part of the community: they are there because of other organisms. As the mycelia of terricolous fungi are in the closest relation with the soil their ability to grow and thrive must be influenced greatly by its chemical and physical nature, which is ever changing depending as it does on the kind of vegetation (tree and undergrowth) and its litter, the demands it makes on the substances present, and the activity of organisms of all kinds including microfungi and macrofungi. If the mycelium of a fungus is able to grow under a wide range of conditions it will be found in most woods; on the other hand where their range is narrower or their requirements more particular they will succeed only where these are met.

The problem is perhaps a little clearer because there is never a carpet of fruit-bodies—what one could call a closed community—on any but the smallest area; there is always room for some intruder both above and below ground, for the mycelia do not form compact sheets permeating every air-space, and those of different species may grow at different depths. Thus there is not the same competition as with flowering plants where some species apparently cannot get a hold in a habitat where they could grow if there were no competition, and are more or less restricted to places where they, but not their competitors, can gain a livelihood.

Many if not most woodland fungi have a perennating mycelium. Whereas, however, the same spot in a wood will rarely fail to provide the same species of flowering plant year after year, the fruit-bodies of many fungi seem to require special climatic or other conditions for their appearance. Even such common species as *Lactarius vellereus*, *Paxillus involutus* and *Armillaria mellea* may be extremely rare in one or other season, so it does not seem as if their mycelia have to amass materials for a burst of fructification, though occasionally there is a suggestion of some kind of cycle. In many years there is an abundance of some infrequent species or a comparative absence of some very common one.

The neglect of the study of fungi in the general ecological survey of woodlands is surprising. The multicoloured beauty of these strange growths, might be thought, of itself, sufficient to warrant more than a mere casual glance. Indeed the two mycologists who founded the modern study, C. H. Persoon (1755-1837) and E. M. Fries (1794-1878), have left it on record that it was the beauty of a fungus which first attracted them, the former by *Peziza aurantia* (Pl. 42c, p. 263), the latter by *Hydnum coralloides* (Pl. XVIa, p. 227), while an illustrious forerunner, A. Battara (1714-89), succumbed to the fascination of *Sarcoscypha coccinea*.

What part do fungi play in the woodland community? Some are parasitic on trees and stress their presence by the destruction they cause. The majority, however, are not parasites, for they live on the ground, or on dead wood, leaves, and other organic substrata.

A woodland is not an inert community, even if only the trees, shrubs and herbs are considered. There is continuous struggle and constant change, but as there is equilibrium which simulates fixity we have the impression of lasting conservation and everlasting stability. But even if disaster does not overtake them the longest-lived trees have only their allotted span, though this in the oak may be a thousand years, and in the Giant Red Wood (*Sequoiadendron giganteum*) four thousand. Shrubs and herbs similarly have their lease of life, with leaf-fall and the shedding of twigs and branches. It is in assisting in the rotting of organic material, which makes the physical and chemical nature of the soil amenable to the physiological discipline of green plants, that fungi play a fundamental rôle, for a continuing fertile soil is a *sine qua non* of all vegetation.

There must be rotting of organic material if only to remove it. In the course of this, substances are formed which are available as nutriment for the plant covering. Microscopic fungi abound in the humus and play a large part in reducing the resistant lignin and cellulose. This underground activity is never ceasing and the number of visible fruit-bodies is no guide to its magnitude for these appear only in their due season and then only if conditions for their formation and growth are suitable: it is the active mycelium which is important. There is competition amongst fungal hyphae and often between them and herbaceous roots for food and for space and there is also the reaction of their products of growth in stimulation or repression. The competition with roots probably accounts for the paucity of fungi in patches of Dog's Mercury, Wood Sorrel, Bramble and Bracken, and along rides where vegetation is luxuriant.

The density of the trees and their overhead canopy determines the amount of light which penetrates below and consequently the constitution of the undergrowth; it has both a direct as well as an indirect influence on the occurrence of fungi. Only a few species are intolerant of shade as, for example, *Lepiota procera*; some others show slight abnormalities or differences in colour where shade is dense, but the majority are not affected and may therefore occasionally prove to be more certain indicators of edaphic conditions than are flowering plants.

An indirect effect of a parasitic fungus is seen in what have been called "light chimneys" in dense conifer forests for the most part bare of ground vegetation. Attack by *Fomes annosus* will kill one or more trees which in falling leave gaps in the canopy admitting sufficient light for the growth of flowering plants.

In glades where trees are few and far apart and there is no shade, and in grassy places and in rides, typical grassland species occur, but with some degree of shade the species usually differ somewhat from those outside the woodland except in its immediate surroundings. The tree canopy affects the relative humidity by preventing insolation and by reducing air movement. This partly explains the difference between woodland and grassland fungi. In Iceland, woodlands are absent except for low birch copses in sheltered valleys and on moist valley slopes. P. Larsen (1932) states that the 150 species or so of fungi recorded include primarily those which occur in similar habitats in continental Europe. " But there also occur species of genera that chiefly or exclusively inhabit woods, such as *Cortinarius*, *Pholiota* and *Russula*. Of these genera *Cortinarius* is almost exclusively an inhabitant of woods in Central Europe; but several species of it are very numerously represented in Iceland in river plains, fiord valleys, and knolly moorland tracts." He believes that their occurrence is accounted for by the relatively greater moisture content of the atmosphere.

A thick layer of leaves prevents rain water from reaching the soil in a dry season, whereas in a rainy season it keeps it from losing its moisture. Leaves, however, as against leaf-mould are not a habitat generally favoured by fungi. In spring the forest canopy retards the rise in temperature and fungi are scarce there as against a fair plenty in the open.

The fungi of damp areas are distinctive and indeed are often special to the particular kind of wood. In very dry seasons the sides of woodland streams often provide good collecting ground if the soil is not waterlogged, and many small species can be found amongst mosses growing in the spray of waterfalls.

It is one of the commonplace facts of field mycology, and one of the most puzzling, that an area of woodland apparently in no way different will be bare of fungi while the remainder is abundantly fruitful, or a large wood may be worked all day with no reward and then a hundred square yards or so will show quantities even of a number of uncommon species.

Certain genera such as *Amanita*, *Russula*, *Lactarius*, *Cortinarius*, *Boletus* and *Hydnum* are almost wholly sylvicolous. Many of them are those principally concerned in mycorrhizal formation. Other genera typical of woodlands are the lignicolous *Polyporus*, *Polystictus*, *Fomes*, *Hydnum*, *Pholiota* and *Flammula*. Though mycologists have always been compelled to take some note of habitats—indeed L. Quélet wrote, " L'habitat est la moitié de la détermination "—we still have only a meagre knowledge of all this entails. Often in systematic works the habitat of a fungus is given simply as "woods." Experience shows that some species are to be found only in a certain restricted habitat—sometimes difficult to describe: the reputed rarity of a species is probably often nothing more than an ignorance of its habitat. The field mycologist soon becomes aware of the sort of spot likely to provide a given species or a group of species but, intent usually on the identification of his finds, tends to disregard the importance of a precise definition of the habitat.

Woodland fungi may be grouped into those forming mycorrhizas; those growing on trees and logs; on leaves; on mosses; in glades and open spaces; and in the shade of trees. There are no clear dividing lines; thus every transition can be found between species growing directly on, to those growing amongst, leaves, on leaf mould, or on bare ground. Amongst these some occur in all kinds of woods, some are restricted either to coniferous or to deciduous woods, whereas others are characteristic of different types of woodland or plantation—beech, oak, alder, pine or larch. As would be expected the main difference is between deciduous and coniferous woods; the fungi of different types of deciduous woods have a general similarity.

Living trees are frequently attacked by the larger fungi, though they are also the prey of microscopic species. Further, their stumps, logs, leaves and twigs provide sustenance for a host of saprophytes. Obviously as trees play the essential rôle, fungi which grow on them are an important biotic factor in influencing their health and survival and in reducing their remains to material available for plant growth.

Microscopic fungi are very frequently strictly limited in their range of host plants: it is likely that some specialisation also occurs in the larger fungi, but, except in a few species, there is little more than a hint of it.

Some parasitic and saprophytic species grow on almost any kind of tree, others prefer or are almost restricted to either deciduous or coniferous forms; again there may be a special preference for a genus, and, very rarely, only one host is known.

Any part of a tree may be affected, but living leaves, flowers and catkins give insufficient mechanical support for the fruit-bodies of the larger fungi, though they are parasitised by microfungi of various kinds.

The timber of growing trees consists of a dead, central heart-wood and a living outer sap-wood. Most fungi which attack trees are wound parasites gaining an entrance through gaps in the very efficient defensive armour provided by the bark. A rough division can be made between species affecting heart-wood and those on sap-wood. As a rule living sap-wood is not attacked; the resistance may be due in some way to the high moisture content, which, possibly, interferes with the respiration of the fungal hyphae. When tree bark has been damaged so that the underlying cells dry out and die, the way is open for penetration.

At first sight, heart-wood, because of its sheltered position, might appear free from danger. Above ground it is exposed, however, by wounds of various kinds, chief of which are the stubs of broken branches; below ground, dead or weakly roots, or roots nibbled by rabbits, provide an entrance, the decay thus caused being usually in the centre of the tree. Fungi restricted in their attack to heart-wood cannot properly be described as parasites, though they frequently cause the collapse and death of a tree by hollowing out the heart-wood, which provides the mechanical strength of the tree.

When a diseased tree falls, any fungus which has played a part in its destruction usually continues to grow on the log or the stump. But, with the change in conditions, other fungi, wholly saprophytic, begin to appear.

The changes which occur in logs after the felling of healthy trees are intricate, beginning with those which follow the drying of the sap-wood. Then various organisms play a part, chief among which are fungi, for the natural protection provided by the bark is lost, while the moisture content of the wood remains sufficient for spores to germinate. A strange effect often seen on sawn surfaces both of stump and log, is caused by *Bispora monilioides*, a black mould which usually grows in radial sectors or patches, giving the appearance of daubs of black paint, as if the timber had been marked for some particular purpose. As decay proceeds through the combined efforts of insects, bacteria and moulds, fungi of larger size appear, and rarely only one species. There is frequently a succession of these, for some need well-rotted wood before they can grow and fruit. Every kind of Basidiomycete is to be found on stumps and logs, but, strange to say, *Lycoperdon pyriforme* is the only Gasteromycete.

In a dry season it is always profitable to examine stumps and logs. Wood retains moisture better than does soil or even humus, and the mycelia of lignicolous fungi are well protected against adverse conditions. Moisture, however, is necessary for their development, but different species require different amounts both for vegetative growth and for the production of fruit-bodies. Thus *Schizophyllum commune* and *Polystictus versicolor* are relatively xerophilous, whereas *Hypholoma sublateritium* and *Pluteus cervinus* are relatively hydrophilous.

GENERAL WOODLAND FUNGI

There are many fungi which grow in all kinds of woods, though some of them prefer one or the other.

Amanita rubescens (Pl. 3, p. 18), abundant after late summer rains; *A. spissa; A. pantherina; A. gemmata* (*junquillea*), uncommon; *A. mappa,* more common in frondose woods, its var. *alba* preferring beech.

Amanitopsis vaginata; A. fulva (Pl. 4, p. 19). *A. nivalis,* infrequent.

Several species of *Lepiota,* including some found in pastures. *Lepiota clypeolaria; L. castanea; L. sistrata* (*seminuda*); *L. lenticularis,* in damp places.

A few species of *Psalliota* which on the whole prefer conifers to deciduous trees. *P. sylvicola; P. rubella; P. sylvatica; P. haemorrhoidaria; P. elvensis; P. augusta.*

Hypholoma velutinum, common along paths; *H. pyrotrichum.*

Tricholoma saponaceum; T. nudum; T. glaucocanum often in beech woods; *T. sejunctum; T. ionides* in damp spots. Several species with greyish to greyish brown caps— *T. terreum,* the commonest; *T. triste; T. (Armillaria) ramentaceum; T. argyraceum; T. chrysites; T. squarrulosum; T. atrosquamosum; T. murinaceum; T. virgatum; T. orirubens.*

Hebeloma crustuliniforme; H. sinapizans; H. elatum; H. radicatum.

Flammula lenta (*Hebeloma glutinosum*), sometimes attached to buried twigs; *F.* (*Riparites*) *tricholoma.*

*Clitocybe nebularis,** very common in late autumn; *C. clavipes; C. odora; C. fragrans* (*suaveolens*); *C. obsoleta,* usually on bare soil under hedges; *C. infundibuliformis; C. catinus; C. inversa* (*flaccida*), preferring conifers; *C. gilva* (*splendens*); *C. cerussata* with its subspecies *C. pithyophylla* under pines and *C. phyllophila* under deciduous trees; *C. candicans.*

Tricholoma aggregatum, T. cartilagineum, T. cinerascens and *Clitocybe connata* in dense clusters often on the side of roads.

Laccaria laccata (Pl. 8a, p. 83), very common and most variable, reddish brown with thick and spaced unequal gills and a tough fibrous stem; *L. laccata* var. *amethystina* (Pl. 8b, p. 83), wholly a beautiful dark violet when moist, becoming lilac when dry.

Paxillus involutus, very common and variable.

Collybia maculata; C. butyracea; C. rancida; C. (Marasmius) dryophila (Pl. 9b, p. 102), with a pale yellowish cap, brown in the centre, whitish gills and yellow to reddish brown stem; *Marasmius (Collybia) confluens,* in dense clusters on leaves and pine needles. '

Amongst species of *Russula* are *R. ochroleuca* (Pl. 14a, p. 119), with ochre-yellow

*The host of the rare *Volvaria Loveiana* (*surrecta*) which grows in clusters on the cap.

cap, whitish gills and white stem becoming grey; *R. xerampelina; R. amoena; R. foetens; R. nitida; R. emetica* (Pl. 14*b*, p. 119), having a scarlet cap, white gills and stem, with several growth forms; *R. fragilis; R. fallax; R. nigricans*—old blackened specimens often attached by *Nyctalis asterophora* and *N. parasitica*—*R. densifolia, R. adusta* and *R. albonigra.*

Lactarius zonarius; L. insulsus; L. piperatus; L. serifluus; L. mitissimus; L. subdulcis. Mycena pura.

Inocybe geophylla; I. pyriodora; I. corydalina; I. hystrix; I. calamistrata, chiefly under pines; *I. jurana.*

Naucoria Cucumis, in damp places. *Cantharellus tubaeformis.*

Strobilomyces strobilaceus. Boletus reticulatus; B. felleus; B. erythropus; B. calopus; B. piperatus.

Growing on tree-trunks or stumps.

Hypholoma fasciculare (Pl. 17, p. 130), the Sulphur-Tuft, is very common: the cap yellow, the gills sulphur-yellow then greenish, the stem yellow and wavy; *H. sublateritium. Armillaria mellea;* (Pl. 11*a*, p. 110). *Pholiota radicosa*, growing from underground wood to which its long rooting base is attached. *Pluteus cervinus. Claudopus varibalis*, on sticks and fallen branches. *Schizophyllum commune*, on logs.

Polyporus sulphureus, attacking all kinds of trees including chestnut and yew which are usually immune; *P. caesius. Polystictus versicolor* (Pl. 26*c*, p. 167), on stumps, fences and posts; the upper surface velvety with satiny concentric zones of many colours, lighter when growing in the shade, the white pores small and round, becoming torn with age.

Clavaria stricta (Pl. 28*d*, p. 175), the only British species of *Clavaria* growing on wood; densely and irregularly branched from a short stem, the branches crowded and erect, pinkish buff above with the tips yellow at first, browning to the touch and usually with a sweet smell.

Calocera cornea. Phlebia merismoides. Merulius tremellosus; M. corium. Stereum purpureum, a common saprophyte but also a troublesome parasite causing " silver-leaf," particularly in Rosaceae; *S. hirsutum*, an important cause of decay in felled oaks lying on the ground. *Auricularia mesenterica. Coryne sarcoides* (Pl. 43, p. 270), purple and rather gelatinous, most common in the conidial stage showing first as small columns then as a convoluted mass from which may arise the top-shaped perfect stage. *Xylaria Hypoxylon*, particularly, and *X. polymorpha* common on stumps, as is also the puzzling Discomycete *Cudoniella acicularis*, which looks like a small white agaric with a convex cap (disc) and slender stem: the absence of gills gives a clue to its identity.

PINE WOODS

The Highland pine-woods are the remnants of an original coniferous forest. The pine-woods of the south-eastern heaths though so characteristic are generally thought to be the result of extensive planting in the eighteenth and nineteenth centuries, though there is evidence that pine persisted in the south until comparatively recent times.

The fungi are distinctive, being characterised chiefly by species of *Boletus, Clavaria, Gomphidius, Hydnum, Lactarius, Russula* and *Tricholoma.*

Plate XV

a. Ganoderma applanatum, on beech. (*Somerville Hastings*)

b. Bulgaria inquinans, often more or less in lines on logs, black and of rubber-like consistency.

(*Somerville Hastings*)

Plate XVI. Two beautiful large white fungi.
(Photographs by Somerville Hastings)

a. Hydnum coralloides

b. Hydnum Erinaceus

Boletus luteus; B. granulatus; B. bovinus; B. variegatus; B. badius; B. pinicola; B. elegans; B. viscidus; the rare *B. cavipes* under larch; *B. tridentinus* under larch and yew; *B. cyanescens* under spruce; *B. sulphureus* usually on sawdust; *B. flavidus,* rare, in bogs; *B. porphyrosporus.*
The characteristic species of *Clavaria* are *C. abietina, C. flaccida* and *C. invalii.*
All five British species of *Gomphidius—G. glutinosus, G. gracilis, G. maculatus, G. roseus* and *G. viscidus: G. roseus* often in close company with *Boletus bovinus.*
Hydnum imbricatum, H. nigrum, H. melaleucum, and *H. auriscalpium*—attached to fallen pine-cones, are the commonest species. Several species of large size are found only in the highland forests.
Lactarius rufus; L. theiogalus; L. deliciosus; L. scrobiculatus; L. helvus and *L. lignyotus* in damp situations; *L. repraesentaneus* under spruce.
Russula drimeia, R. Queletii, R. sanguinea, R. xerampelina var. *erythropoda, R. nauseosa, R. puellaris,* and *R. paludosa,* in bogs, are the main characteristic species.
Amongst species of *Tricholoma* are *T. aurantium, T. caligatum, T. colossum, T. focale, T. robustum,* which formerly were included in *Armillaria; T. vaccinum, T. imbricatum* and the rare *T. psammopum* and *T. inodermum; T. equestre; T. portentosum; T. albobrunneum; T. rutilans,* exceptional in growing on stumps.
Lepiota amianthina; L. carcharias; L. granulosa.
Clitocybe (Cantharellus) aurantiaca (Pl. 11*b*, p. 110), most common under conifers: it is orange-yellow, the gills usually darker; *C. pithyophylla; C. brumalis.* The autumnal *C. conigena (myosura)* and the vernal *C. esculenta (tenacella)* on buried cones. *C. distorta; C. inolens.*
Marasmius scorodonius; M. perforans; M. impudicus.
Several species of *Mycena* on needles and twigs; among them *M. lactea, M. Adonis, M. rubromarginata, M. elegans,* and *M. vulgaris.*
Among other white-spored species are *Amanita porphyria,* and *Armillaria bulbigera,* looking like a white-spored *Cortinarius.*
Many species of *Cortinarius,* including *C. mucosus, C. mucifluus, C. sanguineus, C. anthracinus, C. phoeniceus* and *C. gentilis.*
Hebeloma fastibile; H. mesophaeum.
Hygrophorus hypothejus, a late autumn species; *H. olivaceoalbus; H. agathosmus; H. erubescens; H. pudorinus. Leptonia formosa* in mossy places. *Hypholoma dispersum.*
Thelephora terrestris (laciniata), often encrusting twigs.
Rhizina inflata, Spathularia flavida, Cudonia circinnans and *Mitrula cucculata* are Discomycetes.

On stumps or at the base of trees.
Several yellowish or brownish species—*Hypholoma capnoides, H. epixanthum, Flammula sapinea, F. astragalina, F. hybrida, F. penetrans, F. picrea, F. flavida, F. scamba, Pholiota marginata* (Pl. 11*d*, p. 110), *P. flammans* and *Omphalia campanella.*
Pleurotus porrigens; P. acerosus. Mycena amicta. M. alcalina. Paxillus atrotomentosus, on old pine-stumps. *Polyporus Schweinitzii* on mature pines near ground level or on roots. *Fomes annosus,* causing much damage, fruiting at the base of the trunk. *Polystictus abietinus. Lenzites abietinus. Merulius himantioides,* occasional on logs and stumps. *Stereum sanguinolentum. Sparassis crispa* (Pl. 27*b*, p. 174), looking like a bathsponge growing at the base of trunks; it is creamish yellow to pale buff with a short thick rooting base from which spring numerous flattened lobes.
Tremella foliacea. Tremellodon gelatinosum. Calocera viscosa.

M.T.   Q

DECIDUOUS WOODS

It is convenient to consider the fungi of different types of deciduous woods separately, though the lists of species cannot be exclusive for there is much over-lapping: a fungus may simply be much more common under a certain tree than elsewhere and, at present, we do not know the factors influencing distribution, except for mycorrhizal species.

Amanita phalloides; A. verna; A. virosa; A. strobiliformis (solitaria). Amanitopsis strangulata (inaurata).

Lepiota Bucknalii and *L. grangei,* uncommon.

Tricholoma album; T. columbetta; T. sulphureum; T. acerbum; T. ustale.

Lactarius vellereus, very common, as is also *L. quietus; L. volemus; L. flavidus.*

Entoloma lividum; E. rhodopolium.

Russula is well represented. *R. cyanoxantha; R. grisea; R. heterophylla; R. rosea; R. Velenovskyi; R. pseudointegra; R. lutea* and var. *armeniaca; R. luteotacta.*

Hygrophorus eburneus, H. chrysodon and *H. Cossus* are common; *H. arbustivus; H. dis-coideus; H. mesotephrus; H. Russula.*

The wholly egg-yellow Chanterelle, *Cantharellus cibarius* (Pl. 20, p. 147) is frequent; it is somewhat top-shaped with the gills fold-like, irregularly branched and anastomosing.

Marasmius erythropus. Several small species on twigs and leaves: *M. ramealis, M. rotula, M. epiphyllus, M. epiphylloides* on dead ivy leaves, *M. foetidus* and *M. prasiosmus.*

Pholiota erebia in damp spots; *P. caperata; P. aurea.*

Boletus edulis; B. luridus; B. chrysenteron; B. subtomentosus; B. versicolor; B. appendi-culatus.

Clavaria cristata and *C. cinerea,* common; *C. aurea, C. flavida, C. botrytis* and *C. formosa,* locally common.

Pleurotus ostreatus (Pl. 19a, p. 146), the Oyster-Mushroom, usually at the base of trunks in clustered overlapping masses, sessile, or with a short, white, oblique stem-like base: the cap thick, fan-shaped, dark brown when very young, then slate-blue, pale grey or fawn; *P. sapidus* most frequently on elm; *P. corticatus.*

Crepidotus mollis, common on old stumps, gate-posts and sawdust. *Flammula ochro-chlora,* common on stumps and buried wood, and on cording laid down for drawing timber; *F. gummosa.*

Pholiota squarrosa, also very common on apple and cherry in orchards. *P. spectabilis* (Pl. 11c, p. 110) has a golden yellow fibrillose cap and a lighter yellow ventricose stem with a short root; *P. aurivella; P. mutabilis.*

Hypholoma hydrophyllum, very common, in dense clusters; *H. Candolleanum.*

Hymenochaete rubiginosa; H. corrugata. Mycena galericulata, in dense groups on stumps; *M. rugosa; M. polygramma.*

Polyporus giganteus (Pl. 27a, p. 174), at the base of trees forming tufts composed of a number of imbricated fan-shaped flaps with a brownish yellow zoned surface and yellowish margin passing downwards into stems which fuse below, arising from a tuber-like base.

Fomes pomaceus, common on Rosaceous trees, and *F. Ribis* on currants and goose-berries.

Moss-covered trunks provide a similar habitat to a moss carpet on the ground but the water supply is irregular. A few small delicate, short-lived species of *Mycena* typically occur there: *M. corticalis, M. hiemalis, M. alba* and *M. olida*. Species of *Galera* are also frequent.

Mosses on the ground, especially *Polytrichum*, provide the small *Cyphella muscigena, Cantharellus (Dictyolus) muscigenus, C. lobatus* and *C. retirugis*.

Many Discomycetes, usually small and brightly coloured, may be found among mosses from early spring. *Peziza rutilans* (Pl. 42*d*, p. 263) is one of the larger species, with an orange-yellow disc, externally paler and slightly downy.

P. aurantia (Pl. 42*c*, p. 262) forms large, irregular, thin, reddish orange-coloured fruit-bodies which lie more or less flat on the ground, paler underneath.

The scarlet flattened discs with a fringe of dark hairs are species of *Lachnea (Ciliaria)*. *L. scutellata* on damp rotten wood, *L. umbrorum* on the ground. *Disciotus venosa* and var. *reticulata. Acetabula vulgaris. Otidea onotica*, usually among oaks; *O. leporina; O. cochleata*.

Helvella crispa (Pl. 41*a*, p. 262) has a thin whitish or ochraceous yellow cap usually with three dependent lobes, and a whitish then yellowish ribbed and lacunose stem; *H. lacunosa; H. elastica*.

Morchella esculenta, the morel, has several forms. It is most frequent where ground has been disturbed. The cap is ochraceous yellow to blackish, globose to sub-conical, with firm anastomosing ribs which form irregularly arranged pits with radiating folds; the stem whitish and meally.

Leotia lubrica; L. chlorocephala. Macropodia macropus.

Galactinia badia (Pl. 42*b*, p. 263) has the cups sometimes irregular or ear-shaped; the disc dark umber-brown, externally lighter and minutely granular, with a fleshy base often with a short stem.

Under **Alders** several species of *Naucoria* occur the commonest of which is *N. escharoides; N. scolecina. Lactarius obnubilis (obscuratus)*.

The only British lignicolous *Leptonia, L. euchroa*, is most frequent on old alder stumps; *Pluteus coccineus; Flammula alnicola. Polyporus radiatus* (Pl. 26*b*, p. 167), bracket-shaped, the surface rust-brown with radiating grooves, the pores minute, silvery, glistening. *Clavaria contorta* on dead twigs.

Poplar. The characteristic species under poplar are *Tricholoma pessundatum, Lactarius controversus, Boletus duriusculus, Helvella monachella* and *Mitrophora hybrida*. (Pl. IIIa, p. 50).

Pholiota destruens on the bole and on logs; *P. heteroclita* on alder and willow.

On **Willow** also occur *Pluteus salicinus* and *P. leoninus. Pholiota erinacea* on fallen twigs. *Flammula connissans. Fomes igniarius. Trametes suaveolens; T. rubescens*.

On trunks of **Elms** *Pleurotus ulmarius, P. palmatus, Pholiota aegerita, Fomes ulmarius*. The large *Volvaria bombycina* (Pl. XXII, p. 279) usually grows on old elm-stumps; the cap is generally yellowish at first, then white becoming fawn, silky, the stem and large volva white.

Usually on **Ash**, though frequent on fruit-trees. is the parasitic *Polyporus hispidus. Daldinia concentrica* is also most common on ash.

Under **Hazel**, *Lactarius pyrogalus* and *Boletus Carpini*, which also grows under horn-beam, where *Lactarius circillatus* occurs.

Under **Hawthorn** the small *Tubaria autochthona*, apparently attached to old berries. On **Elder**, the Jew's Ear, *Hirneola auricula-Judae*. *Marasmius Hudsonii* on old holly leaves.

BIRCH-WOODS

Birch-woods. The fungi characteristically associated with birches are *Amanita muscaria*, *Tricholoma fulvum*, *Lactarius turpis*, *L. pubescens* and *L. glyciosmus*, *Russula aeruginea* (*graminicolor*) and *R. exalbicans*, *Cortinarius hemitrichus*, *Boletus scaber*, *B. holopus* and *B. versipellis*, and in damp places *Lactarius cyathula*, *L. uvidus* and *L. vietus*, *Russula claroflava*, *R. venosa* and *R. versicolor*.

Amanita muscaria, perhaps the most noticeable birch species, occurs also under pines. There are other pine-birch species, some such as *Tricholoma saponaceum* and *T. equestre* similarly forming mycorrhizas with both trees while others like *Cortinarius violaceus* (Pl. 18a, p. 131) possibly find conditions of soil and litter in the two habitats comparable. *C. violaceus* may be mistaken for a dark-coloured *Tricholoma nudum* but for the cortina, and the gills becoming rusty brown as the spores mature. *C. hemitrichus* is almost always present. Other species are *C. triumphans*, *C. armillatus* and *C. pholideus*.

One of the commonest sights amongst birches is *Polyporus betulinus* (Pl. 38b, p. 247) which, starting as a roundish white knob on branch or trunk, soon expands to a bracket with a pale brown upper surface and minute white pores.

On old stumps *Lenzites betulina* is common.

Fomes fomentarius seems to be confined to birch in this country though, on the Continent, it is more frequent on beech.

BEECH-WOODS

Beech-woods are rich in species of *Cortinarius*, *Russula* and *Marasmius* but poor in *Lactarius* and without a characteristic *Boletus*.

Of the forty or so species of *Cortinarius* the most characteristic are *C. elatior*, *C. albo-violaceus*, *C. bolaris*, *C. Bulliardii*, *C. torvus*, *C. cinnabarinus*.

Russula fellea and *R. lepida*, common; *R. virescens; R. aurata; R. alutacea; R. lauro-cerasi; R. maculata; R. solaris*, rare.

Lactarius pallidus seems to be the only restricted species though *L. blennius* shows preference for beech.

Marasmius alliaceus, *M. Wynniae* (*globularis*), *M. cohaerens* (*ceratopus*), *M. lupeletorum*, *M. fuscopurpureus*, on leaves, often in clusters.

Coprinus picaceus (Pl. 21, p. 150), the ovoid cap at first covered with a white felt-like layer (veil) which is left as patches on the dark brown skin.

*Mycena pelianthina; the rare *M. crocata*, attached to leaves and twigs; *M. fagetorum* and *M. capillaris* on fallen leaves.

The massive *Clavaria pistillaris* (Pl. 30, p. 183) is broadly club-shaped, light yellow then ochraceous, darkening where touched, often longitudinally rugose.

On trunks and stumps.

Armillaria mucida (Pl. XXI, p. 278), common on the smaller branches, has a shining white, translucent, very viscid cap, white, widely spaced gills and a thin white stem striate above a wide ring. *Pholiota adiposa*. *Pleurotus petaloides* on buried stumps; *P. lignatilis*, on trunks and stumps. *Pluteus leoninus* and *P. chrysophaeus* on stumps.

Plate 33a. *Lycoperdon pyriforme*; often in dense clusters on tree-stumps, logs, or buried wood. The only lignicolous British Gasteromycete (*Paul L, de Laszlo*)

b. *Geaster triplex*; a large species, often in quantity in south country beech-woods (*Paul L, de Laszlo*)

Paul L. de Laszlo

Plate 34. *Geaster fornicatus*; uncommon, but usually occurring in small groups

Panus torulosus, on trunks and on stumps. *Lentinus cochleatus*, on stumps. *Ganoderma applanatum* (Pl. XV*a*, p. 226), a very common parasite forming large broad flattened brackets.
Trametes gibbosa and *T. mollis*, on stumps.
Hydnum Erinaceus and *H. coralloides* prefer beech. *H. Erinaceus* (Pl. XVI*b*, p. 227), on trunks; large, white or yellowish white, composed of numerous branches more or less fused together, the whole lower surface covered with long, straight, hanging spines. *H. coralloides* (Pl. XVI*a*, p. 227), on rotten logs and branches forming pure white tufts; the thick stem divides successively into long, graceful intertwining branches with bunches of awl-shaped spines hanging from their lower surface.
The black rubber-like button-shaped bodies often growing in quantity on logs is the Discomycete *Bulgaria inquinans* (*polymorpha*) (Pl. XV*b*, p. 226); the hard reddish hemispherical one is the Pyrenomycete, *Hypoxylon coccineum*.

OAK-WOODS

Oak-woods have not so many characteristic species as beech-woods, but there are a few species of *Boletus*, though none of them is common—*B. castaneus*, *B. pulverulentus* and *B. albidus*.
Russula vesca, *R. pectinata*, *R. sororia* and *R. brunneoviolacea.*
Lactarius chrysorrheus.
On trunks and stumps; *Mycena inclinata*, in tufts on stumps. *Polyporus dryadeus*, usually at the base of old trees. *Fomes robustus*. *Fistulina hepatica*, the Beef-Steak Fungus, looking somewhat like an ox-tongue with a glutinous upper surface, yellow tubes and streaky flesh exuding a red juice. *Daedalea quercina*, on stumps. *Stereum spadiceum* (*gausapatum*), on stumps and fallen branches.

CHARCOAL

In former times large quantities of charcoal were used for iron smelting, a fact which had a noticeably harmful effect on our forests. The destructive open kiln method still lingers on in Kent and Sussex and in the Wyre Forest and Welsh Marches. The old hearths always provide a number of characteristic fungi, some of much interest. Nowadays one has mostly to be satisfied with the burnt wood or ground which mark the spots of fires of woodmen or picnickers, or more extensive conflagrations. It is not known whether or not fire brings about changes beneficial to the growth of certain fungi by producing some substances favourable to them, or by removing something deleterious, or perhaps by sterilising the ground and so removing competing species.

Many species growing on charcoal are dark-coloured but as this seems to be of no consequence except to mycologists it would be rash to assume that it is protective coloration. Notable exceptions are *Pyronema confluens* and *Neurospora* (*Monilia*) *sitophila* and *N. tetrasperma*, Ascomycetes which have played a prominent part in ancient and modern controversies about sex.
A whole series of Discomycetes are found in burnt places, some of them, however, not appearing until there is an overgrowth of mosses. *Geopyxis carbonaria*. *Humaria* (*Anthracobia*) *melaloma*. *Humaria* (*Anthracobia*) *maurilabra*. *Humaria carbonigena*.

Several small orange, orange-red or reddish species occur chiefly amongst mosses, e.g. *Lamprospora dictydiola*.
Ascobolus atrofuscus (*A. carbonarius*), often covering large patches of burnt heaths. *Plicaria leiocarpa* and *P. trachycarpa*, common. *Aleuria umbrina* (*pustulata*) (Pl. 42*a*, p. 263), rather thick and fragile, externally very scurfy, smoky brown, paler towards the toothed margin which remains more or less incurved; the hymenium pallid or dull brown; *A. violacea*, uncommon. *Rhizina undulata*, frequent in coniferous woods where the mycelium may attack the roots of conifers.

Many Basidiomycetes also are found on burned ground, often growing in troops; many of them are sombre-coloured.

Collybia ambusta and *C. atrata*, practically indistinguishable except for their spores. *Omphalia maura*. *Flammula carbonaria*, probably the commonest species of burnt ground. *Hebeloma anthracophilum*, infrequent. *Cantharellus carbonarius*. *Coprinus Boudieri*.

Polyporus perennis, frequent on old burnt patches.

There are other, rarer species, which may be described as carbonicolous and several, such as *Omphalia Postii* and *Psathyra pennata*, which, though not characteristic of burnt places, are often found there.

CHAPTER 20

DRY ROT

F ROM THE EARLIEST times it was realised that wooden structures in the open were subject to decay, but that it was possible to treat wood so that it would remain sound. There are numerous references to this in ancient writings. Thus Noah's instructions were: " Make thee an ark of gopher wood ; rooms shalt thou make in the ark ; and shalt pitch it within and without with pitch." Classical writers narrate that the astringent properties of the oils expressed from olive, cedar, larch, juniper, valerian and so on, were used to preserve wood from decay and from the attacks of insects. The magnificent statue of Zeus by Phidias was erected in a damp grove at Olympus and the platform on which it stood was therefore imbued with oil. The famous statue of Diana at Ephesus was of wood and outlasted " all the seven times that the temple had been rebuilt." Though its origin was generally assumed to be miraculous its lasting qualities were possibly due to the fact that " by the aid of numerous apertures it is soaked with nard, in order that the moist nature of the drug may preserve the wood and keep the seams close together."

The Romans also knew that wood kept continually wet is less liable to rot. Pliny stated that " The pine, the pitch-tree, and the alder are employed for making hollow pipes for the conveyance of water, and when buried in the earth will last for many years." The old water-pipes of London were mostly of elm.* According to Christopher Wren, " Venice and Amsterdam being both founded on wooden piles

*It was not until about 1808 that iron pipes began to supersede wooden ones, some of which remained in use in part of Piccadilly until 1864.

The New River Company, founded in 1613, used hollowed-out tree trunks, principally of elm, but also oak and sycamore, for their four hundred miles of piping.

" Bond St., covering both its old and new sections, is now littered with decayed and hollow tree trunks. These have been unearthed in the process of laying a new water main, and are said to have reposed 350 years below ground." They were roughly trimmed and from six to eight feet long, and were doubtless to supply St. James's Palace. (*Daily Chronicle*, 23 September, 1902.)

immersed in water, would fall if the constancy of the situation of those piles in the same element and temperature did not prevent the timber from rotting." The timber piles of the original London Bridge (1176) which have been recovered at odd times are always sound; some of elm and oak, discovered during excavations in 1937, were " in a very good state of preservation." Oak found in restoration work at Furness Abbey a few years ago suffered more in a few months after excavation than it did in its original sodden situation during hundreds of years. The fact is that unless there is access of air, fungal decay of wood cannot occur. It is not that fungi are unable to grow in water, for there is a well-marked aquatic fungal flora. Many Chytridiales occur in water, sometimes as parasites on algae, flowering plants or other fungi; the Saprolegniaceae, a family of Phycomycetes, are frequent in decayed plant or animal remains, often indirectly causing the death of fish and often forming constituents of what is known as " sewage fungus," the evil-smelling mass that accumulates in streams where there are sewage effluents or waste from breweries, paper mills, sugar-beet factories, Penicillin plant, indeed, in any place where organic material is discharged into water.* It has also lately been found that there is a well-marked and characteristic mould flora on dead leaves in streams. Another recent discovery is that microfungi, chiefly Pyrenomycetes, develop on timbers used in marine structures.

Wood continuously dry is immune from fungal attack. This is one of the reasons why timber is seasoned before being used for con-structional purposes; another is to prevent warping. Whether seasoned or not, if used out of doors all wooden structures eventually rot unless they are treated with some preservative. Painting gives protection to window frames, doors and exposed parts of houses, garden fences, gate-posts and other wood, which, particularly where in contact with the soil, would be soon rotted. A very common fungus which causes damage at and below the level of the soil is the ubiquitous *Polystictus versicolor* (Pl. 26c, p. 167); its white mycelial strands may also be seen on the buried portions of all kinds of dead roots and on stakes used in gardening. The pink pads so abundant on pea-sticks are the conidial form of *Nectria cinnabarina*, a Pyrenomycete (Pl. 40b, p. 255); later the much darker flask-shaped fruit-bodies may often be seen.

*The Dove, beloved by Isaac Walton and Charles Cotton, being " full of very good trout and grayling," may be endangered unless steps are taken to protect it. The Churnet, which flows into the Dove from the point at which the effluent of a dye works enters it near Leek, has its bed " covered with sewage fungus and there are no fish or weed all the way to Froghall, seven miles downstream."

The jelly-like yellow blobs conspicuous after rain on fences are the fruit-bodies of *Dacryomyces deliquescens*; they dry up and become orange-coloured spots to revive again when moistened.

Wood, whether in its natural form or squared and planed, if liable to become moist, inevitably rots; the fungi causing the rot are species common in woodlands, and for the most part are indifferent to whether the bark has been removed or not.

The out-of-door destruction of household effects is of little consequence; a garden without its troubles would cease to be a whole-time hobby.

What about indoor timber? One indirect result of the bombing of built-up areas was that many owners and hirers of property gained experience of dry rot and have ceased to regard it as merely a picturesque epithet useful to apply to Government departments: what was a journalistic joke has become a frightening reality of death, dearth and destruction. Wood is always subject to natural decay if conditions favouring growth of the attacking organism are present; if they are not the wood remains sound.

However beneficent Nature may be assumed to be to man, who is given to regard himself as both her greatest achievement and her chief care, it would be a strange fancy to imagine that there is any special dispensation about his goods and chattels. Structural timber differs in no way from other wood; it must be kept dry or it will decay.

Though many of the larger fungi are occasionally found in houses most of them are just as harmless as mushrooms cultivated in cellars. The fungus which is chiefly responsible for damage, *the* dry rot fungus, is *Merulius lacrymans*. Two other dry rot fungi are common, *Coniophora cerebella (puteana)* and *Poria Vaillantii (vaporaria)*, but *Merulius* is the chief culprit.

The fruit-body of *Merulius lacrymans* is of indefinite size, from little more than 1 in. across up to a yard or more (Pl. 35, p. 238). When mature it is usually about ⅛ in. in average thickness. The margin is white and swollen and surrounds an orange-brown or cinnamon-coloured surface, which is formed of small projections which are often joined in a honey-comb-like manner. The hymenium covers the surface of the projections and the orange-brown is due to the myriads of spores borne on serried ranks of typical basidia. The spores are elliptical, measuring $8\text{-}10 \times 5\text{-}6$ μ and containing an oil-drop; they are yellowish under the microscope. Deposits of spores are frequent on furniture, floors and other surfaces, and indeed these are often the first sign of unwonted occurrence noticed by the occupant of an infected house. Preserved eggs covered with spores have been sent to me, the chief concern being whether such a remarkable external colour phenomenon denoted internal deterioration. The number of spores in such deposits can be realised by a simple calculation. As a μ is $\frac{1}{25400}$ in., spores $10 \times 5 \mu$ placed end to end would take 2540 to extend an inch, and side by side 5080. Thus for the most sparse layer of spores possible there must needs be roughly 1,300,000 spores. A fruit-body a foot in diameter produces millions of millions of spores.

It is not very consoling when everything connected with housing seems in short supply, to realise that dry rot is a striking exception, and that, moreover, a single fruit-body of average size produces enough spores to infect every building in the kingdom. The abundance of spores is the explanation of the outbreaks which puzzle and confuse the householder to such an extent that refuge in beliefs savouring of witchcraft and medieval occultism is not unknown. It is more likely than not that all buildings are infected with spores, and that when conditions are favourable to the fungus, dry rot develops, much as in some human diseases. The factors which favour the development of dry rot are moisture and lack of ventilation. Temperature also plays a part, but as *Merulius* grows over a range extending from a little above freezing point of water to about 80° F.,* it has no limiting effect in our climate; dry rot does not flourish in the tropics, but is a scourge in the wooden houses of arctic Europe as it is in meat stores and refrigerator vans in this country.

When spores alight on damp wood they germinate, and the thread-like hyphae penetrate into the wood, and, procuring nutriment from it, continue to grow. When spores fall on any substance other than wood, growth, if any, cannot continue after the food-reserve material contained in them is exhausted; they die of starvation. The fungus can get nourishment only from wood, and in extracting the constituents it uses as food, brings about changes both in substance and structure. The hyphae may remain wholly within the wood, giving no external sign of their presence until severe rotting has developed; bulging and cracking are then the signs of attack, as is common in painted wood.

*The upper limit of growth is thus well below the temperature of the human body. The widespread belief that the fungus can be pathogenic to man is consequently without foundation, though it is possible that the inspiration of myriads of spores may occasionally affect the respiratory organs; they have recently been shown to cause respiratory allergy. Conditions in which the fungus thrives, however, may themselves be deleterious to health.

When the only free surface is painted, as in door posts and skirtings, the presence of the fungus can often be detected by noting such bulges and cracks.

In addition to the internal mycelium there is usually an external one, sometimes meagre in development, but more often a dense white fluffy growth, or even a pad-like structure, depending upon the amount of moisture present. At a late stage this superficial growth may become compact and silvery grey, looking much like the skin of a fish—often tinged with light purple. The dense white type of growth soon shows what look like veins. These are formed by some of the hyphae joining laterally, and gradually becoming strands or strings which are at first white but later become grey. Some reach a thickness of $\frac{1}{8}$ in. and these thicker strands show more differentiation than do those of any other fungus and are admirably adapted for the function they serve. They are composed of three different elements: narrow hyphae with clamp-connections which are in every way similar to the ordinary mycelium; long pointed cells with walls which are so thick that there is hardly any internal cavity, obviously strengthening structures which prevent the strand from tearing or breaking; and very wide thin-walled hyphae with large perforations in the cross walls, much resembling the sieve tubes of green plants and, like them, serving for the transport of food material. By means of these strands of various thicknesses *Merulius* is able to spread over material and structures from which it can derive no nutriment. If wood is reached in its wanderings, this is immediately attacked and eventually destroyed. It is this effective method of extending its ravages which makes *Merulius* so dangerous. It enables it to pass through mortar and through the pores in bricks and even stone, under tiles, cement flooring, and plaster, along bell-wires, indeed to extend across anything that gives mechanical support, so long as the originally infected wood continues to provide nourishment. When wood is attacked several yards away from the source it gives the impression of a new infection, but that it is not so is seen when search reveals the threads and cords.

When strands are unable to extend further for physical reasons as, for example, when they reach the exterior of a wall or the top of a joist, they grow out into a pad of mycelium, either whitish, often with a tinge of purple, or light brown, and this spreads out into a flat layer with a thicker rim. The surface of the inner portion becomes folded into shallow pores becoming reddish brown or cinnamon-colour as the spores ripen—for it is the fruit-body—the margin usually remaining white. Owing to luxuriant growth on a vertical surface, or to the contour of the surface itself, the fruit-body may be bracket-shaped. Then the hymenium-folds often become elongated into teeth-like projections. Occasionally the folds heap together into small tubercles.

When fruit-bodies are seen on walls or on concrete floors, possibly square yards in total extent, it is natural to suppose that the fungus is obtaining nutriment from them. It is, however, only the outward and visible sign that there is rotting wood, though this may be some distance away. Thus, when some years ago Haddon Hall was being renovated for residence, a large fruit-body was found in a stone oven without any visible means of support. The interest shown in this fungus apparently growing on stone, led to the discovery that the famous dance floor was beginning to rot; the strands of the fungus had passed through the joints of nine yards of solid stone-work.

Fruit-bodies usually occur on walls, occasionally on an outside wall, on door posts, joists, around skirting boards, almost as if there was a welling out to the surface. The fruit-body itself may be regarded as marking the end of the attack in a particular direction. It is difficult not to imply motive to this insidious intruder of man's habitations; to imagine that when it has caused as much destruction as possible along its path in one direction, it summons up its substance for a prolific output of spores in order to extend the range of its activities, is teleological reasoning, but the end is the same however it is reached.

When *Merulius* is growing in a confined space, as, for example, behind panelling, the mycelium often grows as a white fluffy growth filling the whole of the space between wood and wall. Occasionally similar growths occur in cellars or rooms long unopened; " like a snow scene " or " looking like the Alps " suggest the picture then presented. When growing through walls as in wine cellars the fluff may have a pinkish tinge.

The amount of damage caused by dry rot in this country is normally far greater than is thought, and most of it is avoidable. If a building is well constructed and kept in good repair there need be no fear of trouble. At the present time the amount of destruction, especially in bombed areas, almost passes belief. The majority of houses in certain districts of London are believed to be infected: a survey of four hundred houses in Regent's Terrace showed dry rot in all. Wherever repair work is in progress rotten timber can be seen stacked for removal. It has recently been stated that " Dry rot in buildings is increasing rapidly throughout the country. It is estimated that 50 per cent of all

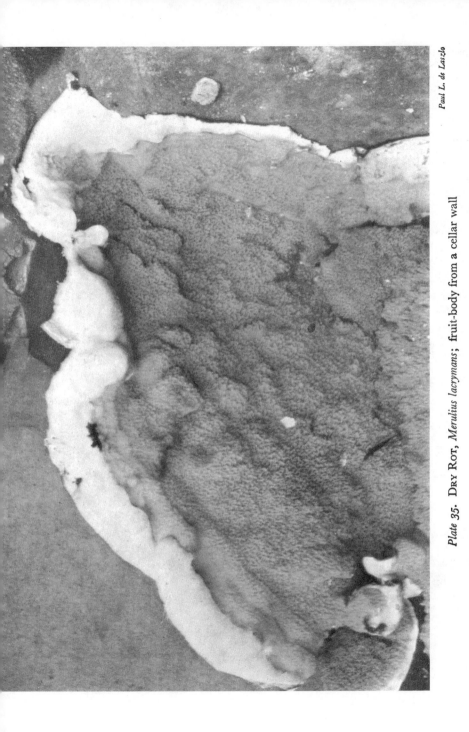

Plate 35. DRY ROT, *Merulius lacrymans*; fruit-body from a cellar wall

Paul L. de Laszlo

Paul L. de Laszlo

Plate 36a. DRY ROT, *Merulius lacrymans*; fruit-body on the

b. DRY ROT, *Merulius lacrymans*; household utensils which

London buildings have become affected since the war. About £20 million is being spent yearly on fighting the attacks, compared with about £1 million before the war."

There is no mystery about the so-called outbreak of dry rot; given the circumstances it was inevitable and was foreseen. When war seemed probable, ventilation-bricks were closed up with paper to prevent the ingress of poison gas, or blocked up with bags containing sand or soil, which rapidly became sodden. When war broke out shelters were constructed which often interfered with ventilation and water-courses, or in other ways made buildings less hygienic in an architectural sense. When the blasts of war really reached us, some houses were shut up and others requisitioned. Moisture and lack of ventilation are the primary factors favouring *Merulius*. Unoccupied houses had their roofs damaged, rain-pipes cracked or blocked, accumulated debris stopped up overflows, and water seeped through walls or poured through broken windows and roofs. Requisitioned houses were in no better plight, for though major repairs were often attended to, minor ones were neglected: carelessness on the part of His Majesty's guests, led to baths overflowing, cisterns leaking and to temporary additions to structures made without thought to moisture and ventilation. The general result was that in empty houses dry rot often got a good hold before it was noticed; in those publicly occupied it was no one's business to trouble about it even if it were noticed.

Plate 35, p. 238, shows a fruit-body of *Merulius lacrymans* from a cellar-wall. The house had been requisitioned, and when left for a period the charged radiators had burst owing to frost and had flooded two floors; dry rot developed and fruited in the cellar. Plate 36, p. 239, shows an attack in an unoccupied house. The drain under the rain-pipe had become stopped up with leaves and overflowed. The water had seeped through the kitchen wall and the fungus attacked the skirting board and floor, which collapsed. The fungal threads passed through the wall into an adjacent room where they grew on to the mat which lay on the hearth, and thence to the various oddments—sweeping brush, kettle, mangle—and there formed a series of small fruit-bodies.

Merulius, when growing on wood, decomposes it and reduces it eventually to powder. During the process water is formed equal in amount to half the dry weight. The fungus when growing strongly is thus able to provide itself with the water it needs for growth, though it must have moist wood to begin its attack. If not interfered with it may spread throughout a house, making floors and staircases unsafe and causing walls to bulge and crack. The fungus hanging from the eaves, the extensive decay and the fissures in the walls in Edgar Allen Poe's story, explain the mystery, though not the imagination, of *The Fall of the House of Usher.*

The worst attack I have seen was in a castle in Eire.* The stone walls had been built with the spaces between them slanting inwards so that when pointing was neglected and mortar perished, water ran through and got behind the panels. The whole of this space was a mass of fungus; most of the panelling was rotten. The threads and strands passed through mortar and even through the large solid stone, attacked floors, fruited on the walls and literally pervaded the building. Renovation was begun but eventually had to stop, and the castle is now left in sole possession of the fungus.

During luxuriant growth and frequently in the formation of fruit-bodies, there is excess moisture and this is exuded in drops. This is the weeping denoted by *lacrymans* and not that of the householder.

All kinds of wood are liable to attack as far is as known, soft woods being for the most part more susceptible than hard woods like oak, yew and teak. The greater prevalence of dry rot in modern buildings is doubtless due in part to the use of the less resistant soft woods, though these readily take up preservatives which confer a measure of immunity. Canadian Western Red Cedar (*Thuja plicata*), which contains a natural preservative, Red Wood (*Sequoia sempervirens*) and Yellow Cedar (*Cupressus nootkatensis*) all show a high resistance to attack.

Though *Merulius* must start its growth on wood, when it spreads to other organic material it may cause considerable damage, partly due to the water exuded, but apparently also to some definite action on the material, especially if containing cellulose. This is not so remarkable as it at first seems, for the fungus can be grown on culture media. Books are sometimes damaged and labels of specimens defaced; even army records are not sacrosanct. Among the more unusual examples sent to me have been boots with the uppers destroyed, though not more than a year in stock; cops of yarn reduced to powder; sacks destroyed and *Merulius* fruiting on emery powder.

Wood infected with *Merulius* gradually discolours and softens, and as it begins to dry out, cracks in three dimensions, so forming cubes. Eventually the whole is reduced to powder; it is to this probably that

---

*" Cottages . . . belong as much to the Irish scene as the unwieldly country mansions whose occupants battle cheerfully with debts, paying guests, and dry rot." *Observer*, 20 May, 1951.

the name dry rot applies. Previous to 1795 all rots were spoken of as " distemper of timber " and though many practical men distinguish in speech between dry rot and wet rot, in practice there is no difference; there must be moisture or there will be no growth, and the fact that *Merulius*, the dry rot fungus, often exudes quantities of water, leads not only to confusion but also to malpractice. All rotting of structural timber should be styled dry rot, and if the name wet rot is to be retained at all it should be restricted to rot in the timber of a growing tree, in other words to timber that is unsuitable for building purposes.

The mycelium continues alive in the decayed wood for some time, often in the form of oidia, formed by the protoplasm massing together in parts of the hyphae and being separated off by cross walls.

Of the two other dry rot fungi, *Coniophora cerebella* is the more common in buildings. It is characteristic of wood which is constantly wet, and does not extend its growth beyond the damp region. Unlike *Merulius lacrymans* which rarely occurs in woods, and then only as a special sub-species,* *Coniophora cerebella* is frequent there. Out-of-doors it is recognised by its fruit-body, which, in my experience, is not very frequent indoors; this is usually irregularly shaped, from 1 in. or so to about two feet in diameter. It is much thinner and more crust-like than that of *Merulius*, and is closely adpressed to the substratum, from which it readily peels away. The hymenial surface is at first flat and yellowish, but usually becomes irregularly warted and gradually changes colour to olive-brown or olive-green as the spores ripen. The margin remains creamy white and is usually indefinite, sometimes with a fringe of thin spidery mycelium. The spores are yellow-brown to olive-brown, 11-13 × 7-8 μ and thus larger and wider than those of *Merulius*. There is rarely much external growth on attacked wood, at most only a small patch of thin yellowish skin and never the thick sheets and pads as in *Merulius*. Mycelial strands, however, occur on the surface of the wood. They are occasionally whitish for a short time, but usually yellowish brown, rapidly darkening and becoming almost black. These strands often cover a considerable surface, branching in a dendritic manner and reminding one of some of the filamentous red seaweeds (Pl. XVIIa, p. 242). The mycelium in the wood has simple clamp-connections. Most text-book figures show it as having a peculiar and characteristic whorl of clamps, but these occur when the fungus is grown in culture; there are as many as five in a whorl.

Merulius silvester Falck probably the same as *M. himantioides* Fr.

Coniophora attacks both hard and soft woods, but these must have a high moisture content; it is very sensitive to drying, for unlike *Merulius* it does not produce water which can serve for its further development. Infected wood immediately becomes discoloured with yellowish brown streaks and patches: it rapidly darkens and finally may be so black that charring may be suspected. The wood cracks mainly along the grain, but also at right angles though not so extensively as in wood rotted by *Merulius*.

The other species of importance, *Poria Vaillantii*, is not so frequent in buildings as are *Merulius* and *Coniophora*. It is, however, very troublesome in damp mines where it is one of the chief agents of timber decay, rapidly reducing pit props to uselessness. It is one of the sights of damp coal mines where long threads of white mycelium hang down from the roof timbers (Pl. XVII*b*, *c*, p. 242).

The fungus forms white mycelial sheets on the surface of the wood and mycelial cords which are not so thick as those of *Merulius* and which remain white. The fruit-body varies much in shape and thickness. It is white or creamy white and sometimes thick and pad-like, or may be little more than a skin. The surface is covered with angular tubes which vary in depth from $\frac{1}{16}$ to $\frac{1}{2}$ in., depending upon the thickness of the fruit-body; the pores are small and round or angular, but when growing on a vertical surface may become torn and tooth-like. An unusual feature is that mycelial strands, often of considerable thickness, are attached to the edge of the fruit-body, some obviously conducting the food material necessary for fruit production, others serving to extend the area of attack. *Poria* requires more moisture for its development than does *Merulius*, and is able to withstand a higher temperature. The rot it produces is similar.

There are several other fungi which occur on woodwork in buildings. One, *Fomes (Phellinus) cryptarum (megaloporus)*, seems to be confined to oak and, consequently, in this country, is found chiefly in old buildings. In France, however, it ranks next to *Merulius* in its frequency in houses: it was responsible for serious damage to the roof of the Palace of Versailles. It requires very moist conditions and a relatively high temperature. It probably causes more rapid decay in oak than does any other fungus, but as it does not form mycelial strands it does not spread, and consequently may remain long overlooked in the oak beams in roofs.* Infected wood rapidly loses colour and finally becomes

*It has, however, been recorded as developing on electric wires having a difference in potential of 110 volts.

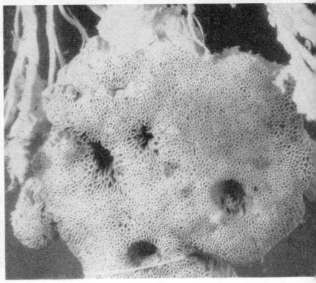

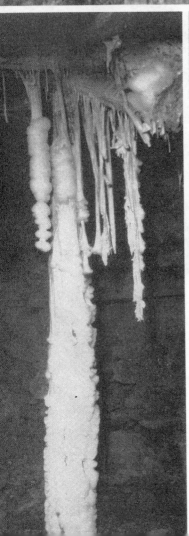

Plate XVIIa (top). Coniophora cerebella. Strands growing over
damp wall. (D. Walker). b (lower left) Poria Vaillantii, hanging
in stalactite-like growths from the roof-timber in mines
(Forest Products Research Laboratory). c (lower right) Fruit-body of Poria
Vaillantii (Forest Products Research Laboratory)

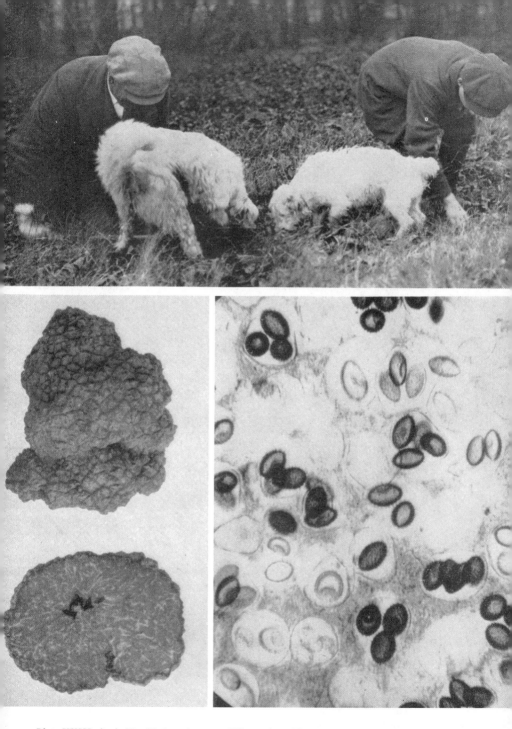

Plate XVIIIa (*top*). Truffle-hunting near Winterslow, Hants. (*The Topical Press Agency*) *b* (*lower left*).
Summer Truffle, *Tuber aestivum,* whole and in section. (*Brit. Mus.* [*Nat. Hist.*]) *c* (*lower right*).
Section magnified showing the ascospores; the number in an ascus varies from one to four.
(*Flatters and Garnett*)

reduced to long white fibrous strands looking like lint. The decayed wood forms a suitable pabulum for the larvae of the Death Watch Beetle which usually is a fellow traveller in the work of destruction. The fruit-body is of variable shapes and sizes. Frequently it is in the form of a pad, at first spongy and flabby, and becoming fairly hard except for the velvety surface; at other times it spreads out as a thick reddish brown plate marked with darker spots where drops of liquid have been exuded. Soon the surface becomes covered with a layer of long tubes with minute pores, often pinkish brown. The fruit-body is perennial and three or four successive layers of tubes may be formed: the flesh is reduced to a thin, hard, woody crust. The spores are creamy white.

Paxillus panuoides is frequent on old sawdust heaps and occasional on decayed conifers. As affecting timber it is found in the same conditions as *Coniophora*, though it is more common in damp coal-mines than in buildings. The fruit-body is shell-shaped and wholly dull yellow, with a slightly hairy upper surface, and decurrent gills which are branched, crisped and crowded. A fibrous yellow mycelium is often seen on the surface of infected wood with fine branching strands which are also yellow. The wood itself is first stained bright yellow but finally becomes dark reddish brown, soft, and longitudinally cracked.

The woodwork of greenhouses is often rotted by *Poria xantha*. The sulphur-yellow fruit-body is a thin layer consisting for the most part of short narrow tubes with small, angular pores which are often torn, and thickish separating walls. There is little or no external mycelium. Infected wood becomes brown and cracked into tubes. The fungus smells like cheap scented soap.*

Daedalea quercina occasionally occurs on worked oak in houses, but more frequently in outbuildings, probably because wood already infected has been used in construction.

From the fact that wood is non-living it follows that even if a fungus attacking it is killed there can be no rejuvenation. Consequently all remedial methods are devised for the prevention of the spread of infection.

There is a vast literature on wood preservation dating back over

---

*The reddish purple patches, the so-called " paint measles," which often disfigure the damp white paint of greenhouses, are caused by one of the Fungi Imperfecti, *Aposphaeria violacea* (*Phoma pigmentivora*), whose fruit-bodies can be seen as minute black dots on the patches.

a century. Creosote, which was introduced in 1838, is still the most successful of all wood preservatives. There are also other preservative oils in use, as well as water soluble chemicals, and chemicals dissolved in oils and non-aqueous solvents.

It may truly be said that dry rot is so prominent in the public eye that for many it will be regarded as a special characteristic of World War No. 2. It is a subject of general conversation, though hardly the talk of the town, as it was before the end of the previous series of continental wars in which this country was engaged. Then, however, it was not the condition of buildings that caused alarm but that of the king's ships, particularly the *Queen Charlotte.*

The story of dry rot in ships and its repeated threats to our naval supremacy is long and fascinating and provides much scope for research. Accustomed to thinking in terms of expensive battleships which may be out-of-date before they are even launched, we are apt to overlook the fact that until about ninety years ago there was no gradual increase in tonnage, and, moreover, the vessels did not become obsolete. The *Royal William*, built in 1719, took part in Howe's relief of Gibraltar in 1782 and bore the flag of the Port Admiral at Spithead in 1805.

Oak was the principal wood used for the hulls of naval ships; indeed if there had been sufficient English oak no other timber would have been employed. The fear of the scarcity of oak through reckless felling led to various timber preservation Acts, and to attempts at re-afforestation.

Wooden ships of all times must have suffered from rotting. The alternate wetting and drying of parts of the woodwork, the poor ventilation and the use of unseasoned wood all favour the development of the ills to which timber is heir.

" In buylding and repaireing Shippes with greene Tymber, Planck and Trennels it is apparent both by demonstration to the Shippes danger and by heate of the Houlde meeting with the greenesse and sappines thereof doth immediately putrefie the same and drawes that Shippe to the Dock agayne for reparation within the space of six or seaven yeares that would last twentie if it were seasoned as it ought."

A striking account of the condition of affairs is given by Samuel Pepys, though not in the *Diary* which gives delight in so many ways. When recalled to the Admiralty Board in 1684, a survey was made of the fleet, and particularly of thirty new ships. A melancholy visit to Chatham showed that " The greatest part of these thirty ships (without having yet lookt out of Harbour) were let to sink into such Distress, through Decays contracted . . . that several of them . . . lye in danger of sinking at their very Moorings." The planks were " in many places perish'd to powder " and the ships' sides more disguised by patching " than has usually been seen upon the coming in of a Fleet after a Battle." " Their Holds not clear'd nor aird, but (for want of Gratings and opening their Hatches and Scuttles) suffer'd to heat and moulder, till I have with my own Hands gather'd Toadstools growing in the most considerable of them, as big as my Fists."

Discussions were many about the effect of the season of felling on the durability of timber and the effect of barking. Few saw that the most reasonable policy was to build a few ships each year and thus be able always to use properly seasoned wood, and that older ships could then be kept in reasonable repair ready for service. What invariably happened, however, seems to have been to regard every period of peace as likely to be permanent, even at times when such a prospect could have been visualised only by the politically mad. War ended, shipbuilding slackened or was suspended, trained shipwrights were discharged, stores neglected, and ships removed from active service (" sea-pay ") and placed in reserve (" in ordinary ") at the dockyards, where they remained unventilated or rotting in what came to be called " Rotten Row." At the beginning of another war some of these ships were found to be unserviceable, and the timber they contained almost a total loss. A fleet formidable enough on paper had decayed into insignificance. In the haste to call a new fleet into being timber was hurriedly acquired and ships hastily constructed with the unseasoned material, material which was also used to patch up the reserve; rushed to sea, the vessels rotted with notorious speed.

After Trafalgar interest was mainly centred on the *Queen Charlotte*. A first rate of 110 guns she was launched in 1810 and rotted so quickly that it was necessary to rebuild her before she could even be commissioned for sea. Repairs up to 1816 cost £94,499 in addition to the original £88,534, before she could be used. By 1859 the total cost of repairs had mounted to £287,837, when her name was changed to *Excellent*—a whimsical choice. She is still remembered by many naval officers as she served as the gunnery school at Portsmouth until she was broken up in 1892.

Various chemical treatments to prevent rot were suggested, and the necessity for preserving railway sleepers gave a further stimulus which led to the use of the oils of coal tar, those heavier than water being called creosote. But dry rot continued to destroy the British Navy. Merchant vessels were in better state, partly because of the beneficial effect of loading and unloading on ventilation. However, decay was not unknown—it was probably owing to dry rot that the *Speedwell* did not accompany the *Mayflower*, and it was " the decayed state " of the *Investigator* that caused Captain Flinders to leave the ship.

Merulius lacrymans was partly responsible for the damage, but various Polypores, including *Polyporus sulphureus*, species of *Poria*, and *Coniophora cerebella* ably assisted. The *Victory* still shows signs of attacks by this last species and many of the figureheads of famous ships which are kept at Portsmouth and other dockyards, have had most of their wood destroyed by this fungus: the several coatings of paint have preserved the shapes, but rain water having percolated through cracks, has provided ideal conditions for the development of *Coniophora*, which has reduced the wood to powder.

It should not be assumed that dry rot no longer troubles men of the sea, for there is a considerable amount of fungal decay in sailing craft of different categories—life-boats, barges, yachts, speed-boats, as well as larger vessels—*Polyporus sulphureus* being the main cause. *Discovery*, when being refitted for Antarctic research was found to have suffered decay and *Pourquoi-Pas?* on her cruise to the Faroes narrowly escaped disaster owing to her planks and beams becoming rotted by *Poria Vaillantii*.

Plate 37a. STINK-HORN, *Phallus impudicus*; the spore-containing gluten has been removed by flies and by slugs

(Paul L. de Laszlo)

b. Clathrus ruber; Bromley, Kent. The spore-containing gluten was eaten by flies

(Paul L. de Laszlo)

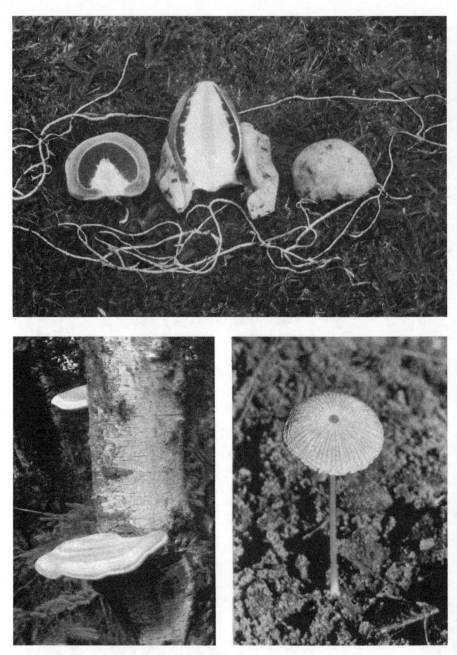

Plate 38a (above). STINK-HORN, *Phallus impudicus;* " eggs " attached to mycelial cords. The sections show the mature spore-mass already formed; expansion is by the rapid enlargement of the cells of the stem. *(Paul L. de Laszlo)* ; *b (below left)* RAZOR-STROP FUNGUS, *Polyporus betulinus;* a very common fungus restricted to birch. *(Paul L. de Laszlo)* ; *c (below right) Coprinus plicatilis;* the gills of this *Coprinus* do not undergo self-digestion *(Paul L. de Laszlo)*

CHAPTER 21

BIRD'S NEST FUNGI AND OTHER
GASTEROMYCETES

PUFF-BALLS are without a true stem, though some species have a sterile base which resembles one, but has the same origin as the fertile gleba; it is in fact a portion of the gleba which does not carry on with its original purpose. There are some nearly related genera, however, which have a true stem, distinct from the glebal tissue from its first appearance. Three of these genera are represented in this country, *Tulostoma*, *Battarraea* and *Queletia*—each by one species.

Tulostoma brumale (*T. mammosum*) is the least rare, occurring here and there in sand-dunes, where it looks like a small puff-ball but with a slender stem, buried in the sand. The peridium is whitish then yellowish, with a friable outer layer, which usually falls away except at the base, and a thin, smooth, papery inner one. There is a slightly projecting umbo which ruptures at maturity for the liberation of the pinkish, acutely warted spores. The stem is whitish at first but becomes reddish brown; it is smooth or fibrillose and slightly narrowed upwards to its junction with the peridium where it fits into a socket, and at its base has a ball of mycelial threads. The gleba is rusty brown and there is an abundant capillitium of hyaline threads which arise from the inner surface of the peridium. *Tulostoma* also occurs on old walls. Sowerby says that he was never in want of specimens " either from the walls of Hyde Park " or from a wall near the halfway-house to Greenwich. Plowright recorded it from between the stone paving setts in a street at Kings Lynn.

Battarraea phalloides is another strange-looking fungus. It is usually about a foot high, rusty brown, with the spores enclosed in a concave-convex receptable, which is borne on a hard tapering stem covered with long twisted fibres, seated in a loose white parchment-like cup (volva). The receptacle splits round the rim to release the spores.

The young fungus is ovate, whitish or slightly brownish, with a wall composed of an outer fleshy and an almost membranous inner layer, the space between them filled with mucilage. As development proceeds the young stem elongates rapidly and, with some force, bursts through the soil carrying the whole of the inner and part of the outer layer of the volva on the top of the cap where it gradually dries.

Barrattaea phalloides was first described by Thomas Woodward in 1784 as " a new Plant of the Order of Fungi." " This extraordinary vegetable production arises from a volva, which is buried six or eight inches deep in dry sandy banks; and, consequently, it is extremely difficult to detect in its earliest state." It had been gathered by W. Humphrey* in 1782 but in a far advanced condition, and it was suspected by some to be a decayed or abortive agaric, possibly *Lepiota procera*. Woodward himself first found the fungus in a dry and withered state near Bungay, Suffolk, in the spring of 1783 and, digging down to see whether the stem had a bulbous base, discovered the volva. He communicated his findings to Dickson who requested him to watch the spot and try to detect the fungus in its early stages. Woodward and his neighbour, R. Stone, found a young specimen in August but, though they visited the locality daily, had no greater success, " for so rapid appears to be its growth that we have found plants of two or three inches high above the ground, the stems of which had lost part of their mucilage, where the day before none had been visible." Woodward held that " this plant agrees with the genus *Phallus* in its volva which has a double coat replete with mucilage." The stem also is filled with mucilage in its early stages. Dickson in 1785 named it *Lycoperdon Phalloides*, thus indicating its similarity to *Phallus*, while placing chief stress on the powdery gleba. Persoon in *Synopsis* (1801) erected the genus *Batarrea*† for its reception; as two cancel pages in a copy of this work in the library of the Linnean Society of London show the name *Bungea* was his first choice.

Battarraea phalloides is a rare fungus recorded from about a dozen British localities. All the early findings were from Suffolk (Bungay, Yoxford) and Norfolk (Norwich, Stoke, Earnshaw, Kirby), but apparently it was not found there again for over a century; it occurred in 1931 near Brandon, Suffolk. It was recorded from Bucks (Dropmore

* Also appears " Humphreys " and " Humfery.'

† The spelling of the name has undergone vicissitudes—*Batarrea, Battarea, Battarrea* and *Battarraea*; as the genus was named in honour of A. C. J. Battarra the last is correct.

1844), Cheshire (New Brighton 1857), Surrey (Nork 1872, Wickham, Virginia Water 1944, Bòx Hill 1953) and Gloucester (Temple Guiting 1915); Plate 39*b*, p. 254, shows this last specimen so displayed that the whole fungus is seen.

Sometimes a single specimen was found, at others several: Sowerby (1792) says, " Mr. Davey, of the Grove, Yoxford, finds it annually in Suffolk." The habitat is always sandy places or (Stoke, Dropmore, Nork and Temple Guiting) outside and inside hollow trees, ash being the most usual. Although fifteen species of *Battarraea* have been described, only three or four seem to be well founded. What is surprising is that *B. phalloides*, the type species originally discovered in this country, is known with certainty elsewhere only from one locality in France, and one (perhaps two) in Italy. It was found near Moulins (Allièr) in 1872 on debris inside hollow oaks 500 metres apart, and appeared every year until 1906 at least.

No question arises here about introduction from abroad but the sporadic appearances of the fungus over a century and a half should be taken into account when considering the distribution of other rare Gasteromycetes.

The spores of *Battarraea* have two walls, a very thick hyaline endospore and a yellowish fawn, punctate epispore. The basidia are club-shaped and have four sterigmata. Sporulation takes place very rapidly, the spores soon becoming detached and completing their ripening before the outer peridium breaks.

Battarraea is remarkable in having two kinds of sterile cells in the gleba. The ones are similar to the capillitium of other Gasteromycetes; the others are called elaters because of their similarity to the structures present in the sporogonia of Liverworts; they are not known elsewhere among fungi though present in some Mycetozoa. Each consists of a single elongated cell with internal spiral or annular, faintly yellow thickenings. Their function is unknown. Apparently they arise in the hymenium and it has been suggested that they correspond to degenerate spores formed as the hymenium is enfeebled and about to cease functioning.

Queletia mirabilis (Pl. XII, p. 195) well deserves its specific epithet. A specimen was brought to me in October 1941 by Mrs. Russell, a member of the staff of the Department of Botany. Her husband, Mr. E. Russell, had found it on spent tan used for cooling white lead mouldings at a foundry in Barnsbury, London. At first glance it looked like a diseased and distorted *Boletus edulis*. The whole fungus was white, with a roundish, stout, stem-like base, covered with fibrous scales; the gleba was rusty brown. *Queletia mirabilis* has been called one of the mysteries of the puff-ball world because of its extraordinary occurrences. It was first collected at Port de Sochaux, France, in 1868, where it grew in large circles on old tan, after summer storms, and sent to Quélet. This eminent mycologist was puzzled by it and forwarded it to Fries who described and named it. It was next found near Saint-Saens in 1884 on a large pile of old tan bark. It appeared in 1891, 1892, and 1893 on a pile of old tan bark at Texlertown, Pennsylvania. Some of the specimens collected in 1892 were sent to the Kew Herbarium: the packing, loose spores and broken fragments, were emptied out of the window under a cedar tree and several fine specimens appeared there the following year. There are two further records from France, both on tan—Mothe-St-Héray in 1906 and Montereau-faut-Yonne in 1913.

The distribution so far as we know it is, therefore, four localities in France, one in U.S.A. and two in England. Of the British records the Kew one is remarkable in many ways, but its source is clear. The other carries its warning. Mr. Russell and his work-mates had often seen toadstools growing on the tan but it was only his wife's comments on the large number of fungi that were then coming to the Museum that caused him to put some in a box. The first consignment comprised *Volvaria volvacea* and the rare *Lepiota Badhami* and *L. meleagris*, all of which were better known when tan-beds were used for heating greenhouses. *Queletia* was in the next consignment but not in the third, after which the supply ended, for the factory was destroyed in an air raid. It would indeed be remarkable if the only naturally occurring specimen in this country should be there at that particular time just for the gathering. We have here again the problem of distribution. It has been suggested that spores were introduced with hides from South America. This would be more convincing if *Queletia* was known from there, and if tan-yards were the only places where tan was used, and that it was in tan-yards that the fungus appeared. The Kew record is clearly an introduction. Of the remaining six, five are European. The species may be an introduction, or more precisely introductions, from some region where it is frequent, and as it is apparently more or less confined to tan, may have been introduced with bark; on the other hand tan is not invariably imported. On the evidence, *Queletia mirabilis* is native in Europe, very rare, and restricted in its habitat.

When young it has the form of a developing puff-ball, white, more or less smooth, rounded above and slightly conical at the base, without any trace of a stalk. Then there is growth below which splits the envelope and gives passage to the stem which gradually enlarges and lifts the upper portion above the surface. Between the end of the stem and the peridium a special tissue is formed which aids separation. When the spores are ripe the foot gradually loosens from the peridium in such a way that with the least shock, even by the action of the wind, the peridium becomes detached and rolls about. By disorganisation and knocks the epidermis tears and the spores are dispersed; there is no definite opening. The basidia which form just as the gleba begins to change colour, develop extremely rapidly and early disappear. They are club-shaped and have three large sterigmata, one at the end and two at the sides. A wall develops in the middle of the sterigma and the spore carries off the end portion with it. The spores have a thick epispore covered with irregular warts. They develop and ripen while the fungus is still buried 3 to 6 inches within the substratum.

BIRD'S NEST FUNGI

When the wondrous shapes assumed by toadstools are discussed, the so-called Bird's Nest Fungi (Nidulariaceae) always arouse interest and provide scope for ingenuity or amusement for those attempting to explain the mimicry. Why should a fungus simulate a miniature nest with a clutch of eggs?

At the time when there was long and earnest argument about the mode by which fungi were propagated, whether they had seeds or "just growed," the " eggs " (*peridiola*) of the Bird's Nest Fungus, *Cyathus* (Pl. XIV*d*, p. 211), were often instanced as proof of seminal respectability. Indeed they were the only obvious structures which could be put forward as evidence, evidence which Ray brushed aside with the comment, " Una Hirundo, *ut aiunt*, non facit Ver "—one swallow does not make a spring—though he did not attempt to explain their nature.*

Obviously they are in no-wise seeds and they are not Gargantuan spores, but their nature and the method of their formation are puzzling at first sight for they seem so unlike what is found in any other group of fungi. They are a further development of what is seen in *Scleroderma*

*J. Goedart says that " after these grains fall out of the cup . . . they are cherished by the heat of the sun, till they begin to live, after wards they get feet; and in three years time they attain to their full growth, all these things I tryed twice Two years together."

where the sterile layers between the glebal cavities persist for a time, in *Pisolithus*, and in Hymenogastracae where these tramal plates form a network of chambers in which the spores are formed and enclosed. In Nidulariaceae the tramal plates round off, harden and separate so forming the "eggs" (peridiola); these are thus enclosed portions of the gleba and they contain the spores.

The peridiolum has a stout wall usually composed of an outer *tunica* of loosely woven hyphae and an inner thick layer of pseudo-parenchyma which, as it dries, becomes tough and horny. Originally the internal cavity is lined with the basidia. These deliquesce soon after the spores are formed, and the mucus serves as nutriment for their further development. The peridioles do not open of their own accord, but liberate the spores only when their walls have been destroyed by insects or in some other way.

There are three British genera in the Nidulariaceae, *Nidularia*, *Crucibulum* and *Cyathus*. *Nidularia* is the simplest genus and has two British species, *Nidularia pisiformis* and *N. confluens*, neither of which is very common. They both grow on leaves, chips and dead branches throughout the year, beginning as almost globular structures with a single membrane. *N. pisiformis* (Pl. XIV*b*, p. 211) is finally brownish and minutely hairy, and opens in a circumscissile manner exposing a number of brown, shining peridioles which lie free in a mass of mucilage. *N. confluens* has a whitish and thinner downy wall which splits irregularly; the peridioles are circular, compressed and deep chestnut-colour. It often grows in so crowded a manner that the fruit-bodies are distorted through lateral pressure.

Crucibulum vulgare (Pl. XIV*c*, p. 211) is common on wood, twigs, dead bramble stems and fern fronds, and begins as a greyish or dirty cinnamon-coloured globular structure with a double wall, and then becomes bell-shaped, the opening being covered in by a flat, yellowish, double-layered membrane (*epiphragm*) which, as maturity is approached, breaks and disappears, revealing the smooth and shining whitish interior. The numerous peridioles are circular and biconvex, pale brown or dingy white, having on the one side a nipple-like projection from which stretches a cord (*funiculus*) attached to the inner wall of the peridium. The funiculus is a delicate sinuous bundle of thick-walled hyaline threads enclosed in a loose bag of partly gela-tinised hyphae, and is brittle when dry, but when wet is elastic and can be pulled out to an inch or more in length. It is usually very obscure after maturity and often gelatinises and disappears.

Cyathus differs from *Crucibulum* in having its wall of three layers, but the essential difference is in the funiculus and its attachment, which is to the middle of a slight depression or umbilicus on the side of the peridiole. In the unopened cup the peridiolum resembles a miniature *Boletus* attached by a very narrow portion to the inside of a cup-like projection on the wall. The swollen part of the " stalk " is a sheath which encloses an extension of the narrow portion as a delicate convoluted thread. If the peridiolum is carefully lifted the funicular thread unwinds and is spun out from two to seven inches; the enclosing sac is consumed during the process, becoming a part of the thread itself. In normal development, as the fungus matures, the funicular sheath becomes gelatinous and disappears and the peridoila remain attached to the wall by the thread. Sometimes the thread itself also gelatinises and the peridiola become free in the cup.

Such a complicated contrivance has tempted speculation about its possible significance, and various suggestions have been made. In recent years, however, it has been known that a rain drop falling with some force splashes an egg from the cup with a momentum sufficient to send it into the air, usually two or three feet, but even up to seven feet. As the flight begins the funicular thread inside the sheath spins out, breaks away from the wall and trails behind, and sticks to, or may entwine, any leaf or twig in its course, the egg dangling down and awaiting the time when its spores should be freed to disperse.* It is probable that rain drops are the effective agents of discharge of the peridioles of the other Bird's Nest Fungi.

There are two British species of *Cyathus*, *C. striatus* and *C. olla* (=*vernicosus*). Both are common, growing on sticks, stubble, twigs, beech mast, fern fronds, garden fences, fibre, and *C. striatus* occasionally, *C. olla* frequently, on the ground. They are rather larger than *Crucibulum* and *Nidularia*.

Cyathus striatus (Pl. XIV*d*, p. 211) is bell-shaped with a broadish base, reddish brown or ferruginous, and strigosely hairy on the outside. In its young stages the edges are incurved and the opening is closed in with a pale fugacious membrane, which, on breaking, discloses the lead-coloured fluted interior and the whitish, circular, compressed

---

*Leptostroma Camelliae which was described from Germany in 1834 remained a mystery for over a century. Then, in U.S.A., the lower leaves of numerous large *Camellia* bushes were found to be liberally speckled with black button-shaped pads. These proved to be peridioles of *Cyathus pallidus* which was growing on the decayed remnants of boxes. With this clue the identity of *Leptostroma Camelliae* was established.

peridioles. *C. olla* differs in being more broadly bell-shaped, tapering to a narrow base, being greyish or ochraceous and invariably silky then smooth on the outside, and smooth and lead-coloured or brownish within, with blackish or greyish, shining peridioles.

At maturity the entire cavity of a peridiole is filled with spores. The basidia and the hyphae of the subhymenium collapse and gelatinise before the spores are fully ripe. These complete their development in the gelatinous matrix; this may be nothing more than a thickening of the spore wall but may involve a considerable enlargement of the spore volume. Something similar occurs in *Scleroderma* and *Pisolithus* (p. 252). The spores of *Cyathus* are sessile on the basidia: *Nidularia* and *Crucibulum* have well-developed sterigmata.

Another genus, *Sphaerobolus*, is often classed in the Nidulariaceae, but is better placed in a separate family. Three species are recorded as British; *Sphaerobolus dentatus* and *S. terrestris* are very rare, whereas *S. stellatus* (Pl. XIV*a*, p. 211) is common on rotten wood, twigs and leaves, old sawdust, sacking, less frequently on horse, cow and rabbit dung, showing as small crowded, pale yellowish or whitish spheres, immersed at first in a white cottony mycelium. At maturity the outer wall splits from the apex and six to eight sharp-pointed teeth are formed, which, bending outwards, disclose the solitary spherical orange-yellow spore-containing mass. Six layers can be distinguished in the young peridium, but at maturity it consists essentially of two membranes, separated by an air space and joined at the extremities of the points—as if it were one cup within another, the inner containing the glebal ball which fits neatly but freely within it, immersed in a slimy liquid. The glebal ball, about $\frac{1}{20}$ in. in diameter, is surrounded by a thin, adhesive, brown skin, and consists of tens of thousands of thick-walled spores and thousands of gemmae embedded in a tough fatty matrix. The spores are at first borne on basidia; the gemmae are larger oval or oval-elongated portions of vegetative hyphae and are capable of germination. Suddenly the inner cup turns inside out and the ball is catapulted out with such a force that it may travel as much as fourteen feet vertically and seventeen feet horizontally. At discharge a slight sound can be heard and also when the ball lands on a solid body. The outer non-everting membrane holds fast the inner membrane by its teeth and prevents it from following after the projectile and interfering with its flight. The glebal ball takes with it a little of the slimy liquid surrounding it (derived from the innermost layer of the peridium) and adheres to any solid object which it

Plate 39a (*above*) *Boletus parasiticus* on *Scleroderma verrucosum*; the only British *Boletus* which is parasitic (*Scleroderma verrucosum* has a thin skin with small warts). (*Paul L. de Laszlo*) b (*right*) *Battarraea phalloides*; Temple Guiting, Gloucester, 1915 (*Paul L. de Laszlo*)

c (*above left*) WHITE TRUFFLE, *Choiromyces meandriformis*; grows partly or wholly underground. (*Paul L. de Laszlo*); d (*above right*) WHITE TRUFFLE, *Choiromyces meandriformis*; specimen removed from the ground (*Paul L. de Laszlo*)

Plate 90a. *Tremella mesenterica*; on dead branches of deciduous trees, lasting through the winter *(Paul L. de Laszlo)*

b. CORAL-SPOT, *Nectria cinnabarina*; the conidial (imperfect) stage, common on twigs, such as pea-sticks *(Eric Hosking)*

strikes, flattening in doing so. There must be a sufficient supply of water for the " mortar " to act, and light is necessary for fruit-body formation: the discharge takes place during the day and the apex is directed towards the strongest incident rays of light. It is possible that the glebal balls shot on to herbage are eaten by animals and pass through the alimentary canal to give rise to the coprophilous forms. But in this country the fungus is commonest on wood and sticks and it seems unlikely that infection is spread there by dung flies as has been suggested. The glebal masses retain their vitality for many years—in my own experience for at least ten.

The fungus was first recorded by Micheli in 1729 under the name *Carpobolus*; he described and figured the shooting of the spore mass. Since then it has always fascinated observers. J. F. Durande, in 1785, instances the explosion of the " mortier " as an example of organisation and mechanism incompatible with the ideas then general that fungi were simply degeneration products of plants. The resemblance to the old piece of ordnance was called to mind by Berkeley and others, and in recent years Buller has paid special attention to the *Sphaerobolus* gun —" not only the largest and the most powerful but also the loudest of all fungus guns."

The remaining group of Gasteromycetes, Hymenogastraceae, grow either beneath the surface of the soil, or half-buried, thus resembling truffles (Chap. 22).

Hymenogastraceae are relatively simple in structure. Such simplicity may be a sign either of primitiveness or reduction. At first sight it might seem that certain features have been lost in adopting so specialised a habitat; the simplest forms among them would, on this view, be the most advanced. Mycologists, however, are generally agreed that the group is the least evolved of the Gasteromycetes.

A section through a fruit-body shows the gleba to consist of cells or cavities; the hymenium forms a lining to them. There are seven genera represented in Britain; none of them is common, but, it should be added, they are not often searched for. They are classified into those with (*Hydnangium, Hysterangium*) and those without (*Rhizopogon, Melanogaster, Hymenogaster, Octaviania*) a simple or branched columella in the cellular gleba, and by the shape, colour and ornamentation of the spores.

Rhizopogon and *Melanogaster* are attached to the soil by branched mycelial cords all over the surface whereas in other genera these occur only at the base. The two British species of *Rhizopogon* grow in groups in sandy coniferous woods. Both are globose or ovate with a thick almost leathery skin, and somewhat superficial. *R. rubescens* is white at first and resembles the " egg " of *Mutinus*, except for the adnate mycelial fibrils, and turns pink when touched; later it becomes yellow then brown, and the rhizomorphs dark brown or black. The gleba is yellowish or brownish, soft, with small irregular cells. *R. luteolus* is whitish, becoming honey-yellow then olive-brown; the gleba is olivaceous, the cells minute and rounded with shining whitish walls.

Melanogaster differs from *Rhizopogon* chiefly in having deeply coloured spores. The fruit-body is irregularly globose, sometimes nodulose. *M. variegatus* is at first yellow or ochraceous, then rusty red becoming duller with handling. The walls of the cavities are whitish then bright orange, the contents black. It grows under beech trees in tufts of five or six, some beneath the surface, some exposed. Formerly it was sold in Bath market as Red Truffle and eaten in preference to the Summer Truffle (*Tuber aestivum*). It has a sweet taste and smells somewhat like bitter almonds.

The most readily recognised of the many other species is *Hydnangium carotaecolor* which is somewhat nodular, pale orange-red becoming dark orange-brownish when dry, and slightly woolly: the flesh is a beautiful orange-red, with minute irregular cells. It grows in woods, or under trees on downs, half-buried or superficial. The carrot colour is contained in globules, which stain paper.

Hymenogastraceae provide much scope for research, and phylogenetic speculations. *Rhizopogon* is probably the simplest type of Gasteromycete both in structure and development and is therefore usually held to be the most primitive. In drawing up a phylogenetic tree (still a practice which seems to fascinate biologists), taking *Rhizopogon* as a starting point, two main lines may be drawn, one leading through *Hysterangium* to Phallaceae, the other through *Melanogaster*, to Sclerodermataceae with a branch on the one hand to Nidulariaceae and on the other to Lycoperdaceae. Such phylogenetic trees are useful so long as they are regarded merely as mnemonics. Half a century ago F. Bucholz pointed out the similarity of the spores of *Russula* and *Lactarius* to those of certain Gasteromycetes and French mycologists have in recent years traced several series in *Russula* and *Lactarius* to genera in Gasteromycetes. Other suggested series, *Paxillus → Boletus → Rhizopogon*—it is remarkable that they are all attacked by the same parasite, *Hypomyces* (*Sepedonium*) *chrysospermus*; *Coprinus → Montagnites → Gyrophragmium* and *Rhodophyllus → Richoniella* show how the problems lend themselves to logic and ingenuity. Whether or not Gasteromycetes include a set of end lines as well as developmental or progressive series amongst themselves such possibilities must always be borne in mind in postulating progenitors. It seems improbable that Gasteromycetes evolved once for all or, in other words, that they are a completely homogeneous group.

CHAPTER 22

TRUFFLES

MOST OF THE LARGER fungi spend the greater part of their existence in the soil as vegetative mycelium. Their physiology is in no wise dependent upon light and so there is no need for special structures such as leaves to ensure its reception in sufficient amount. The fruit-bodies, usually of short duration, are formed at, or soon reach, the surface, their spores being adapted to aerial or biotic dispersal. Those fungi parasitic on trees behave similarly though their fruit-bodies are often of longer duration and sometimes perennial.

There are some fungi, however, which are wholly subterranean. This is not so remarkable as it seems at first sight for if the necessity for spore dispersal by air no longer exists there is no overriding need for emergence from the substratum. Such fungi occur in all the main divisions: Phycomycetes, Ascomycetes, Basidiomycetes. They are also found in Fungi Imperfecti though here the spores are blown about with the soil particles, and these microscopic moulds have no morphological characters which could be considered as special adaptations.* The subterranean habit is obviously biological and, having arisen along several different lines, can have no phylogenetic

*Amongst microscopic fungi present in the soil, leaf mould, dung, rotten wood, etc. are a large number which parasitise microscopic animals, principally eelworms, protozoa and rotifers. Usually attachment is by means of a glutinous substance formed on the conidia, enabling them to stick to the host, on the wall of the mycelium, on capitate projections, or on the inside of loops, on which the animal is caught. *Dactyella bembioides* is remarkable in forming nooses consisting of three cells each of which suddenly projects its inner wall when stimulated by the touch of an entering eelworm and strangles it. These " predacious fungi " are chiefly Zoopagaceae (a family of Phycomycetes proposed for their reception) and Hyphomycetes. One genus, *Nematochonus*, is Basidiomycetous, having clamp-connections, though basidia have not yet been found. The conidia are adhesive and when they germinate the mycelium enters the eelworm; one species has glandule-like processes on the mycelium.

Plate XIX. *Clavaria fusiformis* (cf. Plate 28a). Usually tufted, becoming hollow and compressed. (*J. Thompson*)

significance. It is difficult to regard it as having been gradually assumed, *pari passu* with infinitesimal morphological modifications, though it is true that in some genera the fruit-bodies are only partially buried. The most logical assumption would seem to be that a series of mutations has taken place which has produced modifications in structure of sufficient magnitude that the whole life-cycle can be successfully passed through under the surface of the soil. When once the underground habit had been assumed it is possible that other kinds of change played a part but until then the fruit-body must remain adapted to an aerial existence if it was to survive. Unless it is granted that there was purposeful evolution, either imposed or innate, the changes postulated must have been large and fortuitous. All subterranean fungi have rounded or ovoid fruit-bodies. There is no need for devices to ensure exposure of spores to the agencies of aerial dispersal.

Truffles (*Tuber*) are the best-known underground fungi because of their high repute in cookery but there are several other related general which comprise the Tuberineae, a special family of Ascomycetes.

Truffles have been a cause for wonder since the dawn of knowledge. Theophrastus instances truffles and fungi as plants without root, stem, branch, twig, flower or fruit, without bark, core, fibres or veins; and again in a discussion on roots says that it is not right so to call all that is underground. Pliny regarded as beyond a doubt the very greatest of all marvels of nature the fact that any plant should spring up and grow without a root, " such, for instance, is the vegetable product known as the truffle." Having gone thus far with Theophrastus he hedges, probably in doubt from his other sources and goes on to say,

" It is found, in fact, in no way adhering to the earth, but enclosed within an outer coat, so much so indeed, that though we cannot exactly pronounce it to be composed of earth we must conclude that it is nothing else but a callous concretion of the earth. . . . Whether the truffle grows gradually or whether the blemish of the earth—for it can be looked upon as nothing else—at once assumes the globular form and magnitude which it presents when found; whether too it is possessed of vitality or not, are all of them questions, which, in my opinion are not easy to be solved."

Their origin was a puzzle to which many answers were essayed. Dioscorides thought them tuberous roots, Plutarch and others a con-glomeration produced by the conjoined action of lightning, warmth

Plate XX. Dryad's Saddle, *Polyporus squamosus*; it grows on tree-trunks as well as logs, often in early summer. (*H. J. Howard*)

and water on the soil, whereas Juvenal attributed them to thunder and rain, and Athenaeus believed their number and size was proportionate to the number and force of the thunder claps. Cicero, who may be regarded as a witness of current opinion, considered them children of the earth, whereas Porphyrus called them children of the gods, giving them a designation which was then applied to offspring of irregular civil status because of unknown parentage.

Most of the ancient ideas put forward about the origin of fungi principally concerned truffles. Nicander's central heat of the globe forming them by rarefying the limon of the earth: Rhazes's vegetables arising spontaneously; Encelius's formed by the exudation of trees, and Fortunius Licetus's (1612) by the universal spirit, an explanation which covers everything and signifies nothing.

Theophrastus is the first writer to mention truffles and does so under several names—*hydnon, askion, iton, misy* and *ceraunion*; *hydnon* is still current in Greece. In his *Historia* (repeated in Athenaeus) he speaks of

" the production and generation of these things which seed beneath the earth; as, for instance, of the truffle, and of a plant which grows around Cyrene, which they call *misy*. And it appears to be exceedingly sweet and to have a smell like that of meat; and so, too, has a plant called *iton*, which grows in Thrace."

Of the different truffles Pliny says,

" There are two kinds of them, the one full of sand, and consequently injurious to the teeth, the other free from sand and all impurities. They are distinguished by their colour, which is red, or black, or white within: those of Africa are the most esteemed."

He then copies the remarks of Theophrastus about *misy* not apparently realising that he had described it as the one full of sand, white within, and the most esteemed. As it matured in spring Juvenal called it *Tuber veris*: he praises it in one of his Satires, " Keep your grain, O Libya . . . unyoke your oxen if only you send truffles."

This white truffle which the Greeks and Romans obtained also from Lesbos and Carthage is the " terfez " of the arabs of North Africa, the " kames " of those of Eastern Asia. It is *Terfezia* which differs from *Tuber* in many ways in addition to colour. It usually has a short stem-like base with mycelial threads which compact the sand beneath it. The flesh is not " marbled " with veins but has an outer sterile zone surrounding the fertile tissue which consists of small irregular loose cavities enclosing the asci thus resembling the structure of subterranean Gasteromycetes.

Ludivico de Varthema in his *Travels* (1503-08) found that at Damascus " is sold a great quantity of truffles: sometimes twenty-five or thirty camels arrive laden with them and in three or four days they are sold. They come from the mountains of Armenia and Turkey." G. P. Badger (1853) in a footnote to his translation says that truffles " are found in large quantities at certain seasons of the year, along the banks of the Euphrates and Tigris, and are transported by the Bedawn long distances." Trading still continues; H. R. P. Dickson (1949) mentions that " Truffles and mushrooms, great delicacies to every Badawin . . . form the staple food of the tent-dweller and his family for weeks on end."

They are sold on the markets of Damascus, Baghdad, Smyrna, Aleppo, Baku and Tiflis; one market at Jerusalem has them on sale. It is surprising that truffles are not mentioned in the Bible. However, it has been held by P. Corduque and others, that the *dudaims* which Reuben gathered and gave to Leah, and which were so coveted by Rachel, were truffles. The translation in the Authorised Version is mandrake, but there have been many other surmises; banana, maize, citron, orange, melon, fig, mulberry, strawberry, winter cherry, jasmin, lily, violet, lotus, etc.: Olaus Celsius lists them in *Hierobotanicon* (1745-7). Apart from tradition it is obvious that dudaim must have been something agreeable and desirable to have attracted the attention of Reuben, to have been accepted by Leah and to have excited the cupidity of Rachel, and also it must have been indigenous to the country. The ancients dedicated the truffle to Venus. The food fad that it causes women to become more tender and men more amiable probably originated in the old doctrine of signatures.

Thirty-six species of *Terfezia* are now known, thirty-three of which occur in the sub-desert regions of the Mediterranean basin, Lusitania and Asia Minor. The larger species form a not negligible part of the food of Mediterranean peoples, notably Greeks and Arabs; they are sold all over North Africa.

The fungus when reaching maturity causes the earth to bulge and crack, a fact which was noted by Martial, Leo Africanus and other old writers. Pamphilus in his *Languages*, according to Athenaeus, says, in Parkinson's words, a " certaine herbe groweth above, upon that ground where the *Tubera* breedes, which he calleth " *hydnophyllon*. It seems a strange story—but it is true. The herb is usually one of the rock-roses (Cistaceae). The first suggested identity of *hydnophyllon* is in *Historia generalis plantarum* (*Hist. plant. Lugdunensis*), 1586-87, usually attributed to J. d'Aléchamps. Two plants are described as sent by F. Micó from Spain with the names *Tuberaria major* and *T. minor*, the latter being figured. The name *Tuberaria* was given because the Spanish around Castille called it " yerva turmera," the truffle plant: Micó believed it was the *hydnophyllon* of Pamphilus. J. Bauhin repeated this in his *Historia*—he had been one of d'Aléchamps's chief collaborators. Linnaeus united the two species as *Cistus Tuberaria*: it was later transferred to *Helianthemum*. Other species of both *Helianthemum* and *Cistus* have been said to be associated with truffles. B. M. Duggar found them evidently partly parasitic on the roots of *Artemesia herba-alba* which appeared to be injured about in direct proportion to the size of the fungus.

When Tulasne founded the genus *Terfezia* in 1851 he was under the impression that *T. leonis** comprised both the terfez of North Africa and the kames of Asia Minor. However it apparently does not grow in the deserts of Africa and seems to be limited to the mountainous pine and cedar forests; in Spain in fields where Cistaceae grow; marine sandy places with Cistaceae in Sardinia and commonly in the Smyrna area. " It is probably the truffle the Romans got from Lesbos, but not that they brought from Libya."

Terfezia leonis appears in the list of British fungi but probably through error. Its occurrence here would be unexpected from its general distribution. Unfortunately no British specimen can be traced. There are only two records, both by G. Massee. The first was in 1909 (*Ann. Bot.* xxiii); there is no mention of any locality. The second, in his *British Fungi*, two years later, states that it is " not uncommon in the New Forest, where I have collected several fine specimens at different times in the neighbourhood of Lyndhurst." It is difficult to reconcile these records. At a guess the first was the result of inadvertently mixing specimens, the second a trick of memory.

Gerard (1597) has a figure and description of *Tuber terrae* but this is *Cyclamen*. He has, however, a confused account of truffles.

" There is likewise a kinde of Mushrum, with a certaine round excrescence, growing within the earth, under the upper crust or face of

*The epithet refers to the old Spanish kingdom of León.

Plate 41a (above). *Helvella crispa*; woods, roadsides and ditch banks. Edible. (*S. C. Porter*)
   b (below) *Peziza vesiculosa*; common on old manure heaps (*S. C. Porter*)

Plate 42a. (above left) Aleuria umbrina; on burned places. (Eric Hosking); b (above right) Galactinia badia; on sandy soil in a pine-wood. (Paul L. de Laszlo); c (below left) Peziza aurantia; on the ground in woods. (S. C. Porter); d (below right) Peziza rutilans:

the same, in drie and gravelly grounds in Pannonia and the Provinces adjoining, which do cause the ground to swel, and be full of hils like Molehils. The people where they grow, are constrained to digge them up and cast them abroad like as we do Molehils. Spoiling their grounds, as Molehils are hurtfull unto our soile: these have neither stalks, leaves, fibres, nor strings annexed or fastned unto them, and for the most part are of a reddish colour, but within of a whitish yellow: the Grecians have called this tuberous excrescence, *Idna,* and the Latines *Tubera*: the Spaniards do call them *Turmas de tierra:* in English we may call them Spanish Fussebals."

Johnson, in his edition of Gerard (1633), copies Clusius's figures of truffles with the legend " Tuber terrae. Fuss-balls, or Puckfistes " but repeats Gerard's text. Parkinson (1640) has an interesting account. He says that " in *English* some call them *Spanish* Fussebals . . . but I would rather call them Underground Mushromes, or *Spanish* Trubbes to distinguish them." His description is based on that of J. B. Porta (1588), and he quotes him as saying that " under the outer skinne, certaine, small blacke seede . . . whereby it not onely propagateth it selfe, where it is naturall, but as it hath beene often observed, there hath some of them growne where the parings of them have beene cast."

It is clear that neither Gerard nor Parkinson knew of any English specimens. The attribution to Spain is strange for imported truffles came from France. The Spanish turma is *Terfezia leonis.*

The first record of truffles in this country was in 1693 when Tancred Robinson wrote " An account of the Tubera terrae, or Truffles found at Rushton in Northamptonshire, with some Remarks thereon." The truffles had been found by " that curious and learned Gentleman Mr. *Hatton,*" sent to the Royal Society, and submitted to Robinson who reported that they were " indeed the true French *Truffles,* the Italian *Tartuffi* or *Tartuffole,* and the Spanish *Turmas de Tiera,* which are not noted by Mr Ray to be found in our British Soyl." He was not at all clear about their nature; " what these *Trubs* are, neither the Ancients nor Moderns have clearly informed us; some will have them *Callosities,* or *Warts* bred in the Earth: Others call them subterraneous *Mushrooms.*" He was almost tempted to guess that this " delicious and luxurious piece of Dainty " is the product of some bulbose or tuberose plant such as an orchid if there had been vestiges of any structure that could support the view. However, in a postscript he adds that Mr. Hatton had observed fibres arising out of some split tubers " so that perhaps they may be *Plantae sui generis,* and their sulcated *Papillae* analogous to, if not Seed Vessels." Robinson refers to ancient writers and conjectures that the Rushton truffles were found after the late thunder and rains. " The Wet swells them, and Lightning may dispose them to send forth their particular Scent so alluring to the Swine."

The truffles were *Tuber aestivum*: there is a specimen in A. Buddle's herbarium which now forms part of the Sloane Herbarium. Evelyn (1696) complains that we send for " trufles " into France at no small charge though they are not seldom found in England, particularly at Rushton,* " and doubtless in other places too were they sought after."

It was not, however, generally agreed that the Rushton truffle was native. Many of the trees in Lord Cotton's park had been imported from Languedoc, and as it was only since then that any truffles had been observed it was assumed that their " seed " had been imported with them.

Ray recorded the " Trubs or Trufles " of " that learned Physician D. Hatton " and Dillenius added two descriptive names of other species which C. Merret had given in his *Pinax* (1667): they are un-recognisable but were certainly not truffles. He adds, " Tubera perniciosa terrestria seu cervina "—*Elaphomyces granulatus*—which he himself had found at Cane Wood, near Highgate: from his description the fungus appears to have been *Scleroderma vulgare*.

Theophrastus did not hazard a guess about how truffles reproduce.

" Not but what there are people who believe that they are or can be raised from seed. At all events they say that they never appeared on the shore of the Mitylenaeans, until after a heavy shower some seed was brought in from Tiarae; and that is the place where they are in the greatest numbers."

" Seeds " were seen or suspected by several writers—Porta, Geoffroy the younger and others—before Micheli in 1729 described and figured two to four spores in subspherical asci. Bulliard in 1791, though he saw the spores clearly, did not see that they were enclosed. He thought that they were joined to the surrounding tissue by numerous very delicate fibrils which acted as umbilical cords conducting the seminal

---

*" Truffles are still found there, and until about ten years back specimens were exhibited at the annual flower shows," Notes and Queries, 1900.

The old French name was " tartufe " (tartuffe). Molière (1664) used it for the principal character, a religious hypocrite, in his comedy " Le Tartuffe," doubtless because of its development underground. Molière called his estate Périgord.

When the potato was first introduced into Europe it was confused with the truffle, and called " tartuffi " in Italy, and " truffe " or " truffe rouge " in France.

fluid to the developing seeds, becoming separated at maturity. He considered them to be miniature truffles resembling the mature fungus in shape, colour and ornamentation of the wall, indeed in everything except size. He regarded truffles therefore as viviparous plants. This view, because of Bulliard's eminence, was widely adopted. Turpin in 1827 called the spores " truffinelles " and added some strange superstructures on the false foundation. The monographs of Vittadini (1837) and Tulasne (1862) put the mycology of the Tuberaceae on sound lines. Mycologists accepted them as outstanding works—but to practical men the idea that truffles were fungi reproduced by spores seemed far too prosaic an explanation. There were many controversies particularly in France throughout about half the last century. The interest in increasing the supply of truffles which had become an important article of commerce led to theorising which resembled in kind that of ancient writers. The truffle is formed by a fermentation of the soil; by exudations from branches and leaves; by an excretion of roots; by an extravasation of the sap of roots following insect punctures; as spontaneous tubercular swellings of the roots. All had their supporters but it was the gall hypothesis which was the most popular with the general public, for it was advocated with considerable polemical skill by J. de Valserres, in the press and in pamphlets, from 1857 to 1876; but attacks on the integrity of scientists and disregard of facts led to nothing of worth except that the heated controversy centred attention on the organisms themselves.

The presence of truffles can be determined only by chance, by noting signs with a knowledge of habitats, or by the use of animals. Experience teaches that the odds against casually finding a specimen are considerable.

There are certain guides in searching for truffles, known for several centuries. The two principal ones are " récolte à la mouche " and " à la marque." Truffles are attacked by the larvae of particular flies and beetles which are restricted to them. The commonest truffle-flies are small and usually yellowish, *Helomyza tubivora* and *H. lineata* being the most frequent. About the time the truffles are ripe, swarms of flies ready to lay their eggs may be seen hovering a foot or more above the soil, sometimes for the whole of a sunny day but especially mid-morning and early evening. In truffle areas the poorer peasants and poachers lie flat on the ground facing the sun to get a better view of them. The best-known beetle is *Anistoma cinnamomea*. " Récolte à la marque " has been the longest practised. In early autumn, when truffles are ripening, those which are growing near the surface upraise the soil in little heaps, causing it to crack in short straight furrows radiating from the centre; those which are very superficial may crack the soil without forming heaps. Such truffles are usually the biggest, but poachers seldom allow them to mature.

The strong perfume of some species of truffle, especially the most desired ones, makes their presence known to those wild animals which have a liking for them, including, pig, wild boar, wild cat, wolf, bear, deer, goat, badger, rabbit, squirrel, mouse.* The list is of little interest beyond showing that what in man is usually regarded as a certain refinement of taste is fairly widespread. The natural instinct of the pig for finding truffles has been much utilised. The first reference to this seems to be by Platina, historian of the Popes, who died in 1481. In *de Honesta voluptate* he states that nothing equals the instinct of the sows of Notza for finding truffles and that the villagers use them for their search, strapping up their mouths so that the fungus trove is not lost.

Other references to the Italian use of pigs for truffle hunting are those of Ray, who heard of it in his travels (1663-65) and referred to it in three of his works. " In Lombardy ... Tartufale ... a kind of subterraneous Musheroom ... the way to get them is to turn swine into a field where they grow who find them by the smell ... and set one to follow the swine and gather them up. The usual method employed ... is by tying a Cord to the hind leg of a Pig and driving him, observing where he begins to root, which instantly dis-covers the Trufle "—a method he describes in his *Historia* as "modus ... perridiculus est." Evelyn (1644) says of Vienne, Dauphiné, " Here we supped and lay, having amongst other dainties, a dish of trufles, which is a certain earth-nut, found by a hogg trained to it, and for which those animals are sold at a great price. It is in truth an incomparable meat." In 1699 he said, " *Trufles, Peg-nuts*, and other subterraneus *Tubera* ... are commonly discovered by a *Nasute Swine* purposely brought up."

As pigs naturally search for truffles the training necessary merely consists in persuading them to expect some nutritional recompense for their thwarted hopes. Dogs are also much used for truffle hunting,

---

*There seems only one record of parallel human success. C. G. Nees von Esenbeck (1816) states that a poor lame boy living in his neighbourhood (Nuitzberg) was more successful than any truffle dog in detecting them and used his faculty to earn a living.

but they have to be specially trained for this as for all other organised hunts. Again the method appears to have originated in Italy. At the beginning of the eighteenth century there are several records of dogs having been imported thence to Germany, where for a period, the possession of a " Trüffelhund " seems to have been regarded almost as a badge of nobility. Frederic William I of Prussia imported trained dogs from Lombardy. The chief breed was a kind of poodle. It is probable that trained dogs were introduced to France about the same time.

Goats are used in Sardinia, but not sufficiently to have attained more than casual mention.* Where truffles abound, as in Provence, pigs are mostly used. They work against the wind and sometimes detect up to fifty yards. Usually they begin their hunting when two years old and are at their best after three to four years, giving good service up to twenty to twenty-five years. Their snout is well adapted to rooting out the truffles and little human assistance is ever needed. They are carted to the truffle ground (truffières) if these are distant. Given a meal before the search they are rewarded for finds with acorns, beans, maize or carrot, and carry on without distraction even when other pigs are working the ground.

Dogs do not naturally seek out truffles, but they are fairly easily trained if they are of ordinary intelligence. Traditionally some kind of poodle is preferred, but any hunting breed is satisfactory. In France dogs are employed in districts where truffles are not in abundance; in Italy, nowadays, dogs are generally favoured. Dogs are not so sure and quick in detection as pigs, but do not tire so easily and are more obedient and alert. When they begin to scratch the ground the " rabassier " takes over and does the main part of the digging. Success is rewarded by bread, biscuit or some other scrap. One, or at most two, dogs are hunted together, otherwise serious work is liable to succumb to canine gambols. Alba, between Turin and Genoa, famous for its truffle fair held in November, has a school for training truffle dogs; it is said to be over two hundred years old, and the management passes from father to son.

Neither *Tuber melanosporum*, the Périgord truffle, nor *Tuber magnatum*, the Piedmont truffle, have so far been found in this country.

Truffle hunting was carried on in this country until recently, the last of the professional trufflers, Alfred Collins, having finally given up

---

*Bear cubs are said formerly to have been used for hunting *Choiromyces* near the convent of Sergievsky, Russia.

in 1935. It is difficult to ascertain when it began. T. W. Horsfield, in his *History, Antiquities and Topography of the County of Sussex* (1835), writing of Patching, a village near Worthing, seems to be the source of one tradition.

" The beech woods in this parish and its immediate neighbourhood are very productive of the truffle (*Lycoperdon tuber*). About forty years ago William Leach came from the West Indies, with some hogs accustomed to hunt for truffles, and proceeding along the coast from Land's End in Cornwall, to the mouth of the river Thames, determined to fix on that spot where he found them most abundant. He took four years to try the experiment, and at length settled in this parish, where he carried on the business of truffle-hunter till his death."

Pigs were used for hunting truffles in Sussex and Kent until about 1910, though dogs were more usual: also there were truffle-hunters of the name of Leach until the industry petered out. However, trained hogs from the West Indies is an impossible story, and the date (i.e. c. 1795) is too late.

Gilbert White, in his Journals, has many references to truffles. The first of these is July 1768 when he says that they began to be taken in his brother Henry's beech grove at Tyfield near Andover " will continue to be found in great abundance every fortnight till about Lady Day." In 1773 he says that seven or eight pounds are taken annually at that little spot and divided equally between Henry and the " trufle-hunter." A large quantity were found in July 1775, " near two months sooner than the common season." No mention is made of dogs until 1783 when he writes, " Two truflers came with their dogs to hunt our hangers, & beechen woods in search of trufles; several of which they found in the deep narrow part of the hill between the coney-croft-hanger, & the high wood; & again on each side of the hollow road up the high-wood, known by the name of the coach-road." Meanwhile Henry's trufles had failed for two or three years: " He supposes that they may have been devoured by large broods of turkies that have ranged much about his home-fields, & little groves." In 1789, " A trufle-hunter called on us, having in his pocket several large trufles found in this neighbourhood. . . . Some trufles he informed us lie two feet within the earth; some quite on the surface: the latter, he added, have little or no smell, & are not so easily discovered by the dogs as those that lie deeper. Half a crown a pound was the price he asked for this commodity." Again in 1798, " a trufle-hunter came with his dogs . . . he frequently passes along the village. . . . He is attended by two little cur-dogs which he leads in a string."

Though White gives information, gleaned from truffle-hunters, about the effect of the season on the crop, he makes no reference to the way the dogs are used or to their training, indeed, apparently regarding the finding of truffles in his brother's grove as of more interest than that dogs were used to find them. It seems remarkable that so curious a commentator on natural history should not have given some details about this peculiar local industry unless it is assumed that he had known of it since boyhood. As he was born in 1720 it is probable that truffle hunting with dogs began in this country early in the eighteenth century.

The truffle industry was followed principally in Hampshire, Wiltshire, Dorset, Sussex and Kent, the chalk downs, particularly where there are beeches, and parklands of private estates being worked. The chief centre was the Wiltshire village of Winterslow, well known to students of Hazlitt. According to local tradition the occupation was carried on for more than three hundred years. A Spaniard is said to have introduced the dogs in Elizabethan times and taught the people how to find truffles: the knowledge, once acquired, went from father to son. J. H. Walsh (1882) puts the period about two hundred years ago; his Spaniard brought two dogs, did well by the sale of truffles, and, at his death left his money and dogs to a farmer from whom he had received some kindness. But even 1680 seems too early, for it is unlikely that Ray, Dillenius and others would not have heard of it or that so much stir would have followed Hatton's Rushton discovery in 1693.

The truffle-hunters were scattered throughout the truffle country, but their numbers were never great because of the areas they had to cover: the poorer ones had to make their journeys afoot, those better off used a pony and trap. However at Winterslow* there were at one time from ten to a dozen trufflers: there were many generations of families—Yeates and Collins being the best-known names, Eli Collins having a more than local reputation as he hunted from the age of nine to eighty-three. The owners of large estates allowed the trufflers

*In 1860 the truffle-hunters of Winterslow petitioned Parliament for exemption from the dog tax of twelve shillings a year " being poor labouring men . . . living in a woody district of the county where there is a great many English Truffles grow, which we cannot find without dogs, we do therefore keep and use a small pudle sort of dog wholy and solely for that and no other . . . it has been carried on by our ancestors for generations without paying tax for the dogs."

to hunt their strictly preserved woods through the shooting season, and were also their chief customers. The dogs employed were originally a kind of white Spanish poodle with thick woolly coat and short legs, but there was a good deal of cross breeding. Success was rewarded by a small piece of bread, and dogs seldom continued to work without what they were entitled to expect. Dogs which preferred game to truffles could not be used where so many of the hunting grounds were preserved. Alfred Collins relates how a hare jumped over one of his dogs running in scent of a truffle and was ignored.

Truffles are usually three to four inches underground, though they may be much deeper; one was recorded as being 20½ in. deep. The normal weight for a fully grown truffle is a few ounces but very occasionally reaches two pounds or more, one of 2½ lb. being " as big as the top of a cottage loaf."

Truffles near the surface are easily scratched up by dogs, but so that they should not exhaust themselves, the truffle-man assisted with his " truffle-spike," a staff with a strong iron spike at one end and a two-pronged fork at the other; it was also used for drawing aside briars and boughs in copse woods.

A trained dog scents a truffle at thirty to fifty yards. This is remarkable, but there is on record that a dog jumped a hedge, crossed a field, and secured his prize under a beech tree, a distance of at least a hundred yards; one of the Collins's dogs scented a truffle at 123 yards.

Mr. Alfred Collins informs me that ninety per cent of the finds were under beech, the rest under cedar, hazel, hawthorn and sycamore, and that wherever there are plantations of beech, or beech and fir, on Salisbury Plain truffles occur after a few years, and production continues for ten to fifteen years: also that the chief competitors the trufflers encountered were the truffle beetle, red squirrel, rat and mouse. The season is from October to February. The price in Victorian days was from half a crown to four shillings a pound.

The decline of the industry was doubtless due partly to the breaking up of the old estates and the felling of trees. The new owners did not know the truffle-men as of old, and disapproved of them and their dogs rummaging about their land: and truffles had no gastronomic significance for them.* The first World War and its aftermath of changing social conditions had a deleterious effect in several ways,

*" In the eighteenth century the keepers on this estate [Savernake] were required to keep the family's table supplied not only with game but with truffles."

Plate 43. *Coryne sarcoides*; the perfect (ascus) stage, much less common than the imperfect (conidial) stage which forms convoluted gelatinous masses somewhat darker in colour (*Paul L. de Laszlo*)

Paul L. de Laszlo

Plate 44. *Geoglossum difforme*; in grass among moss

and this strange rural occupation gradually petered out with no apparent chance of revival.

Our best-known species, *Tuber aestivum*, (Pl. XVIII*b*, p. 243), is irregularly globose, glistening bluish black when fresh, becoming brownish black on drying. It is covered with large, hard, polygonal, 4-6 sided pyramidal warts with irregular longitudinal grooves and transverse parallel lines, often depressed at the apex. The flesh is yellowish white at first but when mature is brownish and marbled with very numerous white labyrinthine veins. There is a slight but characteristic odour.

About a dozen species of *Tuber* have been recorded for this country but, excepting *Tuber aestivum*, have little reputation as food; some have none at all, being small and very hard. The flesh of the young fruit-body is white or whitish with sinuous lines, some dull white and opaque, others somewhat translucent and a little darker. The opaque white portions remain more or less unchanged while the others take on successive tints—yellowish, grey, brown or vinous and dark brown or blackish—as the spores form and mature. The density, sinuosity and arrangement of these lines or veins is used largely in classification, and they have received several names. The dark veins (venae internae) are the hymenium and there the spores are formed in oval or subglobose asci. The most conspicuous white veins (venae externae) which run more or less parallel with them are really very reduced spaces left between the hymenial foldings, which the tips of the paraphyses invade and there weave a loose mat. A white vein thus appears to be bordered by two dark lines which are in fact the hymenial layers. In some species the ends of the paraphyses join up at a more or less definite height forming an additional though thinner darkish line: there is then the appearance of five parallel veins or lines running through the gleba.

The genera *Choiromyces* and *Elaphomyces* were formerly classed with Tuberaceae but are now regarded as having developed along different lines. The first is closely allied to *Terfezia*. *C. meandriformis*, the White Truffle, (Pl. 39*c*, p. 254) is globose, or irregular and nodular, with a plicate base, creamy white becoming light reddish brown and often cracking; the hard flesh is whitish then yellowish and is marbled with numerous ochraceous much convoluted hymenial veins. It is edible and is sold in Upper Silesia as Kaiserpilz; in France it is often used to adulterate truffles. It usually grows half buried and I have seen specimens scratched up by hens and pheasants.

The species of *Elaphomyces* grow underground in woods. The wall is two-layered and is very hard, and at maturity the interior is filled with a powdery mass of spores intermixed with whitish filaments. *E. variegatus* and *E. granulatus* are common, and both are often parasitised by *Cordyceps* (see p. 152). They are more or less globose. *E. variegatus* is yellowish and finally reddish brown with crowded, small, pointed, pyramidal warts; the outer layer of the wall is ochraceous or golden in section, the inner reddish brown and veined; the spore mass is black when ripe with greyish veins. *E. granulatus* differs in its minute, rounded warts and in the inner layer of the peridial wall not being veined. *Elaphomyces* had formerly a great vogue as a medicine but chiefly as an aphrodisiac and was long sold by herbalists under the name " Lycoperdon Nuts." It figures as " Fungus cervinus," " Tubera cervina " and similar names " sic dicta quia reperiuntur iis in locis ubi cervi libidinem suam exercent."

CHAPTER 23

PENICILLIN

P ROBABLY the prevalent opinion about fungi, held even amongst men of science, is that they are responsible for a hideous storm of terror. They ravage crops and forests, attack animals—birds, fish, insects and men—destroy stored products, foods of all kinds, buildings and fabrics, and spoil paper and paintings. Indeed they appear to be one of the chief enemies of man, his possessions and his culture. This popular view is obviously correct so far as it goes, but it is one-sided, as has already been pointed out.

Wherever a fungus grows there must be change. This change is called destruction where it is undesirable, but in the modern idiom, " it all depends on what you mean," and sometimes it would be misleading to label the alteration as destruction, though chemically it is so. Indeed, the changes brought about are often advantageous to man.

The extraction of fruit juices and their fermentation date back to antiquity. It was a discovery of considerable social importance when primitive races found that these juices so improved with keeping that they made glad the heart of man. Certainly by the time man's speech had become coherent he sang the praises of wine, as is seen in numerous references in Egyptian hieroglyphics and Babylonian cuneiform inscriptions.

The essential change in fermentation from grape sugar to alcohol is brought about by yeasts. Yeasts occur in the soil and air of vineyards, and so are present on the skins of the grapes, from which they infect the juice (must) as it is pressed out. Different races of yeast occur in different vineyards, though they are usually of the *Saccharomyces ellipsoideus* type. The character of the wine depends upon the kind of grape, the specific yeast, and the manner and period of fermentation.

In fermentation processes such as wine-making, it is common to find that a practice handed down from antiquity was carried on in

273

essentially the same way until recent times. The old methods were empirical; they were not the outcome of scientific endeavour but rather the haphazard development of a gift of the gods. In modern times the essential factors in many of the processes have been ascertained and the various ways in which they may be influenced for good or evil, as well as the parts played by workers, shirkers and intruders. Naturally in so important an industry as wine-making scientific methods have been widely adopted. It is a little too risky to depend upon the yeasts occurring naturally on the grape skin. Consequently the skins are sterilised either by pasteurisation or, more commonly, by the addition of a small amount of a dilute solution of sulphurous acid or one of its salts, usually potassium metabisulphite. Pure culture yeast is then added to the must as a starter.

As fermentation is carried out in the open it is obvious that yeasts other than the species or strain desired enter the fermenting liquor. Though this contamination is now reduced to a minimum it is not always without adverse effects, some of which, unfortunately, do not reveal themselves until later. Although it may seem in outline that the romance of the vineyard tends to become a laboratory schedule there always remains scope for the master hand where drink and food are concerned.

Most peoples, primitive and civilised, have their fermented liquors, and yeasts are concerned in the production of nearly all.

Modern beer-brewing suffers from no lack of knowledge of the special properties of the many strains of yeast (*Saccharomyces cerevisiae*) which are used, with their primary division into top or high yeasts, and bottom or low yeasts, and their special production of characteristic aromatic taste or odour; imperfections in modern beers are in no wise due to imperfections in the biological processes involved!

Cider, perry, whisky and brandy are yeast fermented. Pulque (Mexico), taette (Scandinavia), bitti (W. Africa), sorgho (Manchuria) and other similar alcoholic drinks have yeasts as their main fermenter.

One aspect of fermentation by yeast is the leavening of bread. Brewers' yeast was first used in baking in the early eighteenth century. The compressed yeast industry began in 1860. Now, pure culture strains are used which are physiologically adapted to rapid and abundant gas formation.

In the Orient moulds replace yeasts as the main agents of fermentation processes. Arrack of different nations results from members of

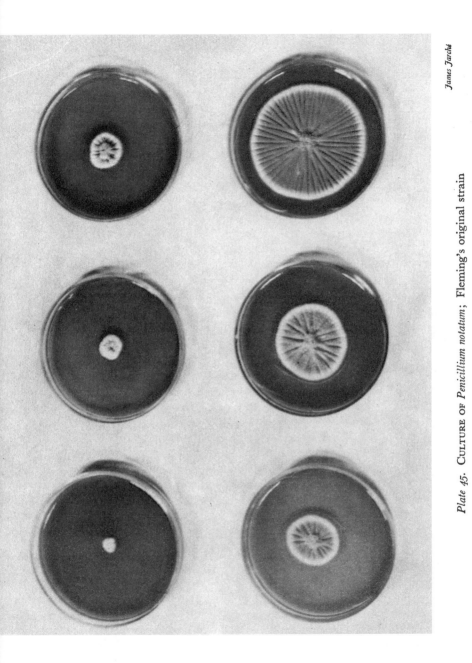

Plate 45. CULTURE OF *Penicillium notatum*; Fleming's original strain

Plate 46. ANTIBIOTIC EFFECT OF *Penicillium notatum*; a preparation made by Sir Alexander Fleming showing how different pathogenic bacteria react towards the products of the fungus (i.e. penicillin)

the Mucoraceae in the " starters," whereas the Koji for the enormous fermentation industries of Japan is *Aspergillus Oryzae*, or closely allied species.

It is difficult to apportion credit for the modern application of moulds to industry. Pasteur was " convinced that a day will come when moulds will be utilised in certain industrial operations, on account of their power of destroying organic matter." He himself had made the first step when he used a mould to bring about a specific chemical action, and was probably thereby led to become interested in ferments. " If I place one of the salts of racemic acid, paratartrate or racemate of ammonia, for instance, in the ordinary conditions of fermentation, the dextro-tartaric acid alone ferments, the other remains in the liquor. This is the best means of preparing laevo-tartaric acid. Why does the dextro-tartaric acid alone become putrefied? Because the ferments of that fermentation feed more easily on the right than on the left molecules."

The best example of the industrial application foreseen by Pasteur is the manufacture of citric acid by *Aspergillus niger*. Citric acid is one of the break-down products of sugar. In 1922 Italy produced about 90 per cent of the world's supply of calcium citrate from the juices of citrus fruits, but within eight years, export had practically stopped because of the commercial production by moulds. Many moulds produce the acid, but *Aspergillus niger* has proved to be the best on a commercial scale. The process is a surface fermentation of a nutrient sucrose solution, with the addition of a comparatively large amount of mineral acid which prevents the growth of bacteria, and most contaminating moulds. *A. niger* forms a thick folded mat on the surface after eight to twelve days, by which time most of the sugar has become converted into citric acid.

Moulds are able to build up their normal cell constituents from an amazingly large and varied series of carbon compounds. Moreover, the same species of mould when growing in slightly different conditions can produce different substances. Thus *Aspergillus niger* is used in the manufacture of gluconic acid, the calcium salt of which is of importance in pharmacy. Oxalic acid, ethyl alcohol and mannitol are other substances which may be regarded as break-down products of the original sugars.

It was not until recent years that it was realised that fungi are also able to synthesise chemical substances. The chief worker in the study of mould metabolism has been H. Raistrick, who, with his collaborators, has isolated over a hundred chemical substances previously unknown to science.

That there is a struggle for existence between organisms of all kinds in face of the various other factors linked together in the term environment, is universally recognised, though its scope is often underrated. Fungi, in common with all other organisms, are affected by this struggle. The non-biological factors of the environment—warmth, moisture, the conditions in the soil and other substrata, including host plants—have been mentioned earlier. There is further the effect of the growth of one mycelium upon another whether these be of the same or of different species. This effect is of several kinds; that which we are now to consider deals with the growth relations between mycelia of different fungi. Some species seem to have no influence on each other: when grown together on a culture medium there seems no opposition but the physical one of space relation, and growth is otherwise no different from what it is when the fungi are grown separately. Other fungi when grown together have either a mutually beneficial effect, or one of them may benefit in some way, as, for example, in abundance of growth or in spore production; the stimulus is presumably due to the production in the medium of some substance or substances favouring growth. A third type is where two fungi are mutually repellent or where one suppresses the growth of the other.

The general facts about the mutual influence of one fungus on another have been known to laboratory workers for many years, for all are victims of occasional unwelcome guests in their cultures. For some time past mycologists have paid attention to the phenomenon of antagonism between fungi because of its theoretical importance in the study of plant diseases, particularly those originating in the soil, whereas the antagonism between bacteria has been studied in the hope of finding inhibitors of those causing human disease. The possible implications of the various known facts are of abounding interest, and world-wide research is being carried on at the present time, as a result of the discovery of penicillin.

In 1928 A. Fleming was working with Petri dish cultures of the bacterium *Staphylococcus aureus*, in an investigation on the destruction of bacteria by leucocytes. One of his cultures became contaminated by a mould, a member of the genus *Penicillium*. The species of *Penicillium* are common in soil, on decaying plants and plant debris, on food such as bread, jam, potted meats, on fruits such as apples, oranges, lemons, in fact on all kinds of organic matter. Most species are green, indeed there are a hundred or so species which are distinct in microscopic characters and in physiology, though to the casual observer they are just green moulds. Even many who should know better, use the name *Penicillium glaucum** in much this sense; in text-books and examination syllabuses *Penicillium glaucum* includes all green species of *Penicillium*. It should be noted, however, that all common green moulds are not necessarily *Penicillium* species; the green *Aspergillus herbariorum* is abundant on the same kinds of substrata; *Trichoderma viride* is common on fallen twigs and rotten wood.

As all species of *Penicillium* produce enormous numbers of spores which are blown about in the air, they are a constant nuisance in culture work; they are veritable laboratory weeds. Everyone who has been subjected to the Lebensraum penetrations of these moulds, has either scrapped the infected culture, or, if expedient, has cut out and removed the unwanted intruder. Fleming, about to discard the culture plate, noticed that there was a zone of dead Staphylococci around the circumference of the colony of *Penicillium*. For a quarter of a century or so he had been interested in methods of destroying pathogenic bacteria and had worked with what are now known as antibiotic substances, particularly those produced in the metabolism of other organisms. Instead, therefore, of disposing of the culture, he decided to try to find out whether it really was the mould which was killing the *Staphylococcus*. He grew it in a nutrient broth and, after a time, filtered off the liquid. He tested the filtrate and found that it was some two or three times as effective as pure carbolic acid in stopping the growth of *Staphylococcus*. He found that it also prevented the growth of many other pathogenic bacteria—*Streptococcus*, *Pneumococcus*, *Gonococcus* and the diphtheria bacillus, but that it was without effect on others, such as *Bacillus coli* and *B. influenzae*.† To avoid the cumbersome

*" Greenness has no more significance in predicting biochemical ability of a *Penicillium* than bayness of a horse in judging his speed in a horse race."—C. Thom. It is of no greater significance in identification.

† H. C. J. Gram devised a stain for bacteria which colours some blue, others red. The first are called gram-positive, the others gram-negative. Penicillin is primarily active against the gram-positive group.

There were several previous reports of substances antagonistic to bacteria being produced by *Penicillium*. Possibly the first was that of William Roberts who wrote in 1874: " The growth of fungi has appeared to me to be antagonistic to that of *Bacteria* and vice versa. I have repeatedly observed that liquids in which the *Penicillium glaucum* was growing luxuriantly could with difficulty be artificially infected with *Bacteria*: it seemed, in fact, as if this fungus played the part of the plants in an aquarium, and held in check the growth of *Bacteria*, with their attendant putrefactive changes."

expression " mould broth filtrate " he called it penicillin. It was not determined what the active principle was, whether a chemical substance or an enzyme, for Fleming is a bacteriologist. His first practical application of penicillin was the isolation of the insensitive Pfeiffer's bacillus, which in the respiratory tract is usually associated with organisms highly sensitive to penicillin. *B. influenzae* has been repeatedly isolated in this way when it could not be seen in films of sputum, and when it was not possible to detect it in plates not treated with penicillin —a neat piece of laboratory technique. But Fleming also stated that penicillin had no poisonous effect and that " it may be an efficient antiseptic for application to, or injection into, areas infected with penicillin-sensitive microbes," for it was non-irritant and non-toxic. In 1931 he prophesied that, " it is quite likely that it, or a chemical of a similar nature, will be used in the treatment of septic wounds."

For some reason or other no special interest was taken in the discovery. In 1932, however, Raistrick and his colleagues obtained a culture of Fleming's mould and tried to isolate the effective principle. They grew the mould on a synthetic medium consisting solely of glucose and inorganic salts and defined the optimum conditions of growth. They acidified the medium slightly, extracted with ether, and on the removal of the ether, obtained the anti-bacterial substance in a crude form: they restricted the name penicillin to this substance, which they found was a very complex acid, unstable in the conditions of their experiments.

From what has been published it is apparent that further work on penicillin would have been carried out if any real interest had been shown by the medical profession. In the circumstances it was regarded merely as one mould product amongst many, chemically not worth particular study. Possibly the indifference was because chemotherapy was no longer thought to be a profitable line of reasearch. P. Ehrlich had tried 605 arsenicals before he succeeded in finding one which acted effectively on the spirochaetes of syphilis—606 was salvarsan. An abundance of further research gave no tangible positive results. This was the position in 1932. A change, however, then occurred. A team of research workers of the I. G. Farbenindustrie under G. Domagk, was set the task of finding some substance with a selective effect on *Streptococcus*. After considerable trials they produced a ruby-red dye (hydrochloride of 4 sulphamido-2; 4-diaminoazobenzol) which cured mice infected with streptococci. French chemists later isolated the

Plate XXI. *Armillaria mucida,* a beautiful glistening white species occurring on beech.

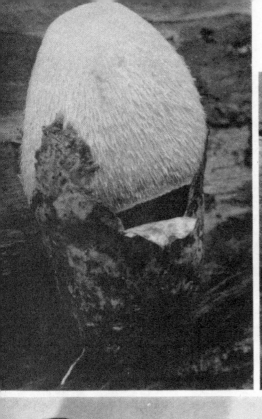

a. Cap bursting through the volva. (*D. A. Pickford*)

b. (*below*) Later stage. (*D. A. Pickford*)

c. Sections before volv ruptured. (*Brit. Mus. [Nat. M*

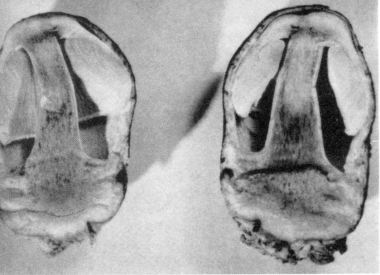

Plate XXII. Volvaria bombycina. The largest British species of the genus, usually growing near or on rotten elm-stumps. The sections show how the volva is continuous at first.

active substance from the dye: it was a white powder—sulphanilamide. Again chemotherapy came right to the front of the stage. Though now attention began to be centred on the production of antibiotic substances by fungi and bacteria, nothing of importance was published until 1939, when R. J. Dubos announced the discovery of tyrothricin, formed by the common soil bacterium, *Bacillus brevis*, which was strongly potent against gram-positive bacteria: he had reasoned like Pasteur and others that there are bacteria in the soil that prey on pathogenic bacteria. In 1938, H. W. Florey, in collaboration with E. B. Chain, had mapped out a programme for the systematic study of the naturally produced anti-bacterial substances. One of the organisms they decided to work upon was *Bacillus pyocyaneus*, up to then the best-known producer of an antibiotic substance (pyocyanase) which had been on the market in Germany for treatment against anthrax and diphtheria; the other was *Penicillium notatum*, as it was thought that from what was already known, penicillin was promising. How right they were! The publication of the results obtained by Florey and the Oxford School in 1940 and 1941, was one of the outstanding medical sensations of all time. Penicillin was really on the stage at last; it dwarfed other performers into insignificance. It was hailed as a " miracle drug," and as the preliminary reports proved to be not only justified but to give it less than its due, it took its place in newspaper headlines. The penicillin used in the clinical trials was obtained from cultures by extracting with amyl acetate. At first it was thought to be pure because it proved to be so active, but is now known to have been only about 1 to 2 per cent pure—presumably very similar to that obtained by Raistrick.

The story of penicillin will often be told, and the long delay before the substance was properly tried out will be accounted for in various ways. But luck, or providence, enters into the story. The spores of the mould which contaminated Fleming's culture plate just blew in through the window or were knocking about in the laboratory in a casual and unwanted manner. The fungus was identified at first as *Penicillium rubrum*, but later it was recognised as *Penicillum notatum*, a species which was first described from decaying hyssop in Norway, but is now known to be frequent in the soil. However, it turned up in the laboratory of St. Mary's Hospital, London, and interfered with the investigations of one of the few men with an outlook on these matters which would ensure scientific curiosity in the manifestations of the intruder.

Another point is that although a large number of species of *Penicillium* have now been studied, as well as other moulds, *Penicillium notatum* and the closely allied *Penicillium chrysogenum*, are the only ones which produce penicillin in appreciable amounts. The luck did not end by the spores of the fungus with such special properties alighting on an experimental culture of one curious in the ways of microscopic organisms. If, after the original account had been published, the mould had been discarded or allowed to die out, anyone desiring to confirm the results would have investigated *Penicillium rubrum*, and failed: penicillin would indeed have been still-born, and, probably, would have received no more attention than an odd reference in text-books.

However, Fleming, convinced of the importance of the mould if only for laboratory technique, not only kept it growing but retained the plate on which he had made his original observation. The cultures of *Penicillium notatum* used by Raistrick, by Florey, and in all the early production on a commercial scale, were sub-cultures of Fleming's original strain. It was by " sheer luck " that Chain came on Fleming's paper describing penicillin. Perhaps luck enters into another matter. When the Oxford School published the account of their epoch-making clinical experiments they were under the impression that they were using practically a pure salt of penicillin, whereas there was something like 98 per cent impurity. The impurities, except in perhaps one case, were fortunately non-toxic, otherwise so clear a picture of the outstanding merits of penicillin as an antibiotic substance might not have been gained, and, possibly, the vast panorama which was so clearly drawn would have been marred if not partly obliterated.

This was a period of intense effort in this country, and of air raids, and it appeared improbable that much headway could be made in getting a supply of penicillin to carry out the necessary clinical experiments, and hopeless to achieve large scale production in time to benefit the fighting forces. Florey, and his colleague N. G. Heatley, therefore went to U.S.A. in July 1941 to try to arouse interest in the problem; they succeeded in obtaining the invaluable assistance of the Northern Regional Research Laboratory at Peoria. It was found that several industrial pharmaceutical manufacturers had already begun the study of penicillin, and information was freely given them. The ball was set rolling for the U.S.A. Government to take over production. There were difficulties: one was the fear of the commerical houses of pooling information because of the Sherman Anti-Trust Laws; another was that the yields of penicillin were so low and costs so high that the task of producing the kilogram of crude penicillin needed for its proper testing seemed beyond accomplishment.

But almost at once a chance discovery altered the shape of things. The workers at Peoria, skilled in the use of moulds as fermentation organisms, at once applied themselves to three obvious problems. Was Fleming's strain of *Penicillium notatum* the only one to produce penicillin —which was unlikely? Was the culture medium used the best for penicillin production? Was surface growth of the fungus better than other methods used in fermentation processes?

In experimenting, a by-product of the local starch-making industry, corn steep liquor,* was added to the medium and the penicillin yield was increased by ten times; milk sugar in the medium gave an additional increase. This discovery probably was the greatest single factor in making the commercial production of penicillin feasible.

Penicillium notatum like many if not most moulds when grown in culture produces variants (mutations) which frequently have the same degree of constancy as the parent strain. Variants were isolated and tested and one (N.R.R.L.) 1249.B.21 was found to produce greatly increased yields and became generally used in commercial production.

Having had experience of growing moulds in submerged culture in certain industrial fermentation processes, they experimented with Fleming's strain but found that it would grow only on the surface. All the cultures of the *Penicillium notatum – chrysogenum* series in the Peoria collections were tried and a strain of *P. notatum* (832) was found to give satisfactory results. All attempts to develop better yielding strains from this being unsuccessful a wide search was made for something more amenable to laboratory technique. Air Transport Command were requested to send soil and mouldy food samples from all over the world. Well over two hundred strains of *P. notatum-chrysogenum* were tested, including many from mouldy food in shops and restaurants. Housewives hearing of the search sent in specimens and it was a strain of *P. chrysogenum* found by one of them on a mouldy cantaloupe in the Peoria market which proved the best! (N.R.R.L. 1951). By selection a strain (B25) was isolated which increased the yield, but nothing better than this could be isolated. Co-ordinated research was in full swing by that time and other laboratories with special problems

*The liquid left after maize is soaked in water (with 0.3 per cent sulphur dioxide) for thirty hours before grinding.

assigned to them took up the task of inducing the production of better yielding strains. It entailed an enormous amount of work, but outstanding success resulted. Conidia of B25 were irradiated with X-rays and one of the mutants obtained from the surviving spores pushed up the yield (X-1612); this in turn was subjected to ultra-violet irradiation and Q-176 resulted. Like the previous best, it was distributed to all manufacturers and was the last organism of which we have full details —for the war ended and with it co-operative research. It is known, however, that further research has resulted in improving the strain in certain desired directions. The stepping up in production is seen in figures published after the war.

The yields of Fleming's strain in surface culture were originally approximately 2 units per millilitre; N.R.R.L. 832 gave 40-80 units in submerged culture; N.R.R.L. B25 100-200 units; after X-rays, X-1612 gave 300-500 units; after ultra-violet, Q-176 gave 1000 or more units. The development of such powerful strains " clearly was the greatest single factor contributing to large scale penicillin production."

At first the production of penicillin was slow. Commercial firms, both here and in U.S.A., took up its preparation but the amounts available were so small that they had to be rationed for clinical tests. These proved so remarkedly successful that the British and American Governments took charge. In September 1942 a meeting was called by the Ministry of Supply which led to a General Penicillin Committee being formed. It needed government aid if any immediate progress was to be made: there were already so many calls on building and other materials that, without priorities, the necessary factories, equipment and chemicals were destined to remain as blue prints or their equivalents. The government promised, and gave, whatever financial or other aid was required. All available knowledge was pooled and research concentrated on producing penicillin on a factory scale. But progress was lamentably slow.

In the States there was much the same beginning, though there, following Florey's 1941 visit, the Medical Research Department of the Office of Scientific Research and Development were in close touch with interested commercial firms. In May 1943 the War Production Board took charge of manufacture and research. " This program was granted the highest priorities accorded to any military item, except the atomic bomb."* By the spring of 1944 penicillin had been

*Bulletin of the U.S. Army Medical Department (1946).

thoroughly tested clinically and its importance for battle wounds and diseases recognised. The armed forces called for large amounts and additional projects were put in hand to find methods of increasing supply. What had seemed altruism on the part of the firms attempting to make penicillin available—the chances seemed too remote for it to have been a gamble—turned into a mass saving of lives, and commercial profit. " The government subsidised the building of plants, the plants were built, and penicillin was made. It was sold back to the government by the manufacturers who, in turn, repaid the government from their profits for the subsidy for building their plants. Some of these plants cost from 600,000 to 2,000,000 dollars to build . . . yet they were completely paid for in a matter of two or three years through profits made on penicillin."

There was a full exchange of information between the two government-sponsored efforts, both research results and production methods, and this was circulated as " restricted." No British firm was allowed to set up a plant without a permit; in U.S.A. a few firms continued privately but twenty-one subscribed to the government scheme.

The pace was startling. Here was a totally new type of fermentation process, producing only traces of a relatively unstable product; owing to the supreme urgency of the demands there could be no waiting for the results of basic studies—they had to be incorporated as they became available.

In comparison the progress in this country was much slower and it was not until the end of the war that we had become penicillin self-supporting. The chief reason for this was the lag in the building of suitable factories, but there did not seem to be at first the general appreciation of the essential mycological foundations of the whole process which was immediately apparent to the American industrial mycologists.

Probably no drug has ever had such publicity as penicillin. This was mostly of the " boost " kind, annoying in that at best it gave fact without foundation: the marvellous cures in war wounds, gas gangrene, burns, meningitis, gonorrhoea, syphilis, pneumonia, osteomyelitis, were recorded, but it was essential that the enemy should be without exact information about this new weapon of war: all investigations in this country were made subject to the Official Secrets Act. It altered completely the British Tommy's conception of what constituted a " Blighty one ": the old-fashioned type of wound proved so amenable to penicillin treatment that it meant merely an absence of a few days from the line, and consequently was not so devoutly to be desired. War is a dirty business in more ways than one, but penicillin cleaned up the filth caused by the bacterial infection of wounds, and takes its place amongst the historic achievements of World War No. 2.

Its discovery, its isolation and the proof of its therapeutic properties, were the accomplishment of workers in this country: it has been rightly claimed as a triumph for British science. But the credit for producing sufficient penicillin for use while hostilities lasted is due mainly to the War Production Board of the U.S.A., which combined the efforts of pharmaceutical and chemical manufacturers and co-ordinated research.

The precise details of penicillin production on a large scale are highly technical. The essentials of the process are the culturing of the mould in a watery nutrient solution containing sugar; the mould, in growing, forms small amounts of penicillin which it excretes into the solution; after several days the fungus mass is removed, and the penicillin is extracted from the remaining fluid. As in all mycological cultures the end result depends upon the particular strain of the fungus used, the constitution of the medium, and the conditions of growth.

The difficulties which had to be overcome in large scale production were consequent upon the facts that penicillin is unstable, that it is present in the medium in very small proportions, and that *Penicillium notatum* grows best in nearly neutral media, which are equally favourable for penicillin-insensitive organisms, some of which produce the enzyme penicillinase which destroys the penicillin as rapidly as it is formed.

An essential of all the manipulations is sterility, and to attain this on a large scale needs the most intricate precautions. The culture medium must be sterile before inoculations with the mould, and must remain free from infection by any other organism. Moreover, the particular strain of fungus must be kept pure and stable.

In the first penicillin plants, milk bottles, Winchester quarts and similar receptacles were used for the culture fluid, being slanted at about 10° so that the greatest surface area was obtained without wetting the cotton-wool stoppers. The bottles were moved on conveyor belts and many devices were adapted from milk-bottling plants. This surface culture method has now been wholly replaced: one defect from which it suffered was the variation in depth of the medium in the bottles, which leads to lack of uniformity and therefore waste.

Another is the great chance of infection by other fungi or bacteria which produce the penicillin-destroying penicillase; a single bottle so infected ruined a day's batch when the whole was added together after incubation, and its effects could not be discovered until the end of the process.

A form of surface culture which has been used on a commercial scale is that of passing the culture fluid through a series of superposed trays; a disadvantage of the method is the difficulty of maintaining sterility. Another method is based on the continuous vinegar process, sterile medium inoculated with *Penicillium notatum* spores being allowed to trickle down a tower containing appropriate packing. Still another was to grow the fungus on bran, an adaptation of the commercial processes used for producing mould enzymes: riboflavin (vitamin B_2) was manufactured in Japan by this method in 1936 using *Eremothecium Ashbyi*.

The bottle method and others have now been replaced by " deep-tank " or submerged culture in vats of 5,000 to 30,000 gallons, made of stainless steel; most other metals rapidly destroy penicillin. One advantage is that the trouble and expense of cleaning, filling, sterilising and incubating many thousands of bottles each day is avoided—as is also the consequent breakage—but the chief merit is that the fungus growing submerged in the medium, which is aerated aseptically with oxygen and mechanically stirred, ensures more rapid and greater production, for the whole of the liquid is constantly acted upon. Space is also saved, for one tank produces as much penicillin as half a million bottles.

The method of submerged growth was first used by A. Calmette, who in 1902 patented a process for the production of gallic acid by the action of *Aspergillus gallomyces* (a variant of *A. niger*) on clear tannin extract.

While war continued penicillin was essential—at any cost. In this country unless plant already in being had been kept in production valuable time would have been lost in making the change over to tank culture. When hostilities ceased ordinary commercial considerations and competition altered the picture and the firms using only the old system went out of production. It is probable that in U.S.A. the possibility of beginning immediate surface culture manufacture with materials already available was the main reason for adopting it: the change-over there was more easily made.

Ordinary medical " yellow " or " amorphous " penicillin is 30 to 80 per cent pure: it contains small amounts of mould pigments, decomposition products, etc. Pure sodium penicillin *G* is obtained by further purification of the solution beyond the usual stage and recrystallisation. It is white and much more stable than amorphous penicillin.

The unit of penicillin activity is now the subject of international agreement. The international standard is defined as the sodium salt of pure crystalline penicillin II (penicillin-G) or benzyl penicillin: the international unit as the specific activity contained in 0.5988 microgram of the international standard.

The early samples of penicillin consisted chiefly of impurities (*c.* 98 per cent), mainly salts of organic acids of varying composition according to the medium and the method of extraction. Chemical titration could not be used to estimate the amount of penicillin, and routine bacteriological methods were at first resorted to. These were soon replaced by the " cup plate " (" cup cylinder " or " cylinder plate ") method developed at Oxford, and still the most widely used. The principle involved is the diffusion of penicillin from small porcelain cylinders placed on a nutrient agar inoculated with a standard strain of *Staphyloccus aureus*: the width of the zone around the cylinder free from bacteria gives a comparative measure of strength when compared with a standard.*

Originally the general opinion was that as so little penicillin was produced, even in the best of the early commercial plants, chemical synthesis offered a better prospect of obtaining the drug in quantity. It was also thought that its activity might reside in a particular chemical grouping in the molecule and that some simpler compounds containing the grouping could be prepared; or possibly, some modification of the structure of penicillin might be brought about which would produce a substance active against organisms insensitive to penicillin itself. Investigation of the chemical structure of penicillin was therefore undertaken as a top priority, both here and in the States: there were ten laboratories in Great Britain and nineteen in U.S.A. engaged on the research. All results were pooled and classified, and collaboration of a unique kind established. This arrangement, which overrode all patents, rested solely on mutual goodwill; it ended before there was a formal Agreement signed between the respective governments on 25 January 1946, that what had already happened should happen during the period from 1 December 1943, to 31 October

*Chemical methods are now used to estimate the purity of samples of penicillin.

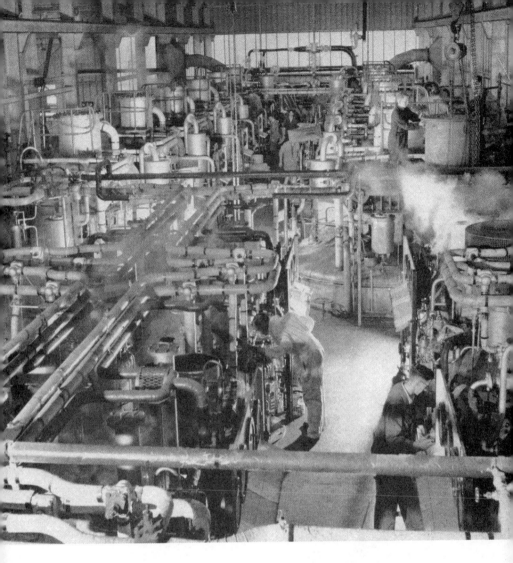

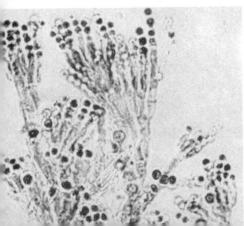

Plate XXIII. a (above) General view of the operating floor of a fermenter hall; b (below) Photomicrograph of *Penicillium notatum* (*Glaxo Laboratories, Ltd.*)

Plate XXIV

A   TOAD

AND

A

TOADSTOOL
(*The Times*)

1945. After this date publication could take place at the desire of either government following consultation with the other.

Soon after the chemical study was begun it was unexpectedly found that there was more than one kind of penicillin. The first two to be recognised were called Penicillin I and Penicillin II in this country, Penicillin F and Penicillin G in America. Penicillin I was then being manufactured here by surface culture on synthetic media whereas the American yields from corn-steep media were Penicillin II. Later Penicillin III (X) and Penicillin IV (K) were recognised as being produced in greater or lesser amounts depending on cultural conditions. A summary of what was known about the chemical structure of penicillin was issued simultaneously here and in America at the end of 1945, followed by a full account in 1950.

There are now five known "natural" penicillins. All are dipeptides with the formula $C_9H_{11}O_4N_2S$ R—the difference between them being in the constitution of the side chain to the molecule, for convenience represented by R. The general structure common to all is:

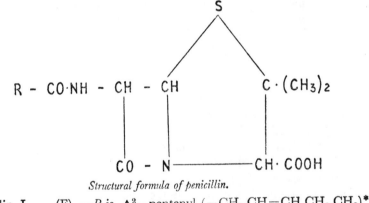

Structural formula of penicillin.

Penicillin I   (F) —R is Δ^2—pentenyl ($-CH_2.CH{=}CH.CH_2.CH_3$)*
Penicillin II   (G) —R is benzyl ($-CH_2.\ C_6H_5$)
Penicillin III   (X) —R is p-hydroxybenzyl ($-CH_2.C_6H_4.OH$)
Penicillin IV   (K) —R is n-heptyl ($-CH_2.\ (CH_2)_5.CH_3$)
Gigantic acid   —R is n-amyl ($-CH_2.CH_2.CH_2.CH_2CH_3$)

All forms are strong monobasic acids. The four-membered β-lactam ring had not previously been met with in biological material: the ring can readily be opened by chemical means or by penicillinase, which is the reason for the high instability of penicillin. Almost any

*The Chemical names are Δ^2 pentenyl penicillin, benzyl penicillin, etc.

strain of the *Penicillium notatum—P. chrysogenum* group will produce some penicillin but this activity is not confined to them. About eleven other species of *Penicillium* are known to form penicillin-like substances, about nine species of *Aspergillus*, the dermatophyte *Trichophyton mentagrophytes*, and *Malbranchea pulchella*, a thermophilic fungus: their yield is usually very low but could doubtless be raised by inducing mutations with radium, X-rays, ultra-violet rays, nitrous acid, colchicine, mustard gas or some other method.

The kind of penicillin produced depends upon the strain of *Penicillium* and any one strain may form a mixture of penicillins according to the conditions of culture.

To round off the summary, mention must be made of what are called precursors, organic compounds which the fungus can assimilate from a medium and incorporate directly into the penicillin molecule. It was found at Peoria in 1943 that the addition of phenylacetic acid to a corn-steep medium increased the yield by 30 to 50 per cent in both surface and submerged cultures: for a time it was supposed that the acid acted as a plant hormone such as indolacetic acid. The clue came from researches in this country when it was found that two different strains of *Penicillium notatum* gave Penicillin I when grown on a synthetic medium and Penicillin II on a corn-steep medium: the medium determined the type produced. The inference was that corn-steep liquor contained a substance acting as a precursor. In further research β-phenylethylamine, a precursor of Penicillin II, and also tyramine, a precursor of Penicillin III, were isolated. So far these are the only penicillins of which the precursors are known. The portion of the penicillin molecule concerned is *R*. Much research has failed to find precursors for the other parts of the molecule.

The discovery of precursors paved the way to the production of biosynthetic penicillins. Many have been made and large numbers are possible some of which may prove to be valuable. In studying precursors it was found that a number of different compounds, but all containing the phenyl group, stimulated the yield of Penicillin II. The next step was to entice the fungus to utilise some " unnatural " compound as a precursor and so introduce a new substance in the *R* position, i.e. a new penicillin.

When the existence of the first three penicillins, I, II and III, was realised it was not thought that they might differ in their clinical effects, and no attention was paid to the selective production of any one of them. Penicillin II was the main type produced in deep tank

PENICILLIN   289

manufacture, and it is in many ways the most desirable for general use. Penicillin IV, the last of the numbered series, has been the cause of much confusion and controversy and some misgiving about the possibility of the development of penicillin-resistant strains of disease organisms. In laboratory tests it is 30 per cent more potent than Penicillin II but is definitely less effective when administered. Coinciding with the introduction of the prolific strain Q176 there was a decided lessening of the beneficial clinical tests of the marketed product. It was found that this was due to the large proportion of Penicillin IV which was being produced where manufacturers had not added phenylacetic acid or other Penicillin II precursor to the medium— a further indication of the paramount importance of the organism in industrial biology.

The discovery of penicillin led to an intensive and extensive investigation of fungi and bacteria in the hope of finding production of other substances having equally valuable therapeutic qualities, or active on organisms insensitive to penicillin, and more easy of manufacture on a large scale. About thirty so-called antibiotic substances have been isolated from fungi, but all fail in some respect. The qualities sought are powerful action, specificity, non-toxicity, action in the presence of body fluids, general stability, stability against toxic enzymes, slow excretion, and non-development of resistance in previously sensitive bacteria. Penicillin is excreted rapidly, which is the reason for the large amounts needed in treatment. Fumigacin (helvolic acid) produced by *Aspergillus fumigatus* has all the necessary qualities except that bacteria readily acquire resistance to it. Most of the others are toxic or too weak in action to be of use.

Large numbers of Basidiomycetes produce antibiotic substances, but so far all found have proved to be toxic, with the possible exception of clitocybin which has received considerable publicity in the popular press, partly because of its being reported as effective against tuberculosis. (*See* p. 124.)

Actinomycetes (Ray fungi) which are characterised by their extremely thin mycelium and which have much in common with bacteria, produce some important antibiotics. These organisms are common in the soil though some are parasitic on plants (*Actinomyces scabies*, causing potato scab) and animals (*Actinomyces bovis*, causing lumpy jaw in man).

The antagonistic nature of many soil Actinomycetes has been known for over sixty years. In 1940 S. Waksman and N. B. Woodruffe isolated the first antibiotic substance in a pure state. Waksman and his colleagues were the pioneer investigators of the subject, isolating numerous antibiotics some active against organisms resistant to penicillin. They isolated Streptomycin from cultures of *Streptomyces griseus* in 1944 and great claims were made for it, some only of which have been substantiated. An enormous literature has grown up around it as it seemed at first that it would complement penicillin. Several other forms have been prepared, e.g. dihydrostreptomycin which are improvements on the original substance.

Considerable research is being carried out on this group, mainly in America. Chloramphenicol (Chloromycetin) prepared from *Streptomyces venezualae* by J. Ehrlich and his associates in 1947, Aureomycin from *S. aureofaciens* by B. M. Duggar in 1948, and Terramycin from *S. rimosus* by the chemists of Charles Pfizer & Co., in 1950, all act on Rickettsia bodies, and the last two on certain viruses. It seems hopeful that eventually substances will be prepared to antagonise most if not all human infections. Chloramphenicol is the only antibiotic manufactured on a commercial basis by chemical synthesis.

It is remarkable that penicillin, the first of the antibiotics, should so far have proved to be the best in the treatment of human diseases.

In the search for substances of use in therapy, that is in the attempt to regulate the activities of fungi for our own ends, there is a tendency to overlook the fact that the production of these chemical substances is a physiological process and can have no immediate biological significance on the occurrence of human disease. On the other hand it doubtless plays a part in the natural distribution of organisms in the soil. Some substances produced are apparently without effect on surrounding organisms. Others stimulate growth as, for example, derivatives of tetronic acid produced by *Penicillium Charlesii*. That other substances have an adverse effect was first shown in 1932 by R. Weindling, who investigating the inhibition of the growth of *Rhizoctonia Solani* by *Trichoderma viride* (*T. lignorum*) attributed it to the secretion of a lethal principle which, with O. H. Emerson, he extracted in 1936 in crystalline form and named gliotoxin. Gliotoxin, which is formed by several other species, inhibits the growth of many fungi and bacteria, and its production is an obvious advantage to its producers in the struggle for space in the teeming soil. It is worthy of note that *Rhizoctonia Solani* causes a disease in potatoes and that *Trichoderma viride* in culture prevents the growth of the destructive *Armillaria mellea*. Leaves of *Eichornia crassipes* simultaneously inoculated with a species of *Corticium* and *Trichoderma* gave little or no infection of *Corticium*, whereas in the absence of the soil organism, invasion by the *Corticium* was extensive.

A much-named substance—patulin, clavicin, clavatin, claviformin, expansin—which is produced by several moulds, when added to soil infected with *Pythium de Baryanum*, checks its growth and planted seedlings do not damp off but remain healthy. Patulin also inhibits the growth of a number of other parasitic fungi. The part the phenomenon takes in the interplay between species is of great importance in the consideration of their distribution in the soil, and, moreover, in soil-borne diseases.

The proposed restriction of the term antibiotic to chemical substances produced by the activity of micro-organisms which inhibit microbial growth or activity, is unfortunate. Antibiosis is not confined to the microscopic, for it is really the antithesis of symbiosis. The expressed juice of many flowering plants inhibits the growth of the usual test organisms *Staphylococcus aureus* and *Bacillus coli*: onion juice was found to be active against forty-two species of fungi, including ringworms: tomatin from tomato juice is active against some species of the mould *Fusarium*. Antibacterial substances occur in water extracts of the litter from forest floors. Too great an extension of the term, however, would interfere with clear thinking, just as too narrow a definition stultifies.

Some of the pieces of the jig-saw puzzle of fungal activities are already in place, and we are gaining glimpses of what appear to be parts of the completed design: it may include " detestable enormities " but that is by no means the whole picture.

There is a world wide shortage of proteins and this has occasioned much search for new supplies. The residual broths from antibiotic manufacture—penicillin, streptomycin, aureomycin, etc., prove to be rich in Vitamin B_{12}, which is an essential part of the " animal protein factor " (APF). Added to poultry and pig foods the broth gives a marked improvement in growth, but the stimulation is greater with some than with others. It was unexpectedly found that this was due to the presence of antibiotics. Research so far shows that the antibiotics decrease the needs for several vitamins and for proteins. " Not all the consequences of this new development in nutrition can be foreseen but some are already visible. These include the need to change or qualify the accepted figures for requirement of known nutrients, the need to re-evaluate the importance of micro-organisms in the

M.T. U

digestive tract of the non-ruminant, and the opportunity to increase materially the efficiency of meat production." Obviously so important a discovery called for much research before the purveyors of proprietory preparations could be permitted to flood the market. The view generally favoured is that antibiotics used in this way exert their effects through an action on the gut flora.

THE   END

BIBLIOGRAPHY

OF WRITINGS ON FUNGI there is no end. Some books and articles, though not referred to in the text, are listed with a view to helping readers to follow up any aspect of the subject which interests them. When full references are given in the text, they are not repeated here. Incidental references are listed mainly because several of them might prove difficult to trace.

ADLER, C. F. (1752). Noctiluca marina. (Linnaeus, Praeses). Dissertationes Academicae.

ALBION, R. G. (1926). Forests and Sea Power. The timber problems of the Royal Navy, 1652-1862. Cambridge, Mass., Harvard University Press.

ANDERSON, O. (1950). Larger fungi on sandy grass heaths and sand-dunes in Scandinavia. *Bot. Notiser Supplement* 2: 1-89.

ANDERSON, E. E., and FELLERS, C. R. (1942). The food value of mushrooms. (*Agaricus campestris.*) *Proc. Amer. Soc. Hort. Sci., 41*: 301-4.

ASCHERSON, F. M. (1836). Ueber die Fructifications-organe der höheren Pilze. *Wiegmann, Arch., 2*: 372.

BARGER, G. (1931). Ergot and ergotism. London, Gurney and Jackson.

BAYLIS, J. S. (1911). Observations on *Marasmius oreades* and *Clitocybe gigantea* as parasitic fungi. *J. econ. Biol., 6*: 111-32.

BAYLIS ELLIOTT, J. S. (1915). Fungi in the nests of ants. *Trans. Brit. myc. Soc.* 5: 138-142.

BECQUEREL, P. (1910). Recherches expérimentales sur la vie latente des spores des Mucorinées et des Ascomycètes. *C. R. Acad. Sc., Paris 150*: 1437-9.

BELT, T. (1874). Naturalist in Nicaragua. London.

BENSAUDE, M. (1918). Recherches sur le cycle évolutif et la sexualité chez le Basidiomycètes. Thèse. Paris.

BERGMEN, S. (1927). Through Kamchatka by dog-sled and skis ... (Trans. F. Whyte.) London, Seeley, Service & Co.

BERKELEY, M. J. (1838). On the fructification of the pileate and clavate tribes of Hymenomycetous fungi. *Ann. Mag. nat. Hist. 1*: 81-101. (1840) On the fructification of *Lycoperdon, Phallus*, and their allied genera. *Ann. Mag. nat. Hist. 4*: 155-9.

BERNARD, N. (1909). L'évolution dans la symbiose. Les Orchidées et leur champignons commensaux. *Ann. Sci. nat. Bot. Ser. 9. 9*: 1-196.

BIGGS, R. (1937). The species concept in *Corticium coronilla*. *Mycologia 29*: 686-705.

BJÖRKMAN, E. (1949). The ecological significance of the ectotrophic mycorrhizal association in forest trees. *Svensk. bot. Tidskr. 43*: 223-262.

BLAKESLEE, A. F. (1904). Sexual reproduction in the Mucorineae. *Proc. Amer. Acad. Arts Sci. 40*: 205-319. (1932.) Genetics of sensory thresholds: taste for phenyl thio carbarmide. *Pro. nat. Acad. Sci., Wash, 18* (1) 128-30.

BLEWITT, M. and FRAENKEL, G. (1944). Intracellular symbiosis and vitamin requirements of two insects, *Lasioderma serricorne* and *Sitodrepa panicea*. *Proc. roy. Soc. B. 131:* 212-21.

BOMMER, C. (1894). Sclérotes et cordons mycéliens. *Mém. Acad. R. Belge, 54.*

BOTHE, F. (1930). Ein neuer einheimischer Leuchtpilz. *Ber. dtsch. bot. Ges. 48:* 394-9. (1931) Über das Leuchten verwesender Blätte und seine Erreger. *Planta 14:* 752-65. (1935) Genetische Untersuchungen über die Lichtentwicklung der Hutpilze I. *Arch. Protistenk. 85:* 369-83.

BOUDIER, E. (1901). Influence de la nature du sol et les végetaux qui y croissent sur le développement des champignons. *Bull. Soc. myc. France 17:* 69-73. (1911) La fresque de Plaincourault (Indre). *Bull. Soc. myc. Fr. 27:* 31-33.

BRUNSWICK, H. (1924). Untersuchungen über die Geschlechts- und Kern-verhältnisse bei der Hymenomyztengattung *Coprinus*. *Bot. Abh. 5:* 1-152.

BUCHNER, P. (1930). Tier und Pflanze in Symbiose. Berlin, Gebrüder Bornträger.

BULLER, A. H. R. (1909). Researches on fungi. The production, liberation and dispersal of the spores of Hymenomycetes. II (1922). Further investigations upon the production and liberation ... III (1924). The production and liberation of spores in Hymenomycetes and Uredineae. IV (1931). Further observations on Coprini together with some observations on social organisation and sex in the Hymenomycetes V (1933). Hyphal fusions and protoplasmic streaming in the higher fungi ... production and liberation of spores in *Sporobolomyces, Tilletia* and *Spaerobolus*. VI (1934). The biology and taxonomy of *Pilobolus*, production and liberation of spores in Discomycetes, pseudorhizae and gemmifers ... of certain Hymenomycetes. London, Longmans, Green & Co. (1915) The fungus lore of the Greeks and Romans. *Trans. Brit. myc. Soc. 5:* 21-66.

BULLIARD, P. (1784). Histoire des plantes vénéneuses et suspectes de la France. Paris.

BURGEFF, H. (1909). Die Wurzelpilze der Orchideen. Ihre Kultur und ihr Leben in der Pflanze. Jena, G. Fischer. (1932) Saprophytismus und Symbiose. Studien an tropischen Orchideen. Jena, G. Fischer. (1936) Samenkeimung der Orchideen und Entwicklung ihrer Keimpflanzen. Jena, G. Fischer.

CARTWRIGHT, K. ST. G. (1938). A further note on fungus association in the Siricidae. *Ann. appl. Biol. 25:* 430-2.

—— and FINDLAY, W. P. K. (1946). Decay of timber and its prevention. London, H. M. Stationery Office.

CATONI, G. (1929). La fruttificazione basiodiflora di un endofita della Orchidee. *Boll. R. Staz. Patol. veg. Rome N.S. 9,* 66-74.

CHAIN, E., FLOREY, H. W., GARDNER, A. D., HEATLEY, N. G., JENNINGS, M. A., ORR-EWING, J., and SANDERS, A. G. (1940). Penicillin as a chemotherapeutic agent. *Lancet 239:* 226-228.

CHATIN, A. (1892). La truffe. Paris.

CLUTTERBUCK, P. W., LOVELL, R., and RAISTRICK, H. (1932). Studies in the biochemistry of micro-organisms. XXVI. The formation from glucose by microbes of the *Penicillium chrysogenum* series of a pigment, an alkali-soluble protein and " Penicillin "—the antibacterial substance of Fleming. *Biochem. J. 26:* 1907-18.

COBB, N. A. (1906). Fungus malady of the sugar cane. *Exper. Stat. Hawaiian Sugar Planters' Assoc. Bull. No. 8.*

COOKE, M. C. (1881-91). Illustrations of British fungi (Hymenomycetes). 1-8. London.

CORDA, A. C. J. (1838). Icones fungorum. II. Prague.

CORNER, E. J. H. (1935). The fungi of Wicken Fen, Cambridgeshire. *Trans. Brit. myc. Soc. 19*: 280-7.

COSTANTIN, J. and MATRUCHOT, L. (1894). Procédé d'obtention des blancs de champignons comestibles. Brevet No. 236, 349, 17/2. *Bull. propr. industr.*

COUCH, J. N. (1938). The genus *Septobasidium*. Chapel Hill. Univ. North Carolina Press.

CURTIS, J. T. (1939). The relation of specificity of orchid mycorrhizal fungi to the problem of symbiosis. *Amer. J. Bot. 26*: 390-8.

DICKSON, J. (1785-1801). Plantarum cryptogamicarum Fasc. 1-4. London.

DIEHL, W. W. (1941). The taxonomy of Zenker's *Leptostroma camelliae*. *Mycologia, 33*: 215-9.

DITMAR, C., von (1886-90). Reisen und Aufenthalt in Kamtschatka in der Jahren 1851-55. *Kais. akad. wiss. St. Petersburg.*

DRECHSLER, C. (1946). A clamp-bearing fungus parasitic and predaceous on nematodes. *Mycologia 38*: 1-23.

DUBOS, R. J. (1939). Bactericidal effect of an extract of a soil bacillus on gram-positive cocci. *Proc. Soc. exp. Biol. Med. 40*: 311-2. *J. exp. Med. 70*: 1-10, 11-17.

DUGGAR, B. M. (1905). The principles of mushroom growing and mushroom spawn-making. *Bull. U.S. Bur. Pl. Ind. 55*: 1-60.

DUMÉE, L. and MAIRE, R. (1913). Note sur le *Queletia mirabilis* Fr. et sa decouverte aux environs de Paris. *Bull. Soc. Myc. Fr. 29*: 495-502.

DURANDE, J. F. R. Mémoire sur le champignon ridé, et sur les autres plantes de la même famille. *Nouv. Mém. Acad. Dijon pour . . . sciènces et arts, 2*: 302-24.

EZEKIEL, W. N. (1950). Mycological problems in deterioration of military equipment. *Trans. N.Y. Acad. Sci. Ser. 2. 12*: 224-9.

FALCK, R. (1912). Die Meruliu-Fäule des Bauholzes. *A. Möller's Hausschwammforsch.* 6, Berlin, G. Fischer.

FAVRE, J. (1948). Les associations fongiques des hauts-marais jurassiens et de quelques régions voisines. *Máter. Flore cryptog. Suisse* 10: no. 3.

FERGUSON, M. (1902). A preliminary study of the germination of the spores of *Agaricus campestris* and other Basidiomycetous fungi. *Bull. U.S. Bur. Pl. Ind. 16.*

FLEMING, A. (1929). On the antibacterial action of cultures of a *Penicillium*, with special reference to their use in the isolation of B. influenzae. *Brit. J. exp. Path. 10*: 226-36.

FRANK, A. B. (1885). Ueber die auf Wurzelsymbiose beruhende Ernährung gewisser Bäume durch unterirdische Pilze. *Ber. dtsch. bot. Ges. 3*: 128-45.

FRIEDERICH, K. (1940). Untersuchungen zur Ökologie der höheren Pilze. *Pflanzenforschung. 22.*

FRIES, N. (1948). The nutrition of fungi from the aspect of growth factor requirements. *Trans. Brit. myc. Soc. 30*: 118-34.

GÄUMANN, E. (1949). Die Pilze. Basel, Birkhäuser.

GIBELLI, G. (1883). Nuovi studii sulla malattia del Castagno detta dell'inchiostro. Bologna.

GILBERT, E. J. (1928). La mycologie sur le terrain. Les livres du mycologue 2. Paris, E. le François.

GLEN, G. (1816). A case proving the deleterious effects of the *Agaricus campanulatus*, which was mistaken for the *Agaricus campestris*, or champignon, *London Med. Phys. Journ. 36:* 451-3.

GOEDART, J. (1682). Johannes Godartius of Insects. Done into English and methodized with the addition of notes [by M. L(ISTER)]. York.

GRAINGER, J. (1946). Ecology of the larger fungi. *Trans. Brit. myc. Soc. 29:* 52-63.

GRAVES, G. (1821) in W. Curtis, Flora Londinensis. ed. ii, W. J. Hooker & S. Graves.

GRIEVE, J. (1764). Translation of S. P. Krasheninnikov. The history of Kamtschatka and the Kurilski Islands with the countries adjacent. Gloucester.

GWYNNE-VAUGHAN, H. C. I., and BARNES, B. (1937). The structure and development of the fungi. 2nd ed. Cambridge, University Press.

HAAS, H. (1932). Die bodenbewohnenden Grosspilze in das Waldformationen einiger Gebiete von Württemberg. *Beih. bot. Zbl. 501:* 35-134.

HARTIG, R. (1873). Vorläufige Mitteilung über den Parasitismus von *Agaricus melleus* und dessen Rhizomorphen. *Bot. Ztg. 31:* 295-7.

HARTIG, T. (1844). Ambrosia des *Bostrychus dispar*. *Allg. Forst. u. Jagdztg. 13:* 73-5.

HARVEY, E. N. (1940). Living light. Princeton, University Press.

HATCH, A. B. (1937). The physical basis of mycetrophy in *Pinus*. *Black Rock Forest Bull. 6.*

HAWKER, L. E. (1950). Physiology of fungi. London, University Press.

HEIM, R. (1942). Les pigments des champignons dans leurs rapports avec la systématique. *Conf. Soc. Chim. Biol. 29:* 48-79. (1942) Les champignons des termitières. *Rev. Sc. 80:* 69-86. (1948) Phylogeny and natural classification of macro-fungi. *Trans. Brit. myc. Soc. 30:* 161-178.

HILL, J. (1764). In Watson W.: An account of the insect called the vegetable fly. *Phil. Trans. roy. Soc. 53:* 271-4.

HÖFLER, K. (1938). Pilzsoziologie. *Ber. dtsch. bot. Gesell. 55:* 602-22.

HOLLANDE, C. E. (1945). Lyse massive des bacilles de Koch chez le cobaye après traitement à la clitocybine. *C. R. Acad. Sci., Paris, 221:* 361-3.

HOUGHTON, W. (1885). Notices of fungi in Greek and Latin authors. *Ann. Mag. nat. Hist. ser. 5, 5:* 22-49.

HRUBY, J. (1928). Die Pilze Mährens und Schlesiens. *Hedwigia 68:* 119-90.

HUTTON, J. (1790). On certain natural appearances on the ground on the Hill of Arthur's Seat. *Trans. roy. Soc. Edin. 2:* 3-11.

ISTVÁNFFI, G. de (1903). Deux nouveaux ravageurs de la vigne en Hongrie (*L'Ithyphallus impudicus* et le *Coepophagus echinops*). *Ann. Inst. ampélol. hong. Budapest.*

JOCHELSON, W. (1906). Religion and myths of the Koryak in Jesup North Pacific Expedition VI, 1. *Mem. N.Y. Amer. Mus. nat. Hist. X:* 1-382.

KAMIENSKI, F. (1882). Les organes végétatifs du *Monotropa Hypopitys* L. *Mém. Soc. nat. Sci., Cherbourg, 24:* 5-40.

KENNAN, G. (1870). Tent life in Siberia . . . London.

KLOTZSCH, F. (1838) in DIETRICH, A., Flora regni Borussici.

KNOP, W. (1865). Quantitative Untersuchungen über den Ernährungsprocess der Pflanze. *Landw. Versuchs. Stat. 7:* 93-107.

KNUDSON, L. (1922). Nonsymbiotic germination of orchid seeds. *Bot. Gaz. 73:* 1-25.

KOBERT, R. (1891). Matières toxiques dans les champignons. *Petersb. med. woehenschr.* 51-52.

KONRAD, P., and MAUBLANC, A. (1924-37). Icones selectae fungorum, I-VI. Paris, P. Lechevalier.

KRASHENINNIKOFF, S. P. (pp.). See Grieve, J.

KÜHNER, R. (1934). Observations sur la localisation cytologique des substances colorées chez les Agarics et les Bolets. *Botaniste 26*: 347-69.

KUSANO, S. (1911). *Gastrodia elata* and its symbiotic association with *Armillaria mellea*. *J. Coll. Agric. Imp. Univ. Tokyo 4*: 1-66.

LA HARPE, J. F. de (1780). Abrégé de l'histoire générale des voyages, 17.

LANGE, J. E. (1923). Ecological notes. Studies in the agarics of Denmark V. *Dansk bot. Ark. 9:* No. 4. (1935-43). Flora agaricina 1-5. Copenhagen.

LANGE, M. (1948). The agarics of Maglemose. A study in the ecology of the agarics. *Dansk bot. Ark. 13:* No. 1.

LANGERON, M (1945). A propos du traitement des intoxications fongiques. *Bull. Soc. myc. Fr. 61*: 14-21.

LANGSDORFF, G. H., von. Bemerkungen auf einer Reise um die Welt in den Jahren 1803-7. Frankfort-on-Main 1912. (English translation. Voyages and travels in various parts of the world . . . London, 1813-4.)

LANSDELL, H. (1882). Through Siberia.

LARSEN, P. (1932). Fungi of Iceland. 2: 3 of Rosenvinge, L. K., and Warming, E. The Botany of Iceland. Copenhagen and Oxford, University Press.

LEACH, J. G. (1940). Insect transmission of plant diseases. New York and London. McGraw-Hill Publishing Co.

LEISCHNER-SISKA, E. (1939). Zur Sociologie und Ökologie der höheren Pilze. *Beih. Bot. Zbl. 69*: 359-429.

LÉVEILLÉ, J. H. (1837). Recherches sur l'hyménium des champignons. *Ann. Sci. nat. Bot. ser. 2, 8*: 321-38.

LUDWIG, F. (1882). Ueber einen einheimischen phosphorescirenden Pilz. *Agaricus (Collybia) tuberosus* Bull. *Bot. Zbl. 12*: 104. (1885) *Agaricus cirrhatus* Pers., ein neuer phosphorescirender Pilz. *Hedwigia 24*: 250-1.

LUTJEHARMS, W. J. (1936). Zur Geschichte der Mykologie *Med. Neerl. Mycol. Vereein. 23*: 1-262.

LYNEN, F., and WIELAND, H. (1937). Uber die Giftstoffe der Knollenblätterpilzes IV. *Liebigs Ann. 533*: 93-117. V (1940) Wieland, H., and Witrop, B., 543: 171-83. VI (1941) Wieland, H., Hallermeyer, R., and Zilg., W., 548: 1-18. VII (1947) Wieland, T., Wirth, L., and Fischer, E., 564: 152-60.

MACRAE, R. (1942). Infertility studies and inheritance of luminosity in *Panus stipticus*. *Canad. J. Res. 20*: 411-34.

MALENÇON, G. (1938). Les Truffes européennes. *Rev. Myc. Paris, Mem. hors-sèr. 1*.

MARTYN, J. (1744). An account of a new species of fungus. *Phil. Trans. roy. Soc. 43*: 263-4.

MAUBLANC, A. (1946). Les champignons de France. Ed. 3. Paris, P. Lechevalier.

MELIN, E. (1917). Studier över de norrländska mymarkernas vegetation. Inaug. Diss. Uppsala. (1922) Untersuchungen über die *Larix* Mykorrhiza. 1. Synthesis der Mykorrhiza in Reinkultur. *Svensk. Bot. Tidsk. 16*: 161-96. (1925) Untersuchungen über die Bedeutung der Baummykorrhiza. Eine okologisch-physiologische Studie. Jena, G. Fischer. (1948) Recent advances in the study of tree mycorrhiza. *Trans. Brit. myc. Soc. 30*: 92-9.

MELZER, V. and ZVARA, J. (1927). *Russula xerampelina* Sch. *Bull. Soc. myc. Fr. 43*: 275-9.

MOLISCH, H. (1904). Leuchtende Pflanzen. Jena. G. Fischer.

MÖLLER, A. (1893). Die Pilzgarten einiger sudamerikanischer Amiesen. *Bot. Mit. Trop. 5*: 1-127.

MÜLLER, O. F. (1770). De musca vegetante europaea. *Nova Acta. Leop. Carol. 4*: 245-9.

MÜLLER, O. F. (1780). in Oeder: Flora Danica Pl. 834.

MÜNCHHAUSEN, O. F. von (1764-70). Der Hausvater 1-6.

NEES von ESENBECK, G. G. D. (1817). Das System der Pilze und Schwämme.

PASTAC, I. A. (1942). Les matières colorantes des champignons. *Rev. Myc., Paris. Mém. hors-sér. 2.*

PAULET, J. J. (1793). Traité des champignons. Paris.

PEYRONEL, B. (1917). Prime osservazioni sulla distribuzione degli Imenomiceti umicoli e sui loro probabali rapporti colle micorize ectotrofiche della fanero-game. *R.C. Accad. Lincei Ser. 5, 26*: 326. (1922) Nouveaux cas de rapports mycorrhiziques entre phanérogames et basidiomycètes. *Bull. Soc. myc. Fr. 37*: 143-6.

PHOEBUS, P. (1842). Über den Keimkörnersapparat der Agariceen und Helvellaceen. *Nova. Acta. Acad. Leop.-Carol. 19*: 169-248.

QUEVAUVILLER, A. (1944). Les poisons de l'*Amanita phalloides* Fr. *Rev. Sc. No. 3229*: 115-121.

RAISTRICK, H. (1949). A region of biosynthesis. *Proc. roy. Soc. A. 199*: 141-68.

RAMAGE, A. (1930). Mushroom—Mineral content. *Nature 126*: 279.

RAMSBOTTOM, J. (1922). Orchid Mycorrhiza in Charlesworth & Co.'s Catalogue 2-17; *Trans. Brit. myc. Soc. 8*: 28-61. (1923) A handbook of the larger British fungi. London. Brit. Mus. (Nat. Hist.). (1926) Special groups of plants. A. Fungi, in Tansley, A. G., and Chipp, T. E. Aims and methods in the study of vegetation, 152-173. London, Crown Agents for the Colonies. (1936) The uses of fungi. Ann. Rept. Brit. Assoc. 189-218. (1940) Taxonomic problems in fungi in Huxley, J. The New Systematics 411-34. Oxford Univ. Press. (1941) The expanding knowledge of mycology since Linnaeus. *Proc. Linn. Soc. London, Sess. 151*: 280-367. (1941) Dry rot in ships. *Essex Nat. 25*: 231-67. (1943) Fungi and the biology of war. *Trans. S.E. Union Sci. Soc. 47*: 1-24. (1944) Fungi and modern affairs. Nature 153: 636-41 Smithsonian Rep. for 1945: 313-26. (1945) Poisonous fungi. London, Penguin Books. (1948) Edible fungi. 2nd ed. London, Penguin Books. (1949) The biological concept of antibiotics. *Soc. d'hist. nat. Afrique Nord, 2*: 273-7.

RAULIN, J. (1863). Etudes chimiques sur la végétation des Mucédinées. *C.R. Acad. Sci., Paris. Sér. 57*: 227. (1869). *Ann. Sci. nat. Bot. 5, sér. 11*: 93-299.

RAYNER, M. C. (1927). Mycorrhiza. An account of non-pathogenic infections by fungi in vascular plants and bryophytes. *New Phytol. Reprint 15.* London, Wheldon & Wesley.

REA, C. (1915). The dominant macrofungi of our woods and pastures. *Worcest. Nat. Club Trans. 6*: 103-111. (1922) British Basidiomycetae. A handbook to the larger British fungi. Cambridge, University Press.

REMSBERG, R. E. (1940). Studies in the genus *Typhula. Mycologia 32*: 52-96.

RIVIÈRE, R. D., de la (1933) Le poison des Amanites mortelles. Paris, Masson & Co.

ROBERTS, W. (1874). Studies on biogenesis. *Phil. Trans. roy. Soc. 164*: 457-77.

ROGERS, D. P. (1935). Notes on the lower Basidiomycetes. *Univ. Iowa Studies, 16,* 160-81.

ROOS, J. C. (1767). Mundus invisibilis. (Linnaeus, Praeses). Dissertationes Academicae.

ROQUES, J. (1832). Histoire des champignons comestibles et vénéneux. Paris.

SACHS, J. (1860). Vegetationsversuche mit Ausschluss des Bodens über die Nährstoffe und sonstigen Ernährungsbedingungen von Mais, Bohnen, und anderer Pflanzen. *Landw.-versuchs-stat. 2*: 219-268.

SCHAEFFER, J. (1933, 1934). *Russula* Monographie. *Ann. Mycol. 31*: 305-516. 32: 141-243.

SCHMIDBERGER, J. (1836). Naturgeschichte des Appelborken käfers, *Apate dispar. Beitr. Obst. u. Naturges. Ostbaum. schedlicher Insecten. 4.*

SCHOPFER, W. H. (1943). Plants and vitamins. Walton, Mass: Chronica Botanica.

SCHULTES, R. E. (1939). Plantae Mexicanae II. The identification of teonanacatl, a narcotic Basidiomycete of the Aztecs. *Bull. Mus. Leafl. Harv. 7*, No. 3. (1940) Teonanacatl: the narcotic mushroom of the Aztecs. *Amer. Anthrop. 42*: 429-43.

SEGER G. (1671). Fungus Anthropomorphos. *Nova. Acta. Leop.-Carol. 2.*, 112-3.

SHANTZ, H. L., and PIEMEISEL, R. L. (1917). Fungus fairy rings in Eastern Colorado and their effects on vegetation. *J. agric. Res. 11*: 191-245.

SLUNIN, N. V. (1900). Country of Okhotsk and Kamchatka. St. Petersburg.

SMEATHMAN, H. (1781). Some account of the termites which are found in Africa. *Phil. Trans. roy. Soc. 71*: 139-92.

SOWERBY, J. (1797-1803). Coloured figures of English fungi. London.

SPRAU, F. (1937). Beiträge zur Mykorrhizenfrage. Die Fruktifikation eines aus *Orchis masculus* isoliertes Wurzelpilzes, *Corticium masculi* nov. spec. *Jb. wiss. Bot. 58*: 151-168.

STÄGER, R. (1903). Infectionsversuche mit Gramineen-bewohnenden *Claviceps*-Arten. *Bot. Ztg. 61*: 111-158. (1910). Neue Beobachtungen über das Mutterkorn. *Zbl. Bakt. 2, 27*: 67-73.

STOLL, A. (1945). Les alcaloïdes de l'ergot. *Experientia 1*: 250-62.

STRAHLENBERG, P. J., von (1730). English translation. An histori-geographical description of the north and eastern part of Europe and Asia ... London, 1736.

THORSEN, P. (1948). *Amanita muscaria* and the fury of the Berserks. *Friesia 3*: 333-51.

TRESCHOW, C. Nutrition of the cultivated mushroom. *Dansk bot. Arkiv 9*: No. 4.

TULASNE, L. R. (1862). Fungi Hypogaei. Paris.

TURPIN, P. J. F. (1827). Organographie végétale. *Mém. Mus. d'Hist. nat. Paris.* 14.

VAILLANT, S. (1728). Discours sur la structure des fleurs.

VANDERLIP, S. (1903). In search of a Siberian Klondike. New York.

VITTADINI, C. (1831). Monographia Tuberacearum. Mediolani.

WAKEFIELD, E. M. (1920). Observations on the biology of some sand-dune fungi. *Trans. Brit. myc. Soc. 6*: 33-6.

—— and DENNIS, R. W. G. (195). Common British fungi. A guide to the more common large Basidiomycetes of the British Isles. London, P. R. Gawthorn.

WAKSMAN, S. A. (1947). Microbial antagonisms and antibiotic substances. New York, Commonwealth Fund.

WALSH, J. H. (1882). The dogs of the British Islands. Stonehenge.

WARNER, R. (1791). Antiquitates culinariae.

WEINDLING, R. (1934). Studies on a lethal principle effective in the parasitic action of *Trichoderma lignorum* on *Rhizoctonia solani* and other soil fungi. *Phytopath. 24*: 1153-1179.

—— and EMERSON, O. H. (1936). The isolation of a toxic substance from the culture filtrate of *Trichoderma*. *Phytopath. 26*: 1065-70.

WHEELER, W. M. (1923). Social life among the insects. London, Constable & Co.

WHELDON, H. J. (1920). Observations on the fungi of the Lancashire and Cheshire sand-dunes. *Trans. Brit. myc. Soc. 6*: 143-8.

WIELAND. See under LYNEN.

WILDERS, W. (1901). Nouvelle substance indispensable au développement de la levure. *Cellule, 18*: 311-33.

WILKINS, W. H., ELLIS, E. M., and HARVEY, J. L. (1937). The ecology of the larger fungi. I. Constancy and frequency of fungal species in relation to certain vegetation communities, particularly oak and beech. *Ann. appl. Biol. 24*: 703-32.

—— HARLEY, J. L., and KENT, G. C. (1938). II. The distribution of the larger fungi in part of Charlton Forest, Sussex. *Ann. appl. Biol. 25*: 472-89.

—— and PATRICK, S. H. M. (1939). III. Constancy and frequency of grassland species with special reference to soil types. *Ann. appl. Biol. 26*: 25-46.

—— —— (1940). IV. The seasonal frequency of grassland fungi with special reference to the influence of environmental conditions. *Ann. appl. Biol. 27*: 17-34.

—— and HARRIS, G. C. M. (1946). V. An investigation into the influence of rainfall and temperatures on the seasonal production of fungi in a beechwood and a pine wood. *Ann. appl. Biol. 33*: 179-188.

WOLLASTON, W. H. (1807). On fairy-rings. *Phil. Trans. roy. Soc. 97*: 133-8.

WOODWARD, J. (1699). Thoughts and experiments on vegetation. *Phil. Trans. roy. Soc. 21*: 382-98.

INDEX

306